THE APE PEOPLE

by Geoffrey H. Bourne

G. P. Putnam's Sons, New York

To my favorite primate—my wife, Nelly

Contents

Introduction

THIS BOOK has been written with the intention of bringing to the layman some of the excitement, some of the pleasures and rewards of working with and trying to understand the great apes. The chimpanzee, the gorilla, and the orangutan are fascinating creatures still poorly understood but astonishingly similar to man in their structure, their physiology, and much of their behavior.

It is only natural that such a book should be based on the only research center in the world which specializes in working with great apes. This is the Yerkes Regional Primate Research Center of Emory University, formerly the Yerkes Laboratories for Primate Biology.

This book is not intended to be a scientific treatise although some of the observations recorded will be of interest to scientists, nor is it intended to be an official history of the Yerkes Center. Although it deals mostly with apes (nonhuman primates without tails), it does discuss some aspects of monkey (nonhuman primates with tails) life which I feel to be of special interest.

Forty years ago Dr. Robert Yerkes, professor of psychology at Yale University, was able to make a dream come true and to found a colony of chimpanzees at Orange Park near Jacksonville in Florida. He built up a colony of forty or fifty chimpanzees. In 1961 the federal government provided funds to move the laboratories to a new Primate Research Center at Emory University and to maintain it. The Center now houses eighty-five chimpanzees, thirty-five orangutans, fifteen gorillas, and five gibbons, together with some seven hundred monkeys.

The collection of apes at the Yerkes Center is unique. Never in the history of mankind has such a remarkable collection of apes been gathered together in one place. Nothing approaching it exists in any other part of the world, and many countries envy us this asset; it is, in fact, not just a national asset but a world asset. Blood samples and tissue samples go from Yerkes to institutions in countries all over the globe. Scientists from different countries come to visit us and some stay and work. They come to see our unique collection of animals, and they come to pay homage to Dr. Yerkes, whose drive and energy and his work in unraveling the ape mind have left mankind such a remarkable heritage.

Dr. Yerkes showed for the first time that it was possible to keep a healthy breeding colony of chimpanzees under laboratory conditions and to work with them in scientific experiments. The know-how which the laboratories developed on the maintaining, handling, feeding, and breeding of these animals enabled the U.S. Air Force to establish a colony of chimpanzees at Alamogordo in New Mexico for experiments related to the country's aerospace program. Unfortunately this colony is now disbanded. The Air Force also had access to the remarkable library on chimpanzees which the Yerkes Center had built up and so was able to produce a comprehensive index of the scientific work which had been carried out throughout the world on these animals. Similarly when the Southwest Foundation for Research in San Antonio, Texas, wanted recently to start a chimpanzee colony for medical studies, it was able to send its scientists and animal technicians to us and to learn in a short space of time how to maintain and care for these animals.

The Yerkes Center over the forty years of its existence has made important contributions to knowledge in the areas of sex development, anatomy, learning ability, cooperation in problem solving, social dominance, auditory capacity, right- and left-handedness, incentives and behavior, problems of vision, personality development and mother-infant relations. Out of these studies has come the kind of exact data that allows the application of man's knowledge of the apes to be used in the solution of many human neurological and psychiatric problems.

Dr. Karl Lashley, the second director of the Yerkes Laboratories, said in an interview in the 1950's that the most important discovery of the Yerkes Laboratories up to that time had been the relation of the frontal areas of the brain to personality. He believed that the one finding justified all the money that had been spent on the laboratories. There is no doubt that the work of the Yerkes Laboratories has opened the way to the better understanding of the human mind, and present studies in other areas of human health and welfare give promise of opening the gates of understanding in these areas as well.

For their help in the preparation of this book, I have to thank Miss Helen M. Cousar, the Center's artist, and Mr. Frank Kiernan, the Center's photographer. Their fine illustrative contributions have done much to bring reality to the presentation of our animals. Some photographs and drawings have also been taken from the books of other authors, but these are acknowledged where they appear in the text.

Atlanta, Georgia   GEOFFREY H. BOURNE

The Ape People

1. Bobby

IT WAS a warm spring day in May. Atlanta's dog-woods and azaleas had turned the city into a luxuriance of white, pink, and red blossoms. The sun gleamed like a spot of brilliant yellow pigment on the palette of a bright blue sky which was flecked with a few wisps of white clouds. Thousands of feet above, a high-flying fighter aircraft, moving at that height with apparent lazy ease, etched white contrails across the sky.

Atlanta basked in the sun, the tops of the houses peeping out of their leafy cover. From above Atlanta, suburbs appear nonexistent; they are masked by a leafy carpet-canopy which seems to the uninitiated to be simply a continuation of Georgia's 3,000,000 acres of forest.

Hidden among this foliage is Emory University. Founded in 1836, it is a fine and powerful educational force in the South. On the campus is the Emory railway station. The trains run right through the campus, and you can get on one at seven o'clock one evening and be in Washington the next morning and New York the next afternoon.

If you start outside the railway station and drive a hundred yards to the Emory post office, you can then turn left across the railway tracks, pass the entrance to the home of Emory's dynamic president on your right, then take the next two turns to the right, ignore a dead end sign, drive 600 yards through the woods, and you will finish up outside the Yerkes Regional Primate Research Center (Ape City). Inside the Center is the greatest collection of great apes, chimpanzees, gorillas, and orangutans ever assembled by man. Among this collection are animals whose names are household words in scientific circles both in the U.S.A. and in many other countries of the world. Many of these I plan to talk about in this book. For the moment I want to tell about just one animal, Bobby, a great friend of mine who has already figured in two books.

On this particular day, I decided to find out what our animals thought of a new canned primate food. I had gone from animal to animal, giving each one a little of the food to taste, watching the reactions. When Bobby exhibited interest I held the can toward him so that he could look into it. However, he kept pushing the can back, and at first I thought he was pushing it away. But no, he wanted to manipulate it into the upright position. He then withdrew his hand and peered through the wire at the can. Then a thick black finger came through the mesh and touched the label, feeling around on it. My eyes followed his maneuvers, and it became obvious that he was touching and trying to feel the picture of a monkey on the label. That was why he had pushed the can upright; he had caught a glimpse of the label from an angle as I held the can toward him, and he wanted to see it more clearly. I knew Bobby was bright, but I hadn't thought his recognition of a drawing of a monkey would have been so prompt.

Bobby shares the Primate Center with 85 chimpanzees, 35 orangutans, 15 gorillas, 600 monkeys, and 125 humans. This book tells its story.

Bobby's life had been an interesting one up to the time he came to live with us at the Yerkes Center. He was born in Sierra Leone and was taken from his mother at about the age of three and flown in a plane, in a packing crate with other animals, to an animal dealer in California. He was rescued by Elizabeth Mann Borgese, youngest daughter of the great German novelist Thomas Mann. Mrs. Borgese, who is an editor for the *Encyclopaedia Britannica* and a participant in the Center for the Study of Democratic Institutions in Santa Barbara, was looking for a chimpanzee for her experiments. In the past she had worked with dogs and with elephants and had even trained some of the former to type a few words on dictation on a typewriter. She wanted to test a chimpanzee's ability to perform the same feat. Bobby succeeded, learning to type very much more rapidly than a dog, as might be expected. His life with Mrs. Borgese is described by her in two books, *The Language Barrier: Beasts and Men* and *The White*

Bobby.

Snake. Bobby lived the life of a gentleman. He attended Santa Barbara cocktail parties; he learned to pour himself a glass of wine without spilling a drop; he embarrassed a Santa Barbara hostess by running up a flagpole at a poolside party; and there is an ugly rumor that he pushed someone in the pool when the party got gay.

He thoroughly enjoyed television, being particularly addicted to programs which displayed the maximum violence. One of his favorites was the barroom brawl in the Westerns. On these occasions he would scream with excitement, jump up and down, and throw things at the television set. He soon learned to recognize the "bad guy," since this individual was nearly always associated with violence, and Bobby would utter cries of excitement whenever he appeared on the scene. On one occasion Bobby saw a television program in which two chimpanzees tore up a house; the following morning the room which he occupied in the house was a shambles. Is it possible to extrapolate from this to humans? There are many humans watching television who are low in intelligence and who have difficulty in distinguishing between reality and fantasy. These are the ones on whom the impact of television violence can be devastating. In the case of normal intelligent adults or even children, television violence is unlikely to modify their behavior very much provided their parents set a rational pattern of behavior. Normal children, anyhow, fantasize violence even without television, but they can discriminate between their fantasy and reality. The subnormal finds this more difficult, and television violence adds to this confusion. That quite a lot of people in our population have difficulty in discriminating between television fantasy and reality is evidenced by some of the people they see on television whom they subsequently elect to public office.

Bobby spent some months with Mrs. Borgese and then spent six months at the Yerkes Center. The following summer he went back to Santa Barbara and I visited him there. He had become very friendly with me during his stay in Atlanta, and although we had not been able to duplicate his California life he had enjoyed a pleasant, friendly existence. When I arrived at the house where he was staying in Santa Barbara, I tiptoed to his room. I looked around the corner, and there he was, sitting on the floor, his head bent, intent on the blocks with which he was playing. I suddenly called out "Bobby." His response was instantaneous. He let out a piercing scream, jumped into the air, and ran to me. Even now he has only to hear my voice to start screaming and jumping up and down with excitement.

After another summer in Santa Barbara, Bobby spent a little time with a California psychologist and his family, and then came to live in the Yerkes Center as a permanent resident. His life was duller but not that dull, for the very next summer he led an idyllic existence with a young lady chimpanzee called Jenera on a small island in a lake situated on the grounds of the home of Emory's president. The island had previously held some Yerkes rhesus monkeys, but they quickly learned to swim the lake and peer in at the windows of the president's house, a behavior which could not be countenanced in any primate, and they were banished from the island. Bobby came back to the Center from the island, and surprisingly enough, although he was retiring to a semicaged existence, he uttered a cry of recognition and excitement when the truck which was carrying him came within sight of the Center. He has now settled down to a comfortable life, sharing his cage, which has an outside patio where he can sit in the sun, with a succession of attractive young lady chimpanzees. Recently we hoped that Bobby would become a father to a bouncing baby, but unfortunately the pregnancy which he produced ended in a miscarriage. We hope it will not be long before he becomes a real father.

During his stay in Santa Barbara, Bobby developed several "civilized" habits, such as a taste for wine and cocktails. He soon learned the significance of the refrigerator and what was kept in it. However, in the beginning he left the door open whenever he helped himself to something from it and this gave away the thief. He rapidly realized how incriminating an open refrigerator door can be and learned to close it. Guava jelly was his special love. Mrs. Borgese says that Bobby was remarkably deft at avoiding breakables in his runs around the room. Only once did she see him kick anything down, and then he turned, picked it up, and carefully put it back in its place. He soon found where everything was in Mrs. Borgese's cottage and once even tried to open a soda pop bottle with a bottle opener. At the chimpanzee cocktail parties which Mrs. Borgese gave, Bobby would sip a martini, eat hors d'oeuvres with a fork from a plate, and occasionally applaud a verbose guest by clapping his hands, often so enthusiastically that the guest could not continue.

I have mentioned that Bobby was used by Mrs. Borgese in experiments designed to see if he could type words dictated to him. Mrs. Borgese had worked for some years previously with dogs. The Olivetti Company in Italy had made her an electric typewriter with keys some 2 inches in diameter. One of her dogs, Arli, proved expert and was able to type such words as *bad, sad, dog, good, ball, dear, fear*, etc., on dictation. Mrs. Borgese told me that Bobby learned much faster. Arli typed by touching the keys with his nose. Bobby, of course, used his fingers. He learned to type *Bob, Arli, banana, grape*, and other words, also on dictation.

We have not kept up Bobby's typing lessons. We hope to use him as a breeder since he is a highly intelligent animal. Bobby's typing ability indicated a talent we would not have thought he possessed; but there is no doubt that man has not yet probed the inherent mental abilities of the ape, even in the case of the chimpanzee. Many experimenters have spent long hours of work on the chimpanzee; the Yerkes Laboratories have spent forty years probing the minds of these animals.

Recently psychologists at the Holloman Air Force Base at Alamogordo, New Mexico, trained chimpanzees to recognize numbers. For example, if the number 8 is flashed on a screen, the chimpanzee will tap eight times on a lever and then touch another lever to indicate that he has finished counting. Similarly if a 7 or a 5 is flashed on the screen the chimpanzee will tap the lever seven and five times respectively. Chimpanzees are also capable of sustained work. At a behavioral laboratory in Silver Spring, Maryland, which is associated with the Walter Reed Army Institute of Research, chimpanzees have to work for their food. To get enough food, they have to work six hours a day. The work involves operating a series of buttons and levers which have to be manipulated to produce a food reward. The animals sit at their panels hour after hour pushing buttons and pulling levers,

Bobby typing.

creating an atmosphere of intense concentration. They do not spare a look at a visitor; they just get on with the job. Some people may consider this cruel, but it may be a lot less cruel than just keeping an ape in a cage with nothing to do at all.

Bobby was not unusual in being house bred. Mrs. Borgese of course made no effort to toilet train him, and in fact all primates are very difficult to train in this respect. Some people have achieved a partial success. A lady who visited the Yerkes Center a few years ago had a pet woolly monkey from South America whom she took everywhere with her, and this animal would invariably go into the bathroom whenever it wanted to defecate or urinate. Cathy Hayes, who kept a Yerkes chimpanzee, Vicki, in her house, obtained partial success with her toilet training. The Gardners, who work in Reno, have been quite successful with their chimpanzee Washoe. His Serene Highness Prince Rainier of Monaco told me a story recently about a chimpanzee which was kept in an apartment in Nice and appeared to be perfectly well toilet trained. Here is His Highness' account of this animal:

"A few years ago I was asked, as it happens quite often, whether I would take a monkey in my Center for Zoological Acclimatization in Monaco, for at least six months.

I enquired about the monkey in question and the owners informed that it was a black-faced chimpanzee, about eight to twelve years old. They also said this chimp lived with them in a luxurious flat in Nice. However, they were leaving Nice to travel for a few months, and thus could not take the chimp with them.

I sent a message that, theoretically, I agreed to take the animal for the duration of their absence, provided they would make a written and signed statement assuming full responsibility for the upkeep of the animal, and that they would supply a proper veterinarian's certificate as to the animal's health as of the moment it entered the Acclimatization Center of Monaco.

I then sent the administrator and the trainer of the Center to Nice on appointment, in order that they might see the chimp and make all final arrangements for its delivery.

The living condition of the 'pet' was related to me by my two envoys after their visit: Much to the amazement of the trainer, when they got to the apartment in Nice and rang the door bell, the door was opened by a black-faced female chimp about one meter sixty-five in height, standing quite erect. . . . The owners were also in the entrance to greet both men. All the group, including the chimp, took seats in the drawing room and started to talk. The chimp observed the visitors with calm indifference: she was quite used to visitors!

The trainer and administrator were shown 'round the apartment, mainly to see the special arrangements made for the welfare of the female chimp. In the couple's bedroom she had her bed, to her size. . . . It was shown that this female ate at the table with her owners, that she knew how to go to the refrigerator to get what she wanted—drink or food—and that she even could sit on the toilet to do her business!

The animal had been living there for many years as the couple had had her when she was very young. It was obvious that the female Chimp preferred the husband and showed great jealousy towards the wife whom she tolerated more than liked!

This chimp had the unfortunate habit of kissing men she liked on the mouth, with quite some violence, as she was very strong. She ate what her "parents" ate, and, sitting at the table, she could also (and would too!) indulge in some French red wine she really did enjoy. This wine ration was on the diet schedule for her daily menus, which the couple supplied when they left her with us! It was explained that this chimpanzee was used to eating cooked food and normal menus just like those eaten by normal adults in France!

One day, as scheduled, the female chimp was brought to us at the Acclimatization Center. We had prepared lovely, comfortable living quarters for her, and had provided her with the food she was used to.

Once her owners had left, she became—day after day—more and more difficult to approach and feed. She would allow only the head-keeper and the trainer to go into her very spacious cage-room and approach her. . . . But we very soon noticed, though she had many toys, that she was upset and unhappy. There was no way or means for us to fight this sort of neurasthenia and melancholy—and the chimpanzee was losing weight, had very little appetite, and would not play with her toys in spite of the trainer's efforts who would even eat his lunch with her! She demonstrated no interest in her fellow ape neighbours, which she seemed to ignore. In a short time she became difficult and even quite disagreeable.

We then wrote to the owners and related how their 'girl' was doing. We requested they take her back as fast as possible as she kept losing weight and health.

About a month later, the couple made arrangements to fetch her and take her back to Nice. This operation, when it took place, could have turned out to be quite dramatic as the chimpanzee was so delighted to see her masters again that she forgot the good education she had professed before: she was rough and quite brutal.

During her entire stay with us she had received the correct food and all the care and even affection that was possible, but it was evidently very far from what she was used to having 'at home'! If we had kept this chimp, I am sure she would not have lived, as she rapidly lost interest in food and just sat and sulked in the corner of her cage-room, refusing to play or entertain herself with any toy or person.

Upon leaving the Center she made a great 'fuss' of jealousy: she wanted to sit on the front seat of her 'father's' car and refused that the wife sit next to him. She then went for the wife and nearly bit her! . . ."

His Highness has a fine Center for Acclimatization of Animals in Monaco where the animals, including several apes, receive outstanding care and excellent food.

The author and friend.

The difficulty in toilet training highly intelligent animals such as the primates is surprising, especially in view of the extraordinary toilet instincts of some of the felines. We have a tree ocelot named Cleo who has been living in our house for eight years. When in need of a toilet, if her toilet box is not available, she will go into the bathroom and defecate or urinate in the bath over the drain where the water runs away. In the London Zoo I have seen an ocelot go to the drain in her cage and squat over it to urinate.

The keeping of Bobby in a house was not a unique activity. Many people have kept chimpanzees and other subhuman primates in their houses. In some cases they have been kept as pets and in other cases with a scientific objective. The stories of some famous ape pets are given in the following chapter. I relate them in some detail so that those who are tempted to keep a little baby ape in their homes will realize what happens when it grows up.

2. Ape People as Pets

SOME years ago Heinrich Oberjohann wrote a book about three apes, Jonny, Nyanya, and Cogo; he described their reactions to being captured by human beings, their reactions to human beings, and their reactions to civilized surroundings.

Jonny was a chimpanzee who was captured in the forest after his mother had fallen into a trap and been killed by natives.

Oberjohann obtained almost immediate affection from the animal. Originally it had been bound when brought to the native encampment where Mr. Oberjohann was staying, but after the bonds were untied the animal threw his arms affectionately around his captor's neck and squeezed him so tightly he gave the impression that he never wanted to be abandoned again. Prior to his capture he had only just missed being eaten up by a leopard, and it seems that the episode of being caught in a cage with his mother, her subsequent death, and the experience of being nearly eaten by the leopard and of seeing the leopard being killed immediately in front of him must have left a big impression on this young animal.

The hunter felt that the baby deserved some genuine affection and decided to behave toward him exactly like a parent. In the evening the animal, who had been named Jonny, showed great interest in a clock. He was fascinated by its ticking, picked it up, shook it, and held it to his ear. It is an interesting thing that chimpanzees appear to be fascinated by clocks and watches. Dr. and Mrs. Keith Hayes from the Yerkes Laboratories (see later) record the interest their chimpanzee Vicki had in watches and the fact that she would even hold a picture of a watch in a magazine to her ear to hear it tick, and Bobby has been observed to do the same thing. At one time when Jonny was holding the clock the alarm went off, an event which terrified him. He threw the clock away, leaped into bed with his new owner, and pulled the bedclothes over his head. In the middle of all this he was howling like a madman. Afterward when awakening in the morning the first thing he looked for was the clock. When he saw it he was seized again by panic and immediately dived back under the bedclothes.

Jonny's first breakfast in captivity consisted of a piece of soap followed by half a bucket of soapy water. He then followed this up with porridge, the remains of which he threw on the bed. Eventually Mr. Oberjohann put Jonny in the care of a little black girl called Sanugra and left Africa.

Some years later, when he was returning to Europe after another visit to Africa, he found Jonny on the boat. The animal had had an encounter with a caged leopard and had reacted in a very excited fashion. Having caused a disturbance and bitten two people, Jonny was on the brink of being destroyed by the captain of the ship when Mr. Oberjohann pleaded for him and was given him as a present. At that time he was carrying animals back to Europe for various zoos, and Jonny joined his collection.

On arrival in Europe with his owner, Jonny was taken to an ex-wrestler who was used to training animals and who was to keep him for a time. The wrestler was very impressed by Jonny's size, and on one occasion, when Jonny was eating bread and cheese and not taking any notice of anybody, the wrestler grabbed him by the ears and tried to pull him to his feet. Jonny sprang up, seized the wrestler by the legs, and threw him over backwards. The wrestler was rather astonished by this; he pointed out afterward that this was the first time in his career that both his shoulders had touched the ground simultaneously, and that this had been done by an ape was a terrible indignity. He tried to get Jonny with a broom, but Jonny seized the broom and broke it in two and with a piece in each hand charged the wrestler. Finally they were both calmed down and shook hands.

Jonny's stay in the wrestler's classroom was marked by many incidents. On one occasion, for instance, he broke a chess board over the wrestler's head; on another occasion he let all the monkeys out of their cages and smashed a window and the bars which protected it with the aid of a piece of bicycle frame. Oberjohann describes how Jonny used to eat the contents of all the sugar bowls while he was in the wrestler's establishment, and on one occasion he decided to teach Jonny a lesson. He filled a sugar bowl with salt, put it in the cupboard, left the room, shut the door behind him, and then looked through the keyhole. To his astonishment he found that the chimpanzee was also looking through the keyhole, and they stared at each other in this way for a minute or two. Then Jonny turned around and went to the cupboard, pulled out the bowl of salt, and hastily swallowed it. Then he opened his mouth and put out his tongue and whimpered in great dismay. After expressing great concern he was finally satisfied by a pint of milk which helped end the unpleasant taste. The salt apparently did not make him sick.

Jonny's behavior in looking through the keyhole at the departing human is very similar to something that happened on one occasion at Oxford University when Sir Charles Sherrington was professor of physiology there. He had some monkeys loose in a room and having been with them came out and locked the door. He then bent down to look through the keyhole to see what the monkeys were doing and found a monkey looking through the keyhole at him.

Jonny became expert at laying the table for meals and was able to prepare sandwiches for cold snacks. He buttered the bread and put slices of sausage and cheese on it, but at mealtime, when it came to eating these sandwiches, Jonny would scoop the sausage and cheese off the bread with his upper lip and would hand the slices of bread to his owner, asking for another supply of sausage and cheese. If this was refused, he would turn around and help himself. He had a unique way of cleaning up after a meal, too—he would sweep all the food that was left on the table into his mouth.

Jonny eventually joined a circus act and became expert at riding a bicycle and roller-skating. He would come onto the stage dressed in a coat, white waistcoat, and top hat and bow to the audience, sit at the table, ring a bell, order a newspaper, drink some wine, smoke cigarettes, and unfold a newspaper, then have his skates strapped on and get up on the stage and skate.

He became intensely fond of the youngest daughter of the owner of the circus act—a little girl of five—and they formed a remarkable relationship. When she was sent away from home in an attempt to break Jonny of his fondness for her, he pined very much, and one night when the household was asleep he got out of his bed and went outside the house; it was a freezing night and the ground was covered with snow. He went to the park, climbed a tree, and spent the night there. The next day he developed a temperature, caught pneumonia, and died.

The wrestler who had worked with Jonny had always wanted to put on a wrestling act between Jonny and himself on the stage in one of the German towns, but he never succeeded in doing so. However, in Columbia, South Carolina, only six or seven years ago, a gorilla was actually on stage and ready to wrestle with anybody. A reporter from the Miami *Herald* was there and decided that he would have a go with the gorilla, whose name was Butch. For the occasion the gorilla was muzzled and given a pair of gloves and the journalist was given a football helmet to wear. The journalist weighed 250 pounds; the gorilla weighed 165 pounds and was only 4 feet tall, but the journalist claimed that each of the gorilla's arms was 4 feet long. He started by grabbing Butch's arms, and the next thing he knew was that he had been spun around and Butch's feet were banging him in the stomach. Butch then belted him across the face with his left hand, sending his helmet flying, kicked him in the chest with a right foot, and sent him across the enclosure. Butch followed him, grabbed him by the legs, and hit him in the abdomen. This was about enough for the reporter. He stayed in with the ape for ten minutes, which was five minutes longer than anyone had ever done before. The reporter claims that it was ten minutes longer than he will ever again stay with any ape.

Later Mr. Oberjohann went to Togoland in Africa, where he acquired a baby gorilla whom he called Nyanya. Nyanya had been brought up with the natives and had never lived with his own species. The only company he had shared was that of an old Negro who was in effect his adopted father. On one occasion when staying in an encampment with other Negroes, an interesting incident occurred. The gorilla had been trained by his Negro owner to do early morning chores such as collecting water. In the morning in this encampment Nyanya had got up and searched for buckets to get water as he had been used to doing. He picked up two of the cook's pails, but the cook saw him making off with them and tried to stop him and get them back. When the gorilla would not give them up, the cook took a stick and threatened the animal with it. But Nyanya, unaccustomed to being threatened and not liking it very much, seized the cook, threw him down on his face, raked his back with his nails, and did a war dance on his back. Later, peace was obtained by permitting the gorilla to do all the morning chores he wanted to do, although there were complaints from the cook that when the ape learned to cook he would get fired.

Nyanya was fascinated by the sight of his master taking a bath and made many efforts by rubbing himself to produce the lather that his owner produced. Given a piece of soap to do the same thing, his first act was to eat it in one gulp. Given a second piece of soap and shown how to use it, he was able to produce soapy lather on his chest to his heart's content. After having done this, he still swallowed the remains of the soap. Nyanya caused concern on another occasion when he chased out the laundry boy and took over the laundry himself, scrubbed soap right through the clothes, wrung them in a way that they had never been wrung before, found himself enveloped in soap bubbles, stormed at them and beat them off with his arms, tried to catch them, and was delighted when they burst between his fingers. Finally he became fed up with everything and picked up the table, the basins, the tubs, and the laundry and threw them all over the place.

Nyanya's posture was surprisingly erect like a man's and not at all like the half-dropped position walking on the knuckles of the hand characteristic of gorillas. Nyanya wanted a share of everything. When he saw that his master had a watch, he wanted a watch and took his master's watch off his arm or out of his pocket if necessary. When his master received a present of cigars, Nyanya had to have a cigar too. So eager was he to have one of

Nyanya gets a bath from Mr. Oberjohann.

these strange objects that he stole one and climbed up a mango tree to smoke it. To teach him a lesson his owner drilled a hole lengthwise through one cigar, filled the cavity with gunpowder, and closed it with a paper pellet. Nothing happened for two days, but on the afternoon of the third day he heard an explosion followed by a howl, and Nyanya appeared with his hair standing on end, very disturbed. The next time he was offered a cigar he was sitting at a table, and when he saw it he let out a scream, jumped up, swept everything off the table, and ran howling out of the tent, his interest in cigars obviously cured.

Nyanya was fascinated by anybody wearing a skirt, and women and girls could handle him just as they pleased; he was not concerned even when they smacked him. Whenever he saw a woman in a skirt he would run up to her and attempt to embrace her. This never happened with the native women because they were terrified of the gorilla, and if he approached them they would turn and run screaming at the top of their voices. One amusing incident occurred when a priest who was a missionary visited the camp. The moment the priest came into sight, Nyanya thought from his long skirts that he was a woman and took off toward him, and despite calls from his owner to come back he continued to run to the priest. However, as soon as the latter saw a gorilla rushing at him he panicked, picked up the hem of his cassock, and ran like a deer. Nyanya, however, simply ran faster and very soon caught up with the priest, flung his arms around him, and clasped him to his breast. At this the priest thought his end had come and fainted away. But Nyanya, who had taken one look at the face with hair on it, was shaken by what had happened, dropped the priest, and returned growling. After that incident Nyanya never again made a demonstration toward women wearing skirts.

After his Negro foster father died, the gorilla became more and more attached to his white master and in fact shared the same bed with him and at night slept with his arm around him. He went everywhere with him in the day, even taking part in the major trapping expeditions that were organized to catch wild animals. On one occasion when he was not going to be taken on a long journey with the native bearers, he got very angry and eventually followed them and insisted upon having something to carry just as the bearers did. He always carried his loads in a very awkward fashion, and after a mile or so he would always want to rest. On this occasion he struggled on after the caravan for some considerable time, and then he suddenly found a practical method of being able to carry the load and still walk without difficulty. He then was very quickly up with the leaders; according to Oberjohann, the moment they halted for the night he would even help the cook collect firewood, fetch water, and pick wild fruits. On one occasion the bearers faltered and came to a halt because Oberjohann had become annoyed when one of them stole one of his personal possessions. They finally finished up by attacking him, and he was saved by Nyanya, who grabbed one of them by the arm and threw him against the tree trunk, followed by another. The other bearers then scattered like birds.

It was obvious to Oberjohann that he would not be able to leave Nyanya in Africa when he went back to Europe with his load of animals, so he had to build him a cage. This the gorilla not unnaturally regarded as a prison, and he displayed considerable resentment at what he appeared to feel was a betrayal by his master. However, he eventually adapted to the cage, joined the cavalcade to the coast, and was loaded with all the other animals on a ship for the journey to Europe. At first Nyanya behaved himself, but on one occasion he got out of his cage, found Oberjohann's collection of poisonous and nonpoisonous snakes which he was bringing home to sell to European zoos, picked up the crates, and threw them into the sea.

When the entourage disembarked in Europe, Oberjohann had no place to put Nyanya while he carried out his business activities, so he left him with a friend, who refused to keep him in a cage. As a result, Nyanya caused all kinds of trouble from which he was eventually rescued, and he was taken by his master in a taxi to be left with someone else. In the taxi he was attracted by the driver's hands manipulating the steering wheel and finally grabbed the wheel. The driver wrenched the wheel straight to prevent an accident, skidded on some tram lines, and stalled the car at a right angle across the street, blocking traffic from both directions. At this point Nyanya climbed over the seat alongside the driver, and when the driver refused to let him fool any longer with the wheel, he opened the door of the taxi, threw the driver out, and then sat in the driver's seat, pulling all the knobs and levers and pressing buttons, manipulating the gears, and blowing the horn continuously. The latter attracted a policeman, who came to investigate. Oberjohann said that they had just stalled, but the policeman saw the gorilla in the driver's seat, was rather shaken by the sight, and demanded to know what it was doing there. Nyanya by this time had climbed out of the driver's seat and run over to a fruit shop, where he proceeded to demolish the window and pick up a bunch of bananas which he carried back to the car. The policeman, however, was threatening to arrest Oberjohann, and the gorilla immediately went for him. At this the policeman took to his heels. In the meantime, Oberjohann gave 100 marks to the keeper of the fruit stand to take care of the window, put Nyanya into another taxi, drove to the police station and explained the situation to them. By this time Nyanya had calmed down and won over all the policemen at the station, and he and his master were allowed to depart.

Still without a place to keep his animal, Oberjohann remembered a zoo director he knew and took the animal to the zoo, where he was accommodated in a large cage. A year later he came back and found that Nyanya was being shamefully mistreated, being flogged and hit with sticks and treated like a wild and ferocious animal. An elderly lady who was a frequent visitor to the zoo became very attracted by Nyanya and was distressed by the treatment meted out to him. She made contact with Oberjohann, who removed Nyanya from the zoo and let him go to live with the old lady. There he lived for two years, completely unrestricted and very happy, but unfortunately he died of a jaw abscess. In her final letter about what Oberjohann described as his adopted son, the old lady said, "I have had Nyanya buried like a man, he deserved that. He lived and died like one among us." Nyanya was a real ape person.

The next animal that Oberjohann tamed was Cogo, a large

and apparently mature chimpanzee he purchased in the mature state. He had several unhappy incidents with the animal, being bitten and slashed very seriously on more than one occasion. At first Cogo was kept in a compound, but he eventually broke away from it and attacked Oberjohann's poultry. Once, in a few minutes he wrung the necks of 27 hens, 4 dwarf antelopes, and 2 ground hornbills. In the confined state Cogo was an assassin, but when he was free he was gentle, obliging, and affectionate.

However, chimpanzees, even when free, do things that human beings would not do. On one occasion when Oberjohann was putting a diaper on a baby chimpanzee, Cogo heard the baby crying and immediately attacked his master. It took Oberjohann a long time to convince Cogo that he was in fact the master, and he had many scars to show for his patience and perseverance. Cogo was once watching a fight in a compound in which there were a large number of mandrills. As he was peering through the outside of the wire in the compound one of the mandrills leaped up and bit him on the lip. This infuriated him so greatly that he rushed along the side of the wire, forced his way in, and attacked the animals, wreaking his vengeance on the mandrill who had attacked him.

On another occasion Oberjohann went into the mandrill compound to stop a fight. He was rushed by a howling mob of mandrills. Two of them bit him on the leg, and the third leaped on his shoulder and began to bite him on the head. The moment he freed himself of these, another wave of attack broke on him. In the meantime Cogo had seen what was happening and had rushed into the enclosure. As soon as the mandrills saw him they all turned around and flung themselves on him. He fought heroically. Two mandrills he killed by fracturing their skulls, but two others held fast to him, and with a dozen other mandrills biting and clawing him Cogo managed to get through the door of the compound. He was covered with blood. Just as Oberjohann raised his gun to shoot the mandrills he saw Cogo collapse. The mandrills had ripped open his abdomen and had torn out his entrails. By the time he was examined, his heart had ceased to beat. Oberjohann had regarded him as a faithful and devoted friend, and he dug a grave for him at the edge of his native forest.

The only person I know who has had close relationships with young orangutans coming from the wild is Barbara Harrisson. In Borneo and Sumatra, the natural habitat of these animals, many of the natives have had orangutans living partly or totally with their families from time to time. But Barbara Harrisson is the only one who has placed on record her details of the orangutans with whom she was associated. She has dramatized for some years the danger of extermination which threatens the orangutan, and her husband, Tom Harrisson, was for a long time director of the museum at Kuching, Sarawak, in Borneo. The term "orangutan" is really two Malay words. *Orang* means "man," and *utan* means "jungle." The native inhabitants of Borneo refer to these animals as *maias*.

The orangutan is not colored black or brown like the gorilla and the chimpanzee but is usually light auburn to bright red, and the hair may be very long, giving the animal a shaggy appearance. The first baby orangutan to arrive at the Harrisson house had been found living with a family of natives who had adopted it after its mother had been shot. In her first relationships with this animal, Barbara found how demanding such a baby can be. Once she left the animal on her own bed, and while she went to prepare his bed she heard a piercing scream and found that he had climbed down to the floor and was crawling toward her. The moment he was taken up and nursed he became quiet.

1563941

The Harrissons' house was in Kuching, the capital city of Sarawak in Borneo. It is a small town of 40,000 people. They found an outside corner of their house where they were able to put up a wire wall to form a cage. Over the cage they put a wooden roof and in it a swing with some ropes and a box for the orangutan to sleep in at night. A check with the veterinary officers showed that the baby had a slight cold. Back home he was weighed and turned the scale at 15 pounds. He had his milk teeth and was apparently about a year old. They named him Bob.

Soon after Bob was installed, a second orangutan called Eve arrived at the Harrisson household. Here again, the mother had been shot and the baby had been brought up in a native house for some weeks. She had then been sold to a Chinese trader and been kept on a chain under his house like a dog and fed on bananas and biscuits. Eventually the Forest Department found the animal and brought it to the Harrissons. The cages where Eve and Bob were kept were close to the bathroom used by the Harrissons, and the animals were very intrigued and watched with great attention the morning toilet of the two humans. They very soon learned to hang from ropes, to bang on the cage, to blow strange noises from their mouths, and to play with everything they could reach outside the cage.

On one occasion when the Harrissons were getting dressed to go out, they heard a tremendous bang from the house, rushed out, and found that Bob had, by fiddling with the fastener on his cage, been able to open it. He had escaped and had started playing with a heavy bronze mirror; he had knocked it off the wall and it was now lying at his feet; in his hand was a Ming jar, but by good fortune Barbara was able to get him to come to her and surrender it before it was broken.

These animals were taken for walks in the garden each day and Barbara has a very good description of the baby orangutan walking: "And now he would stand upright for a second or two with his feet well apart, waving his arms like a windmill to keep his balance. He would stagger a few paces or walk in a semicircle giving the impression of a drunken bear-like dancer. His usual way of walking was on all fours, his arms and legs supporting his head and shoulders, fists close together under the body, feet slightly spread, lurching slightly along." I have seen orangutans walking upright on many occasions, and they hold their hands high in a very characteristic way as they shuffle along with their long red hair hanging down around them. They look very amusing and attractive.

Barbara Harrisson goes to some lengths to emphasize the problem of conservation of orangs in Borneo. The law gave the official game warden the right to confiscate any young orangutan kept as a family pet or sold or found. Such a law was, of course, very difficult to enforce, especially along the Indonesian border, where it was difficult enough to control the humans, let alone the orangutans. In many cases the orangs found in these areas had been brought from Indonesia over the border into Sarawak. As Barbara Harrisson points out, the problem with these native-kept baby orangs was that their food and other requirements for healthy living were not really understood by the natives. The baby orangs have little chance of survival and in most cases die in weeks because they are not protected against human disease, and their chances of survival are not helped by the fact that they are not given the right kind of food. So in recent years in Sarawak it has been necessary to obtain a license to keep an orangutan as a pet in a private residence.

Orangutans that were confiscated by the authorities were handed to the museum, and Tom Harrisson as director and his wife attempted to do something that would ensure a reasonably happy existence for them. They had thought of sending Bob to the San Diego Zoo, but before they could do anything about it they received three new baby orangutans: one, Toni, was named after Sir Anthony Abell, the governor of Sarawak; another one was called Frank after Frank Brown, who was conservator of forests at that time in Sarawak; and the third was named Bill after their friend Bill Smythies, the author of *The Birds of Borneo* and at that time assistant conservator of forests. According to Barbara, Bill had been sold for five Straights dollars (about two American dollars) to a Chinese trader, and Frank had been found in the forest whining over the body of his dead mother, which was already decomposed. A new house had to be built for the new animals, and Eve got extremely jealous of the attention that was paid to them. She would climb up and down the ropes in a frenzy. She would cry and bang her fists, whimpering and glaring at the other babies. Bob was eventually sent off to Singapore, whence he flew to San Diego to become an inmate of the famous San Diego Zoo. He was greeted very enthusiastically by Dr. George Pournelle, curator of mammals at the zoo, and was placed in turn in several different cages, each more difficult to escape from than the last, but he succeeded in escaping from all of them. Eventually he was placed with a little female orangutan named Noëll, who already belonged to the San Diego Zoo, and the two became a very happy pair. Bob appeared on television on a number of occasions.

Back in Kuching, Barbara Harrisson had to cope with the rest of her babies, so she employed a native helper to sit up in the trees with them to get them accustomed to tree climbing. One of the animals adapted quickly to the trees and became a quick climber, using his fists and feet to grip on creepers and small branches; he soon learned to enjoy himself. Another of the orangutans was not as active and a little more nervous. The little girl orang, Eve, found it difficult to adapt to the trees. Another of the animals, Frank, adapted so rapidly that it was difficult to persuade him to come down and eat his supper. Eve, however, despite many attempts to persuade her to take to the trees and to enjoy them, always remained in some kind of fear of them. Perhaps she was more attracted to humans and did not want to leave them. Eventually the Harrissons decided that the only thing for Eve was to get her used to a zoo life before she grew too old. She was eventually accepted at the new ape house in the Berlin Zoo and was transported there by air from Singapore. Barbara Harrisson says, "She has become the youngest and most beautiful spoiled member of the group of young orangs in Germany."

The Harrissons' ape menagerie, however, did not decrease, because about this time they received quite a large male whom they named Nigil, after Nigil Cornwall, the Bishop of Borneo. Barbara points out that in her relationship with Nigil three things about her interested him: the scar on her elbow, her watch strap, and the ring on her finger. She describes how Nigil touched each of these in turn and after touching each one brought the finger he had used up to his nostril so he could smell it. His incorporation into the household was made possible by the departure of Eve. It took Nigil a little while to get used to the trees, but having done so he went up in them and would not come down. About six o'clock in the evening of the first night that he showed this independence he squatted on a fork of the tree and began to bend the branches inward to form a platform just as his wild relations do in the jungle; he was building a nest for the night. At first Nigil would not even come down out of the tree to eat, but eventually he came down and drank his milk and was put back in his cage for the night with the rest of the animals. On another evening when Nigil started making his nest, Frank came to help. He did not object to this at all, although Barbara points out that the two animals frequently undid each other's work. That night Frank came down out of the trees for his milk and to go to sleep in his cage. Nigil took 30 hours to come down out of the trees to get his food this time. But once down, he agreed to go inside his cage for the night. Perhaps he sensed what was going to happen, for it rained all through the night.

Barbara Harrisson pointed out that Nigil was very keen on sacks, and if one was provided for him he would actually get in it with only his head sticking out. We have observed this very often in our own orangutan colony in Yerkes. Given a sack or a towel or anything of this sort, orangs tend to either climb into it or put it on their heads. Recently I paid a visit to one of our younger orangs, Jala, in her cage and brought with me a picture book of various animals which I thought she might be interested in looking through. However, her interest was only to open the book and put it on top of her head as a sort of bonnet. I never got it away from her, and the book was eventually torn out of the cover; she used the contents and the cover as a hat, then finally tore the whole thing to pieces. This was an interesting reaction, for when I showed her the pictures of the book from outside the cage she showed great interest in them, but once she was *given* the book she saw it only as something to put on her head.

In the wild when orangs come into an area where there are plenty of fruit trees they stay there and eat the fruit until they have exhausted the supply. They then move on to another area. This was a problem for the Harrissons because it didn't take the orangs long to consume the fruit on the trees in their garden, and their instinct was then to move on to someone else's garden. Eventually the Harrissons' fruit trees looked in a bad way; there were young branches and twigs broken, tangled masses of dry leaves, and remains of nests stuck on the crowns of the trees; it became necessary to do something to keep the trees from dying. Instead of letting the orangs move into other people's gardens, they were permitted to use the fig tree overhanging the main road outside the house and a rambutan tree which was farther down the garden overlooking the house of a Chinese neighbor.

The animals remained very healthy. They had no colds, diarrhea, or worms.

In giving the animals a degree of freedom and accustoming them to the use of trees as they were doing, the Harrissons were motivated by the hope that eventually they would be able to return these babies to the jungle. They were, however, finding it extremely difficult to do this because the animals so readily developed an attachment for and interest in them.

Barbara Harrisson has made a very serious study of the problem of getting orangs back into the bush. The animals needed to stay a period with her to ensure survival, then they eventually had to fend for themselves. In her book she points out that a few decades ago it would have been possible to release an orang in many parts of Sarawak with the certainty that it would be able to make contact with other orangs very rapidly. But at the time her book was written, in 1963, this was far from the case. One can imagine that now it would be even more difficult for an animal released in this way to find its kind. Several groups of people have gone to Borneo seeking out orangs to study in the wild. In some cases they have not seen any wild orangs at all. Dr. Richard Davenport from the Yerkes Center made an expedition several years ago to north Borneo and was able to see a number of animals over a period of some months. He did not see any significant groups but saw quite a large number of isolated animals.

I went to visit Barbara Harrisson in 1963 at a time when I was doing a tour of Southeast Asia to make contact with animal dealers and scientists and to investigate the availability of various types of monkeys from this part of the world. I flew to Singapore from India and in Singapore stayed at the Raffles Hotel. I had stayed several times before in this hotel; in fact I stayed in it a few days after the Japanese surrender in World War II. It is one of the oldest and possibly the most interesting hotels in Singapore even if it isn't necessarily the most comfortable.

On this occasion I flew from Singapore to Kuching in Sarawak in a Malayan Airlines plane, eating a very good curry on the way and landing about three o'clock in the afternoon. I found that I had been booked in at the best hotel in the town, the Aurora Hotel, and had a corner room which was large and very comfortable. As soon as I was installed there I telephoned the museum and got in contact with Barbara Harrisson. Her husband was out of town at that time and because of his wartime guerrilla experience was helping to cope with the Indonesian guerrillas, but I had the opportunity of going to see the house that she refers to so frequently in her book on the orangutan.

During the course of my stay Barbara arranged for us both to go down to Baku. Baku is a government reservation and park at the mouth of the Kuching River some miles from Kuching itself. The Fisheries Department provided a boat and driver for us. The boat was a canoelike structure, very long and narrow with an outboard motor at the rear which drove it along at considerable speed. We went quite a few miles down the river with a dense jungle, dipping into the water on either side. In the region of Baku we passed a Malayan village with its complex fish traps set on stilts characteristic of that part of the world. To negotiate from the river into the spot on Baku where the animals were kept and where the accommodation is situated, the boat has to go a little way out to sea in the bay, turn right to the swell, and then swing across to the dock on one side of the beach.

This is a part of the world that abounds in black pearls. The sands on the beaches were blackish, and walking on the beach, I was interested to see a number of flat shiny surfaces glinting in the sun. When I got up to them, they proved to be flat oysters which are usually an iridescent nacreous white but in this case were a shiny gray or black. Flat oysters are used by the Orientals for making wind chimes and various types of decoration. The shells of these oysters are almost completely flat, have a mother-of-pearl-like texture, and make a very beautiful decoration. The only habitation in this part of Baku was a couple of huts, one of which was for the native helpers employed by the Harrissons and the other of which was used for the Harrissons and guests when they visited Baku.

As soon as we put our things ashore, we got out and walked along a track in the jungle. The trees were dripping with water and daylight was almost excluded. Along the crest of one hill and along the side of another hill there were a couple of small shacks with wire walls. We were greeted enthusiastically there by two of Barbara's current orangs, Arthur and George. George was rather small, and I wouldn't like to hazard a guess at his age. Arthur was much bigger and four or maybe five years of age. Arthur, when we arrived, was up in the top of a tall thin tree and came scrambling down to look me in the eye and then scrambled back up. He gave an interesting demonstration of how to move from one tree to another. He would get up to the top of one of these tall thin trees and sway back and forth until it swayed over close to another tree, and then he would grab the second tree and let the first one go. This was all to the good if the second tree would bear his weight, but in many cases the second tree would not and he would come crashing down to the ground with some force; but it did not appear to do him any damage. Arthur progressed through several trees in this way, crashing some to the ground and in some cases crashing down only with the branch that he had grabbed. Barbara told me that she sometimes had seen orangs drop suddenly out of a tree 20 or 30 feet to the ground for no apparent reason, and she wondered if they did this on some occasions to avoid a snake.

We went for a walk along a jungle trail accompanied by Arthur and George and sat down after a while to rest on some logs. Arthur was obviously spoiling for a wrestle with somebody about his age and weight and came over and began to push me around a bit, a maneuver which I resisted. I then got a long pole, and as he came toward me I pushed him away. However, the next time I did this he grabbed the pole in both hands, jerked it out of my hand, threw it away, and put his teeth over my ankle, slowly increasing the pressure. At first I thought this was a big joke, but the pressure went on and it was obvious that he was starting to break through the skin. I called to Barbara to give me some kind of aid. She picked up a big stick and beat Arthur across the back until he let go. Arthur still regarded me as a good companion to play with, however, and we set off for the huts with Arthur following alongside the trail, swinging from tree to tree and keeping pace with us. When we got to the wire huts we went inside one of them, locked the door, and left George and Arthur to wander around outside, while we assumed the role of caged animals. When the attention of the animals was focused somewhere else, Barbara and I got out and scrambled up the jungle path and set off for the huts. The orangs had apparently become conditioned to never come past a particular point near these wire huts, and so once we had passed the critical point they made no attempt to follow us. These orangs had been partly reared by Barbara, and she had at that time arrived at the next stage, that of releasing them to an area of jungle where they would be fed. Her native helpers who lived on the spot at Baku fed the animals twice a day. Some time after I left Borneo one of these animals died and the other one was released on an island in the north part of Borneo.

I stayed on at Baku for a while trying to see some proboscis monkeys which have a nose very much enlarged and rather like that of some well fed humans who have an excessive fondness for alcohol. The native name for the proboscis monkey is the Javanese word for "Dutchman," presumably a reference to the well-fed, hard-drinking white pioneers who originally occupied the related part of the world now known as Indonesia.

Gorillas have been known in the Western world for only a relatively short time. In fact the first gorilla came to America in 1927. He was lodged in the Philadelphia Zoo, and his name was Bamboo. Later on, Ngagi and Mbongo were sent to the San Diego Zoo. Mbongo eventually reached a record weight of 618 pounds. Another gorilla that came to America later was Suzi; she was flown across the Atlantic Ocean in the *Graf Zeppelin*. The famous Lincoln Park Zoo gorilla, Bushman, weighed 473 pounds and had very good relations with his keepers. In fact he played football with them for a time, but this sport was stopped after he nearly killed a member of the opposing team by accident.

Probably the most detailed account of a gorilla in captivity was that published by Mrs. A. Maria Hoyt about a gorilla that she secured in the French Congo. In the earlier part of this century her husband was hunting in that part of the world, collect-

Barbara Harrisson rescues a young proboscis monkey from drowning.

ing animals. Mrs. Hoyt had accompanied him and on one occasion was summoned to a hunt where a group of gorillas had been disturbed. Her husband had planned to kill only one gorilla, but the natives, anxious for the meat, ambushed all of them and killed most of the group. Mrs. Hoyt found a tiny baby weighing only a few pounds and still clinging to its dead mother; she picked it up and took it to her camp. She made a little crib in her tent in which the animal slept. The baby was christened Toto, and for a time Mrs. Hoyt was worried about its survival because she could not get it to eat anything. But eventually she found one of the native women who had more milk than her own baby could take, and she suckled Toto on her breasts. There are quite a number of references to this type of human-ape relationship in the literature on apes. Toto learned all kinds of things very quickly, including wiping her face with a handkerchief and after a while blowing her nose in it.

Eventually the Hoyts had to leave the French Congo, and they decided to take the little gorilla with them in a deluxe suite on the steamer which took them from Africa to France; Paris was their destination.

In the suite on the way to Paris, Toto quickly learned that she could come in each morning from the room where she slept and get into bed with Mrs. Hoyt and together they would have breakfast. She soon turned this into a habit, and each day of the voyage she would turn up and go through the routine.

When they arrived in Paris, they had accommodations in a hotel in the Rue de Rivoli. Presumably, Toto felt very insecure under these circumstances and would yell at the top of her lungs if left alone; she always slept in the same bed with either Mrs. Hoyt or her husband. It was not long before the chill air of Paris gave her a bad cold. The best Paris pediatrician was brought in to attend her, but in spite of this care and attention she developed pneumonia, and Mrs. Hoyt went through a traumatic vigil of eight days and nights trying to pull Toto through the crisis. During the course of this illness they even went to the expense of bringing a portable X-ray machine into the hotel room to take pictures of Toto's lungs. Toto eventually recovered from the disease but was very weak for a long time, so much so that the doctor recommended that the Hoyts take her out of Paris to the sea.

They decided therefore to go to a small town near Bordeaux. The retinue which they formed on their departure must have caused great amusement and interest to Parisians, who crowded around to see them leave their hotel. The retinue consisted of Mrs. Hoyt and her mother; Abdullah, a tall, handsome Swahili boy; their chauffeur; two Pomeranian dogs, and Toto. When they got to their destination they received a great welcome. Toto became the pet of everybody, the honored guest, and became very spoiled. In fact she would not go to sleep at night unless Abdullah sat on her bed; often she would pretend sleep, and as soon as Abdullah got up and began to tiptoe out of the room, she would sit up and scream. Mrs. Hoyt noticed at this time that Toto had a very keen sense of hearing. This is a very interesting fact, and a similar ability has been noted by Dr. Kellogg in the

45

chimpanzee Gua. Toto could even hear Abdullah walking on the tiled floor of a neighboring bathroom in his bare feet, and Abdullah was, in fact, a very soft walker. This certainly indicates a very high degree of auditory acuity.

During Toto's convalescence, Mrs. Hoyt found that one of the problems of owning her was that whenever she wore bracelets or necklaces or even earrings, Toto tended to tear them to pieces. Sometimes she would run up to Mrs. Hoyt when she was not looking and grab the necklace from her neck, break it, and run off with it. On many occasions the Hoyts spent long periods on their hands and knees trying to retrieve pearls that had been dropped all over the room in this way. Toto was cured of this behavior by being given a bracelet and necklace of her own.

Eventually Toto recovered her health completely and became strong and well again, and the Hoyts decided to return to the United States. But they were not sure where to go, since they needed a climate that would be suitable for Toto as well as for them.

Eventually they decided that Havana would be the ideal place in which to settle, and one fine day Mrs. Hoyt got on a little launch at Cherbourg to take them to the transatlantic liner which was to convey them to Cuba. They had a suite of rooms on this ship, and had given Toto a sleeping pill before they took her aboard wrapped up like a human baby. Mrs. Hoyt's Pomeranian dogs were also carried on in an invisible kind of way, so that no one on the ship knew that these animals were in the suite. Throughout the journey the Hoyts had everything organized so that whenever the stewards were in any one of the rooms the animals were in another one, so the stewards themselves never even knew the animals were there. I remember once bringing fifty experimental mice by ship from Melbourne to Perth, Australia, in this same secret way; I kept them in an adjacent empty cabin which I had access to because I had bribed the cabin steward to give me the key. On one occasion a lady occupying a neighboring cabin asked me if I could smell mice in that area, but I denied being able to smell anything.

One of the problems with Toto during this period was that she would try to climb out of the porthole whenever it was open, and she also made strong efforts to catch the blades of the electric fan. In spite of great care, Toto managed to break up several chairs, then she tore most of the curtains in the suite to pieces. These they managed to conceal until the last day of the voyage, when Mrs. Hoyt went to the captain of the ship and told him about their wrongdoings and paid for the destruction.

Mrs. Hoyt's husband had reached Havana before they arrived, and he met the ship at the dock accompanied by members of the press, who were all very pleased when they saw Toto dressed up in baby clothes. She was the subject of many pictures and attempted interviews on that day. Toto was incredibly pleased when Mr. Hoyt called out to her, and she threw her arms around his neck. It was a long time before she would let him go. In the hotel where they stayed there was a double bed in one room, and in an adjacent room with a bed in it Toto slept soundly and relaxed as long as the communicating door between the two rooms was left open.

Eventually the Hoyts found a house to rent in the Country Club Park in Havana. It had extensive grounds and gardens which Toto took to instantly. Toto was nine months old. This was the time when she stood upright for the first time and Mrs. Hoyt was called excitedly by Abdullah to come and see Toto walking, while holding his hand. Toto was delighted with herself, murmuring "woo-woo" all the time, and kissed Mrs. Hoyt repeatedly. Once she had made a start at walking, she was soon seen walking with Abdullah all over the grounds. As Toto began cutting her teeth, her mistress made a big fuss of each tooth that appeared. Toto soon got the idea that they were important and used to stand in front of a long looking glass opening her mouth and gazing at the little tooth sticking out from it. Presumably when she did this she knew it was her image, yet there were occasions when she would show anger at the figure in the mirror, attack it, and attempt to destroy it.

Toto took rapidly to picture magazines and spent many hours looking at them, turning the pages and not tearing them as many of our animals will do. Bobby and some of our other animals have been supplied with picture books from time to time, but they look at the pictures only for a little time and then rapidly destroy them. When Toto was supplied with newspapers she would dance on them and would love to crumple them up; she was very pleased with the noise they made when they were stamped on, and she also liked the noise of tearing them. Our tree ocelot, Cleo, also has a weakness for tearing paper. She does this partly to attract our attention and partly because she likes the noise.

Toto reacted in an unusual way to the swimming pool on the grounds of the house where she lived. When Mrs. Hoyt went in swimming, Toto would panic, scream with fear, and run around the edge of the pool in excitement, waving and leaning over. When Mrs. Hoyt came near her, she would grab her bathing cap and try to drag her out of the pool. She behaved as if she were frightened that something might happen to her mistress in the water.

It is of interest that the great apes have a fear of deep water and do not try to swim. During the summer that we had Bobby and the little female chimpanzee Jenera on an island in the lake in front of the house of Emory's president, they would go into the water, on many occasions up about waist high, but they never made any attempt to go any deeper or to swim away from the island. There are records in some of the Continental zoos of gorillas or orangutans drowning by falling into the moat surrounding their dens.

Among the various presents given to Toto, some had special interest for her and others she ignored or destroyed. For example, she was given a toy elephant, a toy teddy bear, and a squeaky ball. These she either threw away or tore to pieces. Then they gave her a spinning top, a hard rubber ball, and white chalk. She very quickly learned to spin the top with her fingers and needed only one lesson before she became expert in spinning it. She bounced the hard rubber balls on the floor and caught them, and she would sit for hours on the stone paths drawing scribbles with the chalk on the stones.

At about this time, 1930, Madame Rosalia Abreu, who had a private colony of primates in Havana, died and her colony was redistributed. Her animal handler became available to the

Hoyts, and they employed him to look after Toto. This Cuban animal keeper, Tomas, used to watch Toto drawing, and whenever she drew something that appeared to be a number he would play it in the lottery. On only one occasion did he actually win. Sometimes Tomas, the gardeners, and the butler could be seen all gathered around Toto deciding what the number was that Toto had just written so they could bet it in the lottery.

With the arrival of Tomas, Abdullah went back to Africa. He had come to Havana in a pair of khaki shorts and shirt, and he returned to Africa with several trunks of ties and shirts, underwear, shoes and hats, etc. Mrs. Hoyt said that in his smart blue business suit he looked more like a prosperous Harlem bandleader than a native African boy. When he got back to Tanganyika he had enough money to start the first of a chain of stores.

Madame Abreu, the previous employer of Tomas, had a remarkable collection of primates. She had started with a macaque monkey and had eventually become interested in anthropoid apes. Later she accumulated a great collection of ape people which we will describe shortly. Madame Abreu was a very religious woman and according to Mrs. Hoyt was convinced that apes had immortal souls; she even had her apes attend mass with her in a private chapel erected on her own estate. One of Madame Abreu's guests described how she went into an enclosure with two chimpanzees carrying a rosary; one of the chimpanzees cowered back when it saw the cross and retired to the rear of the enclosure, whereas the other one came forward and appeared to kiss the cross. Madame Abreu said of the chimp which cowered back, "He has been evil and knows it, but dear little Clochette is good."

Tomas took complete charge of Toto and was with her day and night for more than six years, even sleeping in the same bed in a room assigned to the pair of them. The Hoyts later made a special bed for Toto. In this bed a hole was cut through the mattress and springs, and under it a vessel was placed; Toto used this for her own toilet purposes at night, but in the daytime she used the conventional toilet. She also learned to turn on all the faucets in the new house and in the garden and caused floods from time to time. Tomas trained Toto to sit at the table and eat with him.

Problems of keeping an anthropoid ape in the home now began to bear down on Mrs. Hoyt, because by the time Toto was three years old she was as strong as two men and had the ingenuity of a dozen growing boys. She could open all the doors whether they were locked or not. She knew how to find unused keys, and if she could not open the doors with the keys, she would either break the handle off the door or knock the door down. She learned that she could crash through a door by simply putting her shoulder against it and pushing, so it became impossible to keep her in one room simply by locking the doors. Another of her tricks was to slide down the banisters, and the Hoyts tried very hard to break her of this habit. Her various other activities made the Hoyts realize that it would be extremely difficult to keep her much longer in the house. Among her activities was to move her heavy iron bed across the room and get it close to the wall; from there she could reach the bell to the servants' quarters. She would then set it clanging at any hour of the day or night.

Finally the Hoyts decided to build a house for their mischievous animal. The house had a living room 15 feet by 25 feet, a bedroom 10 by 15, and an outside enclosure 40 by 80 which was surrounded and covered by heavy iron bars. In it they put benches and swings and various play equipment which Toto could use, and usually the door to the outside enclosure was left open so she could go in and out of the gardens at will. Generally, they locked her in this area only when they had visitors.

Even in this sophisticated retreat and with her sophisticated upbringing, Toto would build herself a nest of palm leaves on which she would lie on hot afternoons. By this time Tomas had finally managed to extricate himself from having to sleep with her at night so she became accustomed eventually, by a gradual procedure, to sleep by herself. The Hoyts were greatly impressed by the extreme intelligence of Toto; but they pointed out that although she was highly intelligent, she was not intelligent enough to learn human self-discipline, and this was really the thing which made it impossible to keep her in the house. So she fell between the two stools of being neither human nor a dumb brute and lived in what the Hoyts described as a "half-world" to which she had been conditioned by their companionship. As a result she wanted to share human life to the fullest, but she did not understand why limitations should be imposed upon her.

This was a period when Toto adopted a kitten called Blanquita. She would pick it up very gently, cuddling it in her arms. The kitten was apparently as pleased as Toto with this treatment, and it snuggled in against Toto and purred very happily. After that the cat was constantly with the gorilla, and wherever Toto went she carried the cat; sometimes she carried it under her arms, sometimes just clinging to her back as a baby gorilla does when its mother is walking or climbing, and sometimes she wore it wrapped around her neck like a fur stole. The cat became similarly dedicated to Toto. Eventually Blanquita grew up, and one morning she produced a litter of six kittens in Toto's bedroom. This seemed to upset Toto, and she looked and behaved as if she were angry. She walked over to the new family of kittens, looked them over, and finally picked one out. This was a black and white kitten rather like its mother in appearance. From the moment she adopted the kitten she behaved as if the kitten's mother did not exist, and after having been Toto's loving companion for so long, Blanquita found herself on the outside. She would come and rub against Toto and purr, but Toto would not pay attention to her at all and would even brush her off, demonstrating quite plainly that she did not want anything to do with her. She bestowed all her attention on the baby, who was named Principe by the Hoyts.

Although Toto was capable of violence, with Mrs. Hoyt she was mostly gentle and affectionate and as playful as she could be. Mrs. Hoyt always took her a glass of milk at four o'clock in the afternoon and would play with her for a while in her little garden or playroom. She mentions that when Toto had been very tiny and had a little scratch or cut she would kiss it and blow on it, and now Toto put this in reverse and every time Mrs. Hoyt came to her she would examine her hands and arms and neck; if she found the slightest scratch or abrasion she would also blow at it in a very gentle fashion. Toto was very fond of Mrs. Hoyt's mother and would sit for long periods stroking her white hair. Mrs. Hoyt's mother had taught Toto how to make pictures in the sand with her finger. She would draw a circle to outline a face and put three dots inside, two for the eyes and one for the nose, and she would put a straight line for the mouth. Often Toto was seen to greet the old lady by making this drawing in front of her in the air as she approached. Later, Toto actually drew this representation of a face on the flagstones, but whether she recognized it as a face or whether it was simply a series of movements which she had learned, it is difficult to say.

Toto was also a great eater of mosquitoes and ants. If she saw a group of ants she would brush her arms against them so that a number of them would stick to the fur, and then she would lick them off just like a gorilla in the wild.

Toto was very fond of Mr. Hoyt, but she had no respect for his straw hats or neckties. She was especially fond of his ties, and if they were bright-colored and he came near her she would suddenly grab at the tie and with a quick jerk rip it away from around his neck. Sometimes when the tie did not break, the force of the pull would throw Mr. Hoyt on his face. On another occasion a friend of the family who was a very strong man and a boxer came to visit. He was warned about Toto's strength before he shook hands with her but scorned any danger. The moment Toto got her hands in his, however, she gave him one pull and threw him against the bars of the enclosure with such force that it seemed that he might have broken a shoulder; however, fortunately, only the muscle was bruised.

Toto played one particularly mischievous trick which caused some concern to the gardeners. To trim the tops of the tall trees the gardeners would climb up a ladder leaning against the trees. If Toto was loose and saw a gardener climbing up the ladder she would immediately chase after him and run up the ladder behind him. The gardener would be so terrified he would go up to the top of the ladder over the tree, scramble or fall down the other side, and rush off at high speed. Toto would then jump off the ladder and chase him madly for a little while. On these occasions she would then pick up the pruning shears that the gardener had dropped and throw them after him. It all sounds very much like a comedy sequence from an early movie.

The food that Toto was given is of interest. At 7:30 A.M. she had yogurt mixed with sugar water; at 8:15 A.M. she was given a quart and a half of milk and tapioca; and at 10:00 a large mug of orange juice. At 11:30 she was given eight bananas and some cream cheese. At 1:00 P.M. she had lunch on a tray. At first she was given no meat with this, but since she ate with Tomas she soon began to steal the steak and chicken from his tray and insisted that she also be given the same type of food. At 4:00 P.M. she had a quart and a half of milk with oatmeal or Pablum or cocoa malt. At 6:00 P.M. she was given two baked apples and drank a jug of milk. Between meals, of course, she had water *ad lib.* She had no problem indicating to people that she wanted a drink of water. She would look at a water faucet, indicate it with a hand or a finger, and smack rapidly with her lips.

The actual articles of food included from day to day are of interest: vegetable soup, fresh carrots, potatoes, sweet potatoes, rice, barley, tapioca, eggs scrambled or boiled or served as an omelet, beef steak, lemon meringue pie, apple pie, and fruit compote. Her favorite fruit was peaches, but she also liked grapes and oranges and bananas. She did not like melons at all. Although she loved baked apples, she would only nibble at a raw apple.

The remarkable strength of the animal was shown by the fact that on one occasion when she went into the garage and found the station wagon in her way, she took it by the rear axle with one hand, and even though the emergency brake had been put on, she pushed the car against the wall of the garage with such force as to smash its headlights. Even when she was walking with Mrs. Hoyt there were occasions when she would unpredictably grab her dress, give it a jerk, and either tear a large piece of it off or else pull her onto the ground. Sometimes she would stand erect and then charge, and Mrs. Hoyt said that the only way not to be hurt when this happened was to fall on the ground and roll out of her path. However, sometimes on these occasions Toto would seize her by the arm or even by a portion of her dress and pull her along the lawn or walk, often releasing her only after cries had brought her assistance. Even when Mrs. Hoyt was playing with her in a quite gentle way, kissing her and putting her arms around her, she would every now and again on sudden impulse rip Mrs. Hoyt's dress off and tear it to pieces. Because of this, her mistress always had a special locker in Toto's playroom,

53

and in it she kept a variety of clothes so that she would have something to put on when she left the animal playroom. At about this time Mrs. Hoyt found that the delivery boys who were bringing her groceries refused to come to the house and simply threw their deliveries over the wall into the grounds.

Eventually it was decided that the complications of keeping such a strong animal in a home were too much. All those associated with Toto were in danger, not because the animal was malignant but because she did not know her own strength. She was potentially dangerous to all the neighbors. Mrs. Hoyt found herself forced to make a decision to give Toto to Ringling Brothers Circus, which already had a large male gorilla, Gargantua. It was thought that Toto would make a very good mate for this animal. When they were first brought together, however, Toto would have nothing to do with Gargantua, who eventually retired, frustrated and hurt, to the farthest corner of his cage and sulked. Principe, the cat, had accompanied Toto on this expedition, for she would have been very upset if the cat had been left behind. Unfortunately, in Boston where the circus was traveling, Principe was lost and the circus was forced to move on before she was found. In Chicago Mrs. Hoyt discovered a cat who had some of the appearance of Principe, and she hoped that Toto would accept her in lieu of her pet. But Toto would have nothing to do with her and pushed her away. Toto remained with the circus, and I do not know what her final end was except that she was still there in 1941.

I have dealt with Mrs. Hoyt's experiences with Toto at some length because they demonstrated two points. One is that however intimately you are associated with a young ape, when it grows up it is difficult to keep in a home. The animal just does not understand the restrictions that such an existence places upon it, and it will use its great strength to get rid of any restrictions which are irritating. The second is that Mrs. Hoyt's detailed description of her ape child brings out many remarkable aspects of the animal's intelligence, especially its ability to draw a representation of the human face. These descriptions help to underline the fact that the great apes have an intelligence which we have scarcely penetrated yet, and this is largely owing to our failure to communicate adequately with them.

3. Ape People in Havana

MOST of Toto's life was lived in Havana, Cuba. Perhaps this is appropriate, since Havana had acquired, before the arrival of Toto, one of the biggest private collections of primates, including a number of anthropoid apes, that any private individual has assembled.

This remarkable collection of animals was owned by Madame Rosalia Abreu. Madame Abreu had collected her group of monkeys and apes between 1920 and 1930, and was the first person to show that it was possible to breed and rear the chimpanzee in confinement. Her firstborn chimpanzee, Anuma, was greeted with great interest by Cuban scientists and grew up to maturity in Madame Abreu's care. Madame Abreu and her parents were native Cubans. Her father, a Cuban businessman, died when Rosalia was thirteen; nevertheless, she had established a close friendship with him, and a great deal of understanding had developed between the two of them by the time of his death. Throughout her life Rosalia had a great deal of affection for pets. She had a little dove at one time and on other occasions a Mexican dog, a hummingbird, and various animals. Madame Abreu was herself the mother of five children and was completely occupied in rearing them in the first years of her marriage, but later she became increasingly interested in animals and obtained a great deal of intellectual and emotional satisfaction from them. Dr. Robert Mearns Yerkes had his first exposure to the problems of keeping a colony of apes through his friendship with Madame Abreu and his visits to her colony in Havana. He wrote of his experiences in his book *Almost Human.*

In her thirties, Madame Abreu saw her first monkey in France. It was a macaque, and she bought it and named in Minguita. Toward the end of the decade after she had settled permanently in Havana, Madame Abreu had acquired 75 monkeys and apes. In 1902 she purchased a chimpanzee which was a very bright animal about five or six years old. This first chimpanzee, named Chimpita, was kept at Madame Abreu's residence at Quinta Palatino for nearly ten years. A number of gibbons, orangutans, and other chimpanzees subsequently joined the colony, and of them all the chimpanzee was her favorite. She felt he was the most intelligent of the animals and the one that was most grateful for any kindness. Madame Abreu had a fine collection of South American monkeys, including owl monkeys, howler monkeys, squirrel monkeys, woolly monkeys, and various types of marmosets together with Old World monkeys such as macaques, guenons, and two special Celebes black apes. At one time she also had 10 baboons together with two mandrills; the latter are animals with highly colored faces and bottoms.

In 1924 Madame Abreu's tally of nonhuman primates included 18 anthropoid apes. She had 3 orangs, an adult male called Cachesita and two females, Cachita and Misuita, which she had obtained from Borneo by way of San Francisco. The male was about ten years old and the females six to eight years old. Dr. Yerkes, who had his second meeting with orangs at Madame Abreu's colony, said that it is not easy to become acquainted with them because although they are friendly they are rather Mongolian and their social attitude remains noncommittal or distrustful. I have not found it as difficult to become intimately acquainted with orangutans as Dr. Yerkes indicated. They are very affectionate animals, and one can achieve a close and good relationship with them. Dr. Yerkes felt that superficially, at any rate, chimpanzees resemble man more than the other anthropoid apes.

Madame Abreu did not keep gorillas in her colony. This was not for want of trying; Dr. Yerkes commented that the young gorilla has proved exceptionally difficult to keep in captivity and that captive adult individuals at the time his book was written were almost unknown. This, of course, is not our experience. We

Toto and Principe.

have many young gorillas growing up in our Center, starting from one year old. We have not had the privilege of having any born in our Center as yet, since all our gorilla people are too young for this purpose. Dr. Yerkes did not find the gorilla as appealing a person as the chimpanzee.

One of the things about great apes that makes them so attractive to humans is that so many of the things they do seem to have significance in human behavior or at least to be very reminiscent of it. Probably no single act that I have seen recorded is more extraordinary than the one that Dr. Yerkes describes as having taken place in Madame Abreu's colony one night. One of her servants was attracted to the cage of one of the chimpanzees, known as Monona, who rattled her chain. He released her and then discovered that there was a baby chimpanzee who was apparently dead; the mother had been rattling her chain to get to it, since it had apparently scrambled out of her reach. The mother began to work on this baby by breathing into its mouth and drawing its tongue out with her lips—in other words, giving it some kind of artificial respiration. After a short period of this treatment the infant showed signs of breathing, and the mother then cleaned it up and later chewed the umbilical cord until the remnant was close to the body of the baby. There seems little doubt that if the mother had not been able to get to this infant it would have died. We do not have any record in the Yerkes Center of such extraordinary behavior, which certainly shows signs of intuition or instinct, but we do have instances of mothers mouthing newborn babies, wiping mucus from their mouths, and so on. Whether Madame Abreu's Monona knew what she was doing or not (the latter is most probable), it certainly was the most appropriate behavior for this situation. Dr. Yerkes, in writing about this particular occasion, wonders how many inexperienced human mothers would have acted so appropriately with a baby who was not breathing. Later, one of Madame Abreu's rhesus monkeys produced a baby who appeared lifeless, but the mother paid no attention to it and it was taken away from her. This time it was Madame Abreu who performed on it the same kind of activities that Monona performed on her baby and was able to bring the little rhesus baby back to life. It has since grown into a

59

not completely normal but very healthy animal. The rhesus mother obviously did not show the same "instinct"—or was it "insight"?—as the chimpanzee.

There are other examples from Madame Abreu's colony which presumably indicate a high level of intelligence in her animals. One day her first chimpanzee, Chimpita, and his mate, Cucusa, managed to escape. The guard at Quinta Palatino began to shoot into the air in hopes that this would frighten the animals and make them go back into their cages. At the same time they were called and commanded to come back. Chimpita did do so, but Cucusa climbed up a tree, climbed down again, came up to the guard, took him by the hand, and took the revolver away from him. Probably the animal felt that this was a device that made a frightening noise, and she did not want to hear the noise again; the possibility that she interpreted this revolver as being death-dealing is remote.

On another occasion Madame Abreu was giving Chimpita some grapes and he kept the seeds in his mouth. She was frightened that these might cause some upset in his gastrointestinal tract, so she told him to give her the seeds. He spat all the seeds he had in his mouth into her hand, and then with the aid of his lips and his hands retrieved more seeds from the floor and gave them to her. Eventually, there were only two seeds left; they were in the angle between the wall of the cage and the floor, and he couldn't get at them either with his lips or with his fingers. So Madame Abreu said to him, "Chimpita, when I have gone you will eat those seeds." He then went into the cage next door and found a little stick, and with it he poked the seeds out and gave them to Madame Abreu. Understanding what his mistress required was probably geared not so much to what she said as to the accompanying gestures which gave the animal a clue to what she wanted. At any rate the incident does give some indication of the intelligence of these animals.

Higher primates seem to be aware when they have been injured and that the attempts by humans to treat the injury is being done to help them. Madame Abreu's Chimpita escaped on one occasion, broke a window, and got pieces of glass in his arm.

60

He sat very quietly and very patiently just like a human being while the arm was worked over, the pieces of glass withdrawn with forceps, and the arm properly dressed. On another occasion one of the chimpanzees had to receive a blood transfusion directly from another animal. The donor chimpanzee was placed on a table alongside the chimpanzee who was to receive the blood, and although she was quite an active type of animal she lay quietly on the table and remained virtually quiet during the whole of the period of the operation. The sick chimpanzee was of course too weak to make any struggle. It was almost as if the donor chimpanzee was aware that something very important was being done and she had to contribute.

Dr. Yerkes described his experience in treating some chimpanzees for hookworms. One of them was a little male. His jaws were wedged apart and he had a stomach tube passed, but he acted entirely as though he understood what was going on and that it was all done with the best of intentions. This is not always the case, of course; an older male and female did not behave this way, but struggled continuously. There is no doubt that there is a good deal of individual variation in the behavior of such animals during this type of handling.

There is a tendency for apes to use tools. Jane Goodall has described the use of straws and sticks by chimpanzees to poke ants out of holes, and Dr. Adriaan Kortlandt has described how chimpanzees pick up sticks and throw them at a threatening object such as an imitation leopard. Dr. Yerkes noted that he had found only one monkey, as distinct from an ape, who had any aptitude for the use of tools. Yerkes says that the use of objects as tools by the chimpanzee is very common, and anything which can be found is bound to be used not only as a plaything but something "to be monkeyed with." He claims that he has seen a chimpanzee who has been separated from his mate by a wire partition use a straw to caress her face. The animal would use bits of grass and sticks and wires or anything else that was in the cage to draw in objects which he desired as food. The gorilla does the same type of thing, and the orangutans are also great manipulators.

61

Another interesting thing about the great apes is their eagerness to play. They will accept as playmates children, human adults, or members of their own kind or another species of ape. We have put chimpanzees in with gorillas and with an orang, and in both cases the animals had great fun wrestling and playing together before they settled down and accepted each other. They still have bouts of play from time to time. The play seems to be running and chasing with wrestling and play biting, and they never seem to injure themselves during these activities. It is a different matter, of course, when they do it with a human being, because often bites intended as play bites are pretty painful and possibly even dangerous to human beings, who have a much softer skin. Madame Abreu and Yerkes came to the conclusion that gibbons were very much less intelligent in play and in the matter of handling tools than the other apes.

Yerkes also describes how in visiting one of Madame Abreu's chimpanzees, the chimpanzee picked up a mango and threw it with considerable skill and accuracy at him. When the mango was thrown back he caught it with remarkable assurance. This particular animal had in fact an abundant opportunity to play with balls, so he had obviously developed a certain amount of skill in throwing. The chimpanzees that inhabit the islands surrounded by moats at the zoo in the town of Chester in England spend a great deal of time pulling up sods of grass and heaving them across the moat with considerable accuracy at cars containing visitors to the zoo which are driving past. Another chimpanzee of the Abreu colony acquired the trick of handclapping, and we have two at the Yerkes Center who are very experienced in this respect.

A description is given by Madame Abreu of what she describes as the "vision of death" by her chimpanzees.

I was in Cambo les Bains. It was on the death of Cucusa. A moment before she died she took my head in her two hands and kissed it very long. She saw that death was coming and was saying goodbye. Then she jumped from me to her bed and died. Jimmy who was outside in the park began to scream. He continued to scream looking about as though he saw something. The next day he still kept watching far away towards the mountains. Here at Quinta Palatino, when Mimosa died, he did the same thing. He screamed and screamed and screamed, and kept looking and looking with lower lip hanging down as if he saw something that we could not see. His scream was different from any I have heard at other times. It made my flesh creep. On two or three other occasions when little monkeys have died he has screamed in the same way and watched and looked out. I had him observed to see if there were animals passing or if it was one of his cage companions that excited him. There was nothing passing by, yet he screamed. Then later after he had stopped, we let other animals pass his cage, but he paid no attention. So it seems that it was nothing outside that disturbed him. It is five times, I think, that he has done this. The other day when little Minina died, Jimmy did not scream. Perhaps this was because he did not know Minina.

Yerkes mentions that possibly this so-called vision of death is one of the reasons why Madame Abreu believed that chimpanzees had souls. Madame Abreu noted that primate mothers were strongly attached to their young. She records this in a rhesus monkey and also in baboons. Even when the baby died, she found that the mother continued to hold him. An orang will put a dead baby on her head. In fact, we have seen our orangs carry a live baby in the same position. Madame Abreu described how she had problems getting a dead baby away from one of her chimpanzees:

When Cucusa's second baby was born, Anuma was about three years old. With the baby he was as gentle and affectionate as could be, taking care of it and playing with it without interference from the mother. When the mother became ill the baby was affected and shortly died. Cucusa would not let us take away the baby, so I contrived to put a cord around its neck to conceal it so that the mother would not notice anything unusual. Then I began to play with Cucusa, to caress her and divert her attention from the little one. When I saw my opportunity I signaled to my helpers and they, jerking the cord, pulled the body of the baby from Cucusa's arms. She was not holding it very tightly so we succeeded in this way to get it away from her. She cried and cried as I did my best to console her.

Madame Abreu records quite a number of cases of her animals becoming jealous or defending their colleagues. She describes one occasion on which a young lady who liked monkeys and was usually accepted by them was petting a capuchin, a good-natured male animal, and a little female capuchin, who was also supposed to be gentle, bit her hand. It appeared to be a true act of jealousy.

One thing noted by Madame Abreu is that young chimpanzees and orangutans when frustrated or unable to get what they want have been noted to strike their foreheads on the wall or floor of their cage, a procedure which is also to be seen in young human children.

Dr. Yerkes first visited Quinta Palatino in Havana at Madame Abreu's invitation in January, 1924. At that time she showed him a letter she had received from the famous Dr. Élie Metchnikoff, who had shown great interest in establishing a colony of chimpanzees for medical research. His letter was of great interest and is reprinted here. It is dated in Paris, August 29, 1915, and was addressed from the Institute Pasteur, 25 Rue Dutot.

Dear Madame:

I am infinitely obliged to you for your interesting letter accompanied by the splendid photographs which I have just received. It is indeed marvelous that you have been able to obtain them, for to my knowledge, it is the first time that attempts to photograph an anthropoid ape in captivity have been successful. All the advice that I have had from doctors in Africa and Guinea and in the Congo is to the effect that they have never been able to obtain a likeness of a chimpanzee. I congratulate you then on your result which presents something of great importance for the future in the study of the infectious diseases such as scarlet fever, measles, and diphtheria.

All that you say about the relations between the male and female, about gestation, and about the birth and rearing of the young is of vital interest. Since you are continuing your observations perhaps it will be possible for you to tell me still more details of the life of your chimpanzees. What is the procedure by which the male arrives at intercourse with the female? How does he behave in taking his particular position and does she manifest any coquetry? Does copulation continue during pregnancy? Or does the female cease to accept the male? Does the latter caress the female before and after the act?

How many interesting observations will you be able to make on the education of the little one? Does the mother take care of the infant and does she give him some cuffs? How does the male behave face-to-face with his offspring? Does he continue to live maritably with his mate? And does he not make advances to the dry nurse? (The question as to whether the anthropoids are monogamous or polygamous is particularly interesting.)

You thought, Madame, that your letter would appear to me too long. I have read and re-read it many times, but I find it all too short. So vital is the subject of your observations.

In thanking you again I pray you, Madame, to accept the expression of my respectful homage.

Élie Metchnikoff.

Dr. Metchnikoff was an international authority on medical research and one of its founders. At that time, the appreciation which he showed of Madame Abreu's work naturally considerably encouraged her. At the same time the Pasteur Institute was considering the establishment of a special research station and laboratory for the study of monkeys and apes and their utilization in the study of many medical problems. The Institute finally decided to establish such an anthropoid station, but because of World War I the implementation of this idea was delayed for a good many years. By 1924 the Pasteur Institute had in fact established in French West Africa (French Guinea) an anthropoid institute for medical research and was working actively in a number of medical areas. Dr. Yerkes believed that Madame Abreu's achievements and her letters to Dr. Metchnikoff played an important part in stimulating the Pasteur Institute to go ahead with the establishment of such a colony.

The first chimpanzee born on Madame Abreu's estate was Anuma. He saw the light of day on April 27, 1915, and was the son of Cucusa and Jimmy. Cucusa had been with Chimpita for some time but had refused to mate with him. Subsequently Jimmy was with a young female called Mimosa, and these two for some reason or another also did not breed, yet Cucusa and Jimmy bred very well together. This indicates that there are certain sex preferences among chimpanzees. Madame Abreu advised bringing animals together slowly if they are going to be mated, and she suggested that prior to mating the animals, the male and female should be placed in separated and adjoining cages so that they become completely acquainted with each other before they are put together. Dr. Yerkes introduced this procedure into the tradition of the Yerkes labs; it is still carried on in the present Center, but not exclusively. The reason for putting animals in adjacent cages is that if two strange adult animals are put together in a cage situation, the cage is too small to give either of the animals an opportunity to escape from the other if it is being seriously attacked. So they need to get to know each other first. Madame Abreu made many important observations about the sex and mating behavior of ape people which were confirmed by Dr. Yerkes. We will refer to these subjects again when we are dealing with the sexual life of apes.

Madame Abreu was the first person to make any extensive study of the care of captive primates, particularly of the large primates. Dr. Yerkes emphasized that it is difficult to exaggerate the importance of the knowledge of how to keep great apes healthy and contented and have them breed in captivity. Madame Abreu, through her twenty years of experience, made an invaluable contribution to the practical knowledge of keeping primates, especially apes, in captivity. Dr. Yerkes developed it to near-perfection.

The Abreu estate was situated on the outskirts of Havana. It had many beautiful buildings and grounds and an abundance of fruit and shade trees around, which helped the caged animals to feel that they were more or less in their native habitat. This type of design was characteristic of that which Dr. Yerkes used when he first built the Yerkes Laboratories in Orange Park, Florida, but we will have more about that later.

The climate of Havana is very mild throughout the entire year, but there are cool nights not only in the winter but also in the summer. It was adequate under those circumstances simply to have nest boxes or small rooms where the animals could curl up, particularly if there was a storm. There was never frost, so there was no need for artificial heating.

About 100 to 150 feet from her house in Quinta Palatino Park,

Madame Abreu built 50 cages in a half-circle. She had small cages only 3 or 4 feet in diameter for marmosets; they were 3 feet above the ground and 4 to 5 feet in height. Her cages varied from this to the large-size cage Jimmy, the chimpanzee, and his family occupied, which was 60 feet long, 30 feet wide, and 20 feet high. In some of her cages the steel framework which carried the roof and the walls of wire netting was covered with a decorative coating of concrete which imitated the trunks and branches of trees. This gave a very attractive, rustic effect. The cages had cement floors to facilitate cleaning. Madame Abreu made a point of having a good deal of sun and shade available for the animals, pointing out that it is essential that the animals retreat into the shade at any hour of the day that they wish to. It is possible for them to get heat stroke, as we have found to be the case especially with gorillas, who can stay in direct sunlight for only a relatively short period of time.

Dr. Yerkes has suggested that it would have been a big advantage for the apes at Madame Abreu's Quinta Palatino to have had a separate room as a kind of special dining room or dining cage with access from the other cages and fitted with a long table and chairs. It could also be used for a playroom or schoolroom as well as a dining room. Madame Abreu had experimented with these arrangements, but had never been able to find anyone with sufficient time and interest to train the animals to feed like humans and to play. It can be done, of course, easily with one or two animals, but with a large family of apes it would be a major undertaking.

Every morning Madame Abreu made a round of the cages, giving to each animal or each group some cooked fruit from her own table or any special delicacy she had at that time. This was kind of a social visitation, a friendly greeting, and a petting which was appreciated by the animals not only for the food, but for the social relationship with Madame Abreu. At three in the afternoon a main meal for the day (dinner) was distributed by the keepers. That meal consisted of cooked food, usually with vegetables such as white and sweet potatoes, squash, and corn. For the evening meal the animals often received rice. In season the corn was fed green on the cob. Sometimes there was baked plantain. The food supply varied, of course, with the season, and Yerkes pointed out that although some authorities thought at one time that apes needed meat to be able to survive, there was no evidence that this was so. In his experience with apes and also in current Yerkes experience, meat is not a necessary article of diet although it is accepted. Our animals have eaten hamburgers, they have eaten eggs, and they will eat fish, but this is an expensive way to give protein to large apes. They can get it more easily from milk, from soybeans, etc. There is little doubt that in the wild state apes do eat animal protein. In a wild colony of chimpanzees in Africa studied by Jane Goodall, the animals would sometimes grab and kill a baby baboon and then eat it. They have also been seen eating the meat from animals that various predators had killed.

The value of insects in ape and primate diet has been greatly underestimated even by primatologists. A vegetarian diet is not adequate to keep great apes in perfect health, hence the desirability of milk in their diets and also of giving them some kind of vegetable which has high protein in it. Madame Abreu was very much opposed to overfeeding her animals. If you overfeed them, they not only eat too much but they leave food lying about in the cage and it ferments and attracts insects of all sorts. For this reason she fed the animals smaller amounts of food on a number of separate occasions. Madame Abreu used to take some of her animals, such as the orangs and most of her chimps, into her house for the night. They were, of course, caged securely, but her idea was that this would protect them from taking cold and possibly getting pneumonia.

Dr. Yerkes was very impressed with the health of the great ape colony at Quinta Palatino. He concluded that the climate of Cuba seemed to suit them extremely well, but that their care and feeding was also an important factor. Many zoos and a number of individuals have had great difficulty in trying to breed apes in captivity. At the time of the Abreu colony there were records of a number of chimpanzees being born in captivity at various zoos and institutions, but the story usually finished up with the infant's death. Dr. Yerkes was probably ahead of his time in suggesting that the cause was nutrition. At the time Dr. Yerkes

Miss Alyse Cunningham with John Daniel II.

was writing, which was in 1924, the relationships between captive gorillas and man had been very unfortunate. Dr. Yerkes thought that the gorilla's temperamental resistance to being caged and his inability to become reconciled to loneliness had caused him to perish, whereas the more resilient orangutan and chimpanzee did very well. The captive life of the chimp and orang, he said, could be measured in months; that of the gorilla had been measured only in days. Up until a few years prior to 1926, there had been no record of a gorilla's being kept in captivity outside Africa in a reasonably healthy contented condition for more than a few weeks.

Yerkes subsequently became impressed by the work of Miss Alyse Cunningham, who had set a new record for keeping gorillas. She had devoted a great deal of care and affection to her gorillas and had been able to keep three young animals at various

69

times for periods from a few weeks up to several years. The first of these was John Daniel, whom she kept until he was so large it was no longer possible to keep him in the household. The second had been injured when he was captured and died after only a few weeks in her possession. Her third, called Sultan or John Daniel II, had been a captive for two years by the time she got him and at the time Dr. Yerkes was writing was flourishing very well. He gave the appearance of being a healthy, contented, happy person. The lesson from the Abreu colony and from Miss Cunningham's success and the efforts of others was that it is really necessary to treat these higher apes in a similar fashion to a human person. Without companionship, the gorilla, in particular, becomes a sulky and despondent animal. He may refuse to eat, may become sick and die, especially if he is not caught at a very early age. It is important to remember that primates are social creatures. They are as eager or anxious as human beings to have the company of their own kind or, in its absence, human attention. They depend upon it for real contentment and happiness. Some companionship and some play are quite important for their health and contentment. Dr. Yerkes points out that no primate should be kept in isolation if it can possibly be avoided. Madame Abreu made many observations on the development of the infant ape and its childhood, but we will come back to that in a later part of this book.

Madame Abreu was very concerned about the sanitation of her animals as an aid to the prevention of disease. She says that "the requirements are simple—fresh air, sunshine, pure water, and protection from drafts when the animal sleeps." Dr. Yerkes qualifies this by saying that he would emphasize the following points:

Freedom, or reasonably spacious quarters; fresh air and sunshine, preferably coupled with marked variations in temperature; cleanliness of surroundings as well as of the body; clean and carefully prepared food in proper variety and quantity; a sufficient and regular supply of pure water, congenial species companionship and intelligent and sympathetic human companionship, which, transcending the routine care of the animal, provides for the development of interest if not friendliness; and, finally, adequate resources and opportunites both in company and in isolation for work and play. Given these conditions of captive existence, primates originally healthful and normal should without difficulty be kept in good condition of body and mind and should naturally reproduce and successfully rear their young.

4. The Founding of the Yerkes Laboratories for Primate Biology

THERE is no doubt that the valuable information Dr. Robert Yerkes obtained at Madame Abreu's colony stimulated his earlier interest in anthropoid apes. The knowledge and experience he obtained in the methods of caging, handling, breeding, and feeding such animals enabled him to prepare finally for the establishment of his own institution.

The scientific reasons for Dr. Yerkes' infatuation with these animals are given in his book *Almost Human.* They provide a background for Dr. Yerkes' thinking which is as true today as it was then. They help us to understand the motivating forces which caused him to found the original Yerkes Laboratories for Primate Biology.

The reasons for the scientist's neglect of the higher primates are important only as their discovery and consideration may enable us to escape them. It might naturally be supposed that we should know most about the creatures in our world which, superficially, at least, most closely resemble us. Why is this not true? There are several contributory causes, first among which is the relative scarcity of primates other than man in the principal areas of scientific enquiry. The monkeys and monkey-like animals, as well as the anthropoid apes are, in general, denizens of the tropics or of the subtropical regions, whereas science flourishes and has developed most highly in the temperate zones. Supplementing this geographical factor is the relative nuisance, difficulty, and expense of keeping the animals in closely restricted captivity. Unlike a lot of other wild creatures, they do not, generally speaking, thrive and breed readily in captivity. In this connection it must be remembered that scientific enquiry and discovery has usually been ill supported. The determined but self-sacrificing observer, eager to extend the bounds of knowledge, as a practical necessity has selected the most accessible, most easily dealt with, and most economically maintained materials for the study of his problems. Consequently, the frog, small rodent, such as the rat and mouse, the guinea pig and rabbit, have been much used for biological enquiries, whereas even the commoner and more readily accessible monkeys have been neglected. In the case of the anthropoid ape there is the additional essential fact of relative scarcity and high cost of specimens as well as of maintenance. These are some of the facts which appear when one examines the history of biology. *Are they to restrict research in the future?*

Dr. Yerkes also pointed out:

Most of us readily admit that we cannot have too accurate and detailed knowledge of our own organization and of its relations to environment. But some of us overlook the fact that many biological enquiries, which are pursued with the hope of improving the conditions of human life, may best be conducted, in some, at least, of their

Dr. Robert M. Yerkes holding Panzee and Chim.

stages, with other animals as subjects. In studies of structure, function, and mind it is often far more difficult and expensive to use human subjects than other primates or other mammals. So the principal, practical argument for the more extensive scientific use of the infra-human primates is such an increase of our knowledge of the facts and laws of life as will enable us to more wisely and effectively regulate or control individual social and racial existence. It is primarily an argument of econony.

Monkeys and apes are invariably the most popular exhibits in any zoo. People are fascinated by the semihuman acts which these animals put on in circuses and in the music hall. Yerkes has made the point that in the past 50 or 100 years there have been hundreds of thousands of dollars spent by zoos, circuses, and variety shows in which these animals were used exclusively for entertainment of the general public. Up to the time of the establishment of the seven primate centers by the federal government, the amount of money spent on the study of these animals in order to obtain a contribution from them to the health and welfare of the community at large had been negligible. Even now the sum spent on them is minute compared with what should be spent considering the dividends which would arise almost certainly from this study. Unfortunately, even as I write, the federal government has scheduled a severe financial cutback in the primate center programs.

Much that is of value comes from working with caged animals, but in the process of working with them we need also to have a good knowledge of how these animals behave in their natural habitat—what they live on, how they breed, their relationships between the various members of their community, and so on. Yerkes underlined the importance of providing expeditions, observation stations, support of field naturalists, etc. Since his time we still lack a good permanent station in this field for the observation of the great apes under natural conditions. There have been sporadic visits to study the orangutans, such as that made by Dr. Richard Davenport from the Yerkes Center and by one or two other investigators, and there have also been the excellent studies by Jane Goodall and others of the chimpanzees in Africa. More recently Diane Fossey has made some fascinating studies of gorillas.

Yerkes felt that research with anthropoid apes in the area of human behavior and mental life would supply an indirect approach to certain problems in human psychology which have been proven insoluble by other methods. He was very impressed with the possibility of using monkeys and apes as subjects for educational experiments because he believed that the similarity between the hereditary equipment and educability of the higher primates and man would enable experiments to be undertaken which could not be carried out with children. An experimenter can have no scruples in making a slight modification in the course of life of a monkey, an orangutan, or a gorilla by certain novel methods of educational treatment, but it would be impossible to take such unpredictable risks with a child, since the whole course of his life could be altered by the experimental procedures used. Dr. Yerkes also believed that a great deal of profitable information could be obtained by the study of primate social behavior. "Naturalistic studies of primates should give us adequate working knowledge of their social relations and organization of the chief factors of their social environment. There may appear, also, significant facts concerning social evolution and development, eugenic and euthenic practices or opportunities." Information gained from primates has enabled us to see in a quite different light the social problems of the day, and there is no question that the social studies that have already been carried out have contributed significantly in this area. Social studies with primates undoubtedly stimulate the further development of work in social psychology and sociology, and there is little doubt that in the years which have elapsed since Yerkes wrote, particularly in the last ten years, work with primates has made a significant contribution to the humanistic sciences. Studies of apes will make very significant contributions in the area of hygiene, preventive medicine, curative medicine, surgery, and allied practical arts. The medical significance of these apes was realized 50 years ago in the early twenties when the Pasteur Institute established its primate laboratories for medical research in French Guinea, but from then to the present day primate research seems to have been forgotten except for single special purposes.

The reader will see in the following pages something of the contributions which Yerkes Primate Center has already made to our understanding of the subject of human health and welfare. He will see something of the studies already being carried on and something of the promise for the future, provided those who handle federal funds still understand that the primary function of a government is the health and welfare of its people.

Three major areas of medical research in which monkeys have played a major role are: the conquest of yellow fever in Panama, and as a result in the rest of the world: the production of vaccines for poliomyelitis; and the discovery of the Rh factor in blood groups. This last discovery, which is probably less known than the others, has led to the saving of lives and the mental integrity of hundreds of thousands of children all over the world.

Although Dr. Yerkes' association with Madame Abreu's colony of primates was one of the factors in helping to encourage him to go ahead with the founding of a research colony of anthropoid apes of his own, the idea of doing so had originated some time before. Back in 1902, when Yerkes was only twenty-six years of age, he began to think of doing research with apes. He was a graduate student and an instructor in psychology at Harvard University. During this period he dreamed of a research institute for comparative psychobiology, in which the study of primates and particularly of great apes could make a fundamental contribution to our knowledge of the functioning of the human mind.

In 1916 he was motivated to write an article for *Science* magazine, "Provision for the Study of Monkeys and Apes." In this article he pointed out that while it was usually agreed that the study of primates, especially of anthropoid apes, was very important, nobody seemed to have taken any particular action to remedy this deficiency. He pointed out that although these animals are closest of all living animals to man, scientists knew practically nothing of their behavior, very little of the structure of their tissues, their embryology, and less still of their physiology or of diseases to which they are heir. And nothing was known of their hereditary processes, their instincts, and their habits. Yerkes felt that such a research institute should be located at a site which would offer facilities for maintaining a variety of primates under normal healthy conditions. This would provide for the successful breeding and rearing of animals for many generations, and would provide for the systematic and continuous observations under near-natural conditions. These animals could be used for experimental studies of every aspect of biology.

The institute had to be located in a region where the climate was favorable to the life of monkeys and apes, in other words, in a warmer climate than can be found in Massachusetts. At that time, before the modern development of central heating, this was obviously an important factor in keeping primates; it is not so important now. A number of places where such an institute might be located were considered. Some suggestions were: Borneo, Hawaii, southern California, Florida, the Panama Canal

Zone, Jamaica, or the Canary Islands. Of these Dr. Yerkes seemed to be convinced, at that time, that California was the preferable place.

A wide variety of studies which could be carried out on apes were outlined by Yerkes; it would be very wasteful to maintain a primate or anthropoid station purely for psychological operations, or indeed for any narrowly limited biological research. The most should, therefore, be made of every animal for as many purposes as possible. It was also important that the establishment be permanent. There are many kinds of investigations that can be carried out on apes; some of these need to be continued for the life of the animals. Dr. Yerkes was not aware when he wrote his article for *Science* just how long-lived his apes would later turn out to be. We have in our institution a chimpanzee called Wendy who was actually one of the first in the Yerkes chimpanzee colony and whose age is forty-seven. Dr. Yerkes believed that a primate center such as he planned would not reach its maximum activity before 50 or even 100 years had passed. He gave much study to the type of staff his dream institution should have. There should certainly be an expert interested primarily in behavioral psychology and sociology; there should be a comparative physiologist, an expert in genetics, and one in experimental zoology; there should be someone with an interest and training in comparative anatomy, histology, and embryology. There should also be someone who was expert in experimental medicine, and there should be an assistant trained especially in pathology and neurology. Then he would add a business manager, a clerical force, a skilled mechanic, a carpenter, and four laborers. Dr. Yerkes calculated that if such an institute were built in 1916 in southern California, it would cost about $50,000 a year to run, and an endowment of approximately $1,000,000 would enable it to function perpetually.

Dr. Yerkes closed his article in *Science* magazine by saying: "It does not seem extravagant to claim that the securing of adequate provisions for the systematic and long continued study of the primates is by far the most important task for our generation of biologists and the one which we shall, therefore, be most shamed by neglecting."

It was during 1916 that Yerkes got an opportunity to actually carry out some studies on subhuman primates. These were his first studies. He worked with monkeys and with an orangutan at a primate station established in 1910 by G. V. Hamilton in Santa Barbara, California. There was only one anthropoid ape, the orangutan, in the group of primates; the others were monkeys. Mr. Hamilton, who was both owner and scientist, was interested mainly in the problems of psychopathology of primates. He used them in a study of the nature of behavioral adjustment and maladjustment. He abandoned the work in Santa Barbara in 1918.

In 1912 a German research station for the study of anthropoid apes was established at Tenerife in the Canary Islands. Originally this station was to be used for studies of functional neurology and psychology. The first resident was a psychologist, Dr. E. Teuber. The second, also a psychologist, Dr. W. Köhler, worked at Tenerife for five years. His book *The Mentality of Apes* was a landmark in our knowledge of the mental processes of these creatures.

Way back in 1806, Professor L. I. Fischer, the first professor of zoology at Moscow University, had studied 21 specimens of monkey which had been obtained by the zoological museum. It is believed that these were actually lemurs of a variety known as the Galago.

During a tour around the world from 1803 to 1806 Russian scientist Dr. V. L. Tigelius gave the first descriptions of the orangutan. Other species of primates were described by Dr. I. F. Escholtz, who toured the world from 1815 to 1818. Just before the turn of the twentieth century and afterward, a number of Russians worked with primates. In 1897 Dr. Zabolotny and Dr. Vysokovitch used monkeys for a study of the plague. In 1892 Dr. O. Buyvid studied immunity to tuberculosis in monkeys.

In 1927 probably the world's first primate center was established at Sukhumi on the Black Sea. It was called the Institute for the Study of Experimental Pathology and Therapeutics. It has made some important contributions to medical science.

Besides Sukhumi, other cities in Russia were the scene of studies with primates. These were Leningrad, Kharkov, Kiev, and Moscow, which had several laboratories.

Madame Ladygin Kohts of Moscow and her chimpanzee, Joni. (*From Yerkes Archives.*)

The first psychological studies on primates in Russia were made by Madame N. N. Ladygin Kohts, who worked in the Department of Zoopsychology of the Darwinian Museum of Moscow. She made some very important observations which earned her an important place in the international literature on ape behavior. She also worked with a number of monkeys to study a variety of psychobiological problems.

The Sukhumi Primate Center is still active today under the direction of an outstanding Russian scientist, Dr. Boris Lapin. The Russians are rapidly expanding their work on primates. In sharp contrast, the United States is actively engaged in cutting it back. Recent Russian successes in the field of primate research are the development of prophylactics and therapy of infectious diseases such as diphtheria, tetanus, Asiatic cholera, gas gangrene, dysentery, tick relapsing fever, spotted fever, virus encephalitis, measles, etc. Studies of the higher nervous activity of monkeys has enabled the Russians to produce experimental neuroses and thus to induce physical diseases such as high blood pressure, coronary disease, heart disease, and stomach ulcer. The Russians have also produced a number of human neurological diseases in subhuman primates. More recently they have shown it to be possible to induce cancers in monkeys. This is of special interest because these animals seem to be resistant to the induction of tumors. The Russians are now making a strong effort to isolate viruses from human tumors and leukemias. If they are successful, it will have been research with monkeys which paved the way. If they do it, it will be a breakthrough of major proportions and exceptional importance. The United States is, of course, also working in the same area.

Immediately after the First World War, in 1919, the Pasteur Institute in Paris decided to develop a station for the study of anthropoid apes in Kindia in French Guinea. The apes were to be used principally for the study of medical problems. Yerkes was greatly stimulated by the development of this station. It had, in fact, been established in response to the urgings of the famous Russian biologist Élie Metchnikoff, and was called Pastoria. It was directed by Dr. Albert Calmette, an expert on tuberculosis.

Although Russian by birth, Metchnikoff studied for a number of years in France and had worked extensively there with monkeys and apes he obtained from the various French colonies. Even before 1910 Metchnikoff was convinced that many of man's ills could be studied and probably be cured by carrying out research on these animals. He stressed that facilities for primate research should be made widely available.

About 1912 or 1913, another scientist working in France started a series of studies which would lead him eventually to the establishment of a colony of chimpanzees. He was Dr. Serge Voronoff, who on October 18, 1919, in the amphitheater of the medical faculty of Paris before the 28th Congress of French Surgeons, rose to his feet and startled his audience with these remarks, "I have found a remedy for old age. I have already rejuvenated a number of animals."

Three years later in the laboratory of experimental physiology in the Collège de France, at the time of the 31st Congress of Surgery, Voronoff demonstrated a human patient, Arthur Liarded, whom he had rejuvenated. This of course led to a flood of publicity throughout the world.

What had Dr. Voronoff done which enabled him to make such spectacular claims? He had, in fact, been grafting the sex glands of chimpanzees (the testicles) onto those of human beings. The Voronoff rejuvenation operations now became almost a household subject of discussion. The monkey gland operations were discussed in polite drawing rooms all over the world, but it was either tacitly assumed or else deliberatedly misconstrued as being a graft of the thyroid gland which was responsible for this rejuvenation and not a transplant of the testicles, a subject which was taboo in polite drawing rooms at that time and probably in a lot of drawing rooms even now. The suggestion that Voronoff's operation was a graft of the thyroid gland had some foundation because the doctor had some years before transplanted thyroid glands from chimpanzees to children who had deficient thyroid glands. He claimed that these operations had some spectacularly successful results, asserting that this operation had brought the children from a subnormal to a normal mental level. So there was probably some nondeliberate mix-up between this type of grafting operation and the type of operation which Dr. Voronoff carried out for the purposes of rejuvenation.

Dr. Voronoff's operation for the transplantation of monkey testicles was a very simple procedure. The human being was given a local anesthetic on one operation table; the chimpanzee was fast asleep on another. The scrotum which holds the testicles was opened. Within it there is a loose membranous sac called the tunica vaginalis which is traversed by many blood vessels and in which the testicles lie loosely. The tunica vaginalis was opened and the testicle exposed. The testicle itself is covered by a white, lustrous, pearlylike, tightly fitting cover called the tunica albuginea. Within the tunica lie the two elements of the testicle which will be referred to a little later. With his scalpel Dr. Voronoff then excised two or three or more slices of the chimpanzee testicle, usually about one or two centimeters wide and long and a few millimeters thick. While he was doing this someone else had been opening the skin of the scrotum and the tunica vaginalis of the human subject on either one or both sides according to how extensive the graft was to be. The membranes in man are exactly the same as in the chimpanzee. Then with the handle of a sterile scalpel Dr. Voronoff scarified the surface of the tunica albuginea of the human testicles so it exuded a little fluid and perhaps a little blood, and with a few stitches he fastened the piece of chimpanzee testicle onto the scarified areas of the human testicle. A couple of stitches pulled the tunica vaginalis together and a few more closed the scrotum, and the job was done. The patient was up and out, and by the next day none the worse for his operation.

Of course the newspapers, the music halls, and the cabarets found this operation perfect for entertainment purposes. They talked of people having the operation and swinging from the chandelier. They pictured them back in the cradle or as elderly men indistinguishable in appearance from their children and grandchildren. Such wild claims were never made, of course, by Dr. Voronoff. What he did, in fact, claim was that an elderly person who was forgetful, who was physically hesitant in his walking, and who had lost a good deal of strength would be rejuvenated to the point where he was thinking clearly again and was able to stride out and indulge in a reasonable amount of physical exercise, in other words, to knock about ten, fifteen, maybe twenty years off his physiological life.

The inside of the testicle is made up of two parts. The greater part consists of a mass of continuously coiled tubules, and it is on the inside of these tubules that the spermatozoa are manufactured. As they ripen they drop off into the cavity of the tubule and slowly pass down it to the various tubes which lead from the testicle to the penis; upon appropriate stimulation they are discharged mixed with a solution of various fluids from the accessory sex glands and appear as semen. In between these tubules in the testicle are a number of irregularly shaped cells which produce the male sex hormones. The male sex hormones have an identical composition in man, chimpanzee, other apes, various monkeys, lions, tigers, kangaroos, and all other mammals, so that fundamentally there is no difference between the type of sex hormones found in the various members of the vertebrate kingdom.

The sex hormones carry only the ability to stimulate the secondary sex processes, which in man produce the deep voice, facial hair, strong muscles, and coarse bones (compared with the female). Chimpanzee sex hormone carries these properties and no chimpanzee characteristics. Chimpanzee male sex hormone will produce or accentuate maleness in humans, other apes, monkeys, cats, dogs, guinea pigs, and other mammals and will do nothing else.

What Dr. Voronoff hoped, in sewing little pieces of ape testicle onto the outside of the human testicle, was that the blood vessels from the human testicle would pass into the graft and keep it alive. Then the hormones present in what are called the "interstitial cells" which produce sex hormone in the young male chimpanzee testicle would secrete directly into the bloodstream of the man, producing a rejuvenating effect. There obviously is no connection between the cells of the graft outside the tunica albuginea of human testicle and the spermatozoa-producing tubules inside it, so the graft could not possibly contaminate the human spermatozoa. However, even if the graft had been made into the interior of the testicle there is still no likelihood that anything would have happened. The immunological processes that would have taken place against the sperm-producing cells of the chimpanzee would have been so great that they would have been inactivated and rejected very shortly after having passed into the human testicle.

In any case, the immunological processes go into operation very quickly after the grafting of the chimpanzee testicle onto the human, and one of the problems that Voronoff found was that within six months or a year these grafts were almost completely resorbed, so anyone who imagined that he had derived any benefits from them needed to go back frequently to be regrafted.

In order to have an adequate supply of chimpanzees for his rejuvenation experiments, Dr. Voronoff established in Europe what he described as a "monkey farm." He found a spot only a few hundred yards from Menton which was sheltered by the mountains from the winds of the north. Here tropical vegetation grew very actively; in fact, he got fruit from his palm trees, and even banana trees would grow and ripen in this environment. The place that he established was known as the Chateau Grimaldi, and it was situated on the Franco-Italian frontier. He had monkeys from all over the world. In the winter months he had the indoor cages centrally heated, but the monkeys could remain in the open air in the outdoor cages if they wanted to. Most of these animals later were placed in large open spaces or compounds. They lived there both day and night without having a heated place to go even in the winter. The whole conception of this establishment was to breed monkeys and chimpanzees. Dr. Voronoff established a monkey hospital, a kind of farm, so he could isolate sick animals, and at the time he wrote his book in 1928 two baboons had already been born there.

Dr. Voronoff envisaged that as his operation became more and more popular, a string of chimpanzee farms would be established all along the Mediterranean coast from Naples to Marseilles. This was also the view of his colleague Dr. Rambaud, who was at one time director of the New York Pasteur Institute. In the beginning Voronoff obtained almost all of the chimpanzees from West Africa and his baboons from Abyssinia. The latter were probably gelada baboons. By 1928 he was receiving regular consignments of these animals, but he still found great difficulty in getting enough chimpanzees. The first people who came to his help were missionaries of the Order of the Holy Ghost scattered all over the French colonies. One of his missionaries, Father Maurice, who was a Doctor of Sciences, went to French Guinea as a priest to find out the best way to capture chimpanzees without damaging them. He returned after three months, bringing Dr. Voronoff five chimpanzees. Dr. Voronoff used the testicles of these chimpanzees for his first human grafting operations.

Later Dr. Voronoff found that he was able to obtain chimpanzees only at a very high price, and he hoped that his breeding farms would in the end make it unnecessary to purchase them from Africa; he then got the idea that baboons, which are very prolific, and which were more plentiful and easier to capture than chimpanzees, would be equally successful. He had used one on November, 1920, for grafting into a man of seventy-four. Dr. Voronoff claimed that his patient secured very considerable improvement from his operation with a remarkable restoration of

85

physical and intellectual faculties. He then began to import baboons from the Sudan, French Guinea, as well as from Abyssinia. He always had about a hundred of them on hand ready to provide materials for grafting.

The first two humans whom Dr. Voronoff "rejuvenated" were an engineer and a priest. Both of these men had suffered from what was described as tuberculosis of the testicles when they were twenty-two and twenty-seven years old, respectively. According to Dr. Voronoff, the grafting operation resulted in a remarkable restoration of youthful appearance and activity in both these individuals.

What led Dr. Voronoff to the idea that perhaps transplantation of the testicles of apes would be the way to secure rejuvenation in humans? One might ask first of all why he did not use the testicles of young humans for this purpose. He points out that there were serious drawbacks to doing this. One of the problems was to get testicles from normal young live people, and the only other testicles available from young people would be from those who had died by accident. There were not that many of these people available. In addition, it was not always possible to get at the body in time to obtain the testicle fresh enough to make it possible to transplant, so for this and a number of other reasons Voronoff decided it would be best to go to one of man's closest neighbors, the chimpanzee.

So why the testicle? The testicle was used partly because it contained the interstitial cells which produce the male sex hormone presumably deficient in old men.

Perhaps at this point we should divert briefly to talk about hormones. These chemical substances are produced by the glands of internal secretion which are also called the endocrine glands. The existence of the glands was established toward the end of the nineteenth and in the beginning of the twentieth century.

There are a variety of endocrine glands in the body. One of them is the pituitary gland, at the base of the brain, which has a general control over most of the other endocrines and is actuated to some extent by nerve impulses and secretions from the brain itself. Then there is the thyroid gland (with its associated parathyroid glands), which is situated in the neck over the trachea;

the adrenal gland, situated over the kidneys; and the sex glands, which in the male consist of interstitial cells between the testicular tubules, as already explained. In the female the interstitial cells in the ovary produce hormones, and so do the cells surrounding the egg, and other cells which grow in the ovary after the egg has been discharged into the oviduct. These latter cells form either a temporary or a permanent corpus luteum, depending on whether or not the egg is fertilized.

Dr. Voronoff said all the endocrine glands were dominated by the secretions from the sex glands. He deduced from consideration of the effects of removal of the testicles from both animals and humans that this loss of sex hormone secretion was responsible for aging. If you caponize a cock the comb withers away and the bird stops crowing and loses its spirit to fight, its courage, and its instincts of domination and protection of its females. Voronoff compared the ox, which is a castrated bull, with the intact bull and pointed out that the beast that was once ferocious has now become a very gentle animal which can be driven placidly by a child. He even claimed that if you look at the external appearance of the brain of the bull and the ox, that of the bull has a glossy appearance resembling porcelain, whereas the brain of the ox is either dead white or has a yellowish tint to it.

He pointed out that a spirited stallion which is hard to manage becomes a very docile animal once it is castrated. The circus horses which have been trained to perform all the skillful steps that these horses demonstrate so well are all stallions and not geldings. The castrated sporting dog does not have the hunting quality of the normal dog. Dr. Voronoff spent a time in Egypt, and there he had the opportunity to make some personal studies of a number of eunuchs. All these people were emasculated at the age of six or seven, they were often tall, they had smooth faces without hair, and their cheeks drooped, giving the appearance of a lack of elasticity of the skin which he said made them look like women. They were usually fat and had rounded figures, and the pectoral area was overdeveloped, as if they had hanging breasts. Their flesh, he said, was flabby, and their muscles were undersized; the voice remained childish because of the interruption of the development of the voice box, or larynx. They had much less physical strength than normal humans, and their physical decline appeared to have affected every organ. They were lazy and without energy, were selfish and did not learn very well. They became prematurely old; at forty to fifty years of age their skin became scaly, and after fifty the senile circle, or the arcus senilis, which is present around the cornea and is a typical sign of old age, was common. They rarely appeared to live to be older than sixty. Dr. Voronoff also studied a number of men who had been deprived of their testicles when they were young because they had become tuberculous, and all these people had defective memories. They found it hard to concentrate and difficult to make continuous intellectual effort over a period of time.

When he was lecturing at the Catholic Institute in Toulouse in 1924, Dr. Voronoff found that the ecclesiastics there would not permit a castrated man to be made a priest, and this was not because he needed his testicles when he became a priest, but because the authorities had found by experience that a priest who had had his testicles removed did not have the same intellectual faculties as those who still had testicles.

All these studies led Voronoff to the conclusion that the interstitial cells of the testicle can be regarded as the "source of energy for the whole of the human organism." Voronoff pointed out that decrepit old men were in reality eunuchs. They had been emasculated not by the hand of man, but by nature and by the inexorable progression of old age. When this occurred, there was a definite degeneration of their strength and their mental faculties. Voronoff pointed out—and I think that probably most scientists and scholars would endorse this—that the greatest geniuses had a very strong sexual function. Goethe, who was described as a universal genius, continued to produce first-class work until his death. At the same time that he provided proof of astonishing physical activity and energy he also preserved his reproductive faculties to the last. At the age of seventy-four, Goethe was still ardently in love with a girl of nineteen, and at the age of eighty on his deathbed his last words were: "Look at this lovely woman's head with black curls on a black background." Victor Hugo was also a great lover, and if the facts were known about many outstanding people one would probably find that all of them have a very high sexual drive which is expressed in various ways.

Voronoff pointed out that only the poets have the courage to tell of their loves. In his book Voronoff listed a number of people who lived to a great old age and who maintained their sexual ability into old age; from this he correlated the continuation of sexual function with the extension of life. One example of this is Thomas Parr, who was invited to London by the King of England at the age of one hundred and thirty-two. Parr had remarried when he was one hundred nineteen. Nine months after having been invited to London and living too rich a life, he died, and at the autopsy Dr. William Harvey (who discovered the circulation of the blood) was amazed at the healthy nature of his organs. Another example was Peter Albrecht, who lived one hundred and twenty-three years, remarried in his eightieth year, and had seven children. George Douglas, who was born near Göteborg, Sweden, lived more than one hundred twenty years, remarried at eighty-five, and had eight children, the last of whom was born when he was one hundred and three.

Prior to Dr. Voronoff's activities, some interest in the possibility of using the sex organs for rejuvenation had already been suggested by a distinguished intellectual, Dr. Brown-Séquard, who was the occupant of the Chair of Physiology at the College of France in the late nineteenth century. Séquard prepared an extract from ground-up testicles and advised elderly men to have injections of this. It is rumored that after news of this treatment got around there was a traffic jam in the street where the Collège de France was situated. Hundreds of old roués hastened to Brown-Séquard to get his injections. However, there is little doubt that most, if not all, of the benefits obtained from these injections were psychological.

Dr. Voronoff carried out his first studies on sheep, cattle, and other animals, and some of the photographs of the apparent rejuvenations, for instance those taken before and after the operation on the famous bull called Jackie, were very convincing. So were some of the photos and case reports of human subjects. The work attracted interest from veterinary and agricultural specialists all over Europe, and many of them visited Voronoff to see the results of his experiments.

The passage of time and the advances of medical science have not permitted support of the claims Dr. Voronoff made. In 1930 a group of scientists headed by Dr. F. A. E. Crew from the University of Edinburgh, an outstanding world authority on reproduction, made a comprehensive study of Dr. Voronoff's work. They decided that the work was too poorly controlled to really prove anything. Subsequently in the 1930's the male sex hormones were isolated, their chemical structure was worked out, and they were synthesized in the laboratory. It was thus possible to inject or implant pure hormone into the tissues of old animals and even old human beings. In a wide variety of very carefully controlled animal experiments it was not found possible to secure any prolongation of life or any amelioration of the onset of old age by the continuous injections of the hormone. Even implantation of tablets of the hormone under the skin so that there would be a continuous supply similar to that which the animal would get from its own interstitial cells produced no good results. The results of all these experiments have thus demonstrated that, however hopeful Dr. Voronoff's results may have been, he did not really prove anything.

In fact recent immunological work has shown that there is rapid rejection by the host tissues of any grafted tissue taken from a different species of animal. Even between animals of the same species grafting is only partly successful, and then only if extreme suppression of the immunological mechanisms is carried out by drugs or radiation. Examples of this are difficulties encountered on human heart and kidney transplants. Dr. Voronoff's work slowly faded away, and eventually his primate breeding station, which was probably the most useful thing which came out of the whole series of experiments, was discontinued.

By 1923 the French Primate Station in Pastoria in French Guinea had been going for a number of years, and that was the year that Robert Yerkes saw the beginning of the fulfillment of his own dream. His first opportunity to get chimpanzees for his research occurred in the summer of 1923. He was on vacation in New Hampshire when he received a letter from William T. Hornaday, director of the Bronx Zoo in New York. Dr. Hornaday said he had a pair of young chimpanzees temporarily at the zoo which were for sale. One of the chimpanzees was rather unusual in appearance and behavior, and Dr. Hornaday thought it was either a new species or a rare type of animal. Both animals were three or four years old. The female was not in a very good condition, but the male was a fine specimen. Their owner would not sell them separately and wanted $3,000 for the pair, which was very expensive, since the market price in New York at that time was $200 to $500 per animal. All the money Dr. Yerkes had apart from his life insurance amounted to less than $3,000. Finally he offered the owner, Mr. Noel Lewis, $2,000 for the pair, Mr. Lewis accepted it, and Dr. Yerkes was delighted with his two acquisitions. The two animals were named Chim and Panzee.

They were brought up to the Yerkes farm on a hilltop in New Hampshire one day in August, 1923. Chim and Panzee adapted very well to the woods and pastures of New Hampshire. The Yerkes family came to enjoy Chim, the male, very much, but Panzee was apparently a continuous problem. She was chronically ill when they got her. In the sunshine and the mountain air of the Yerkes farm she seemed to improve slowly, but in September their stay in New Hampshire ended and they had to go back to Washington. There they had to set up a room with indoor and outdoor cages for the chimps. Panzee lived under these conditions for only a few months. Apparently she had tuberculosis of the intestines. The following summer, instead of going back to New Hampshire for his vacation, Dr. Yerkes went to Cuba to study Madame Abreu's collection of primates. He took Chim with him to Havana in June, 1924. Chim arrived in good health, but unfortunately the Abreu colony had an epidemic of a respiratory infection. Chim became ill, got pneumonia, and died within a month. Madame Abreu felt very guilty about the situation and gave Dr. Yerkes $500 to buy himself another chimpanzee. In 1923 Dr. Yerkes thought of finding himself a new place to work that would not only yield him an adequate livelihood but also give him the opportunity to follow his scientific interest with apes. He said he had been waiting with "faith, if not with patience" for the appearance of an angel. One certainly turned up with an extra *l* in the person of James Roland Angell.

Angell, the president of Yale University, conceived the idea of organizing an institute of psychology which could be supplemented by outside resources, and he was able to secure funds for such an institute. Dr. Yerkes was invited to be a member of the new organization and was appointed professor of psychology at Yale. There was an understanding that he was free to devote himself primarily to research with subhuman primates and would work with advanced students in psychology. Shortly after that, Dr. Yerkes got the opportunity to work with a young mountain gorilla in Jacksonville, Florida. This was a very productive opportunity, and Dr. Yerkes published a book and a number of papers on the mentality of the gorilla. At this time he had to decide which of the great apes he should use for his studies. The gibbon, he felt, stood midway between the monkey and the ape, and was obviously not as highly developed or as manlike as the three types of great apes, so his choice was narrowed to the orangutan, the chimpanzee, and the gorilla. To work with all three seemed impracticable because of the cost. He eliminated the gorilla because it was too large and strong, and he eliminated the orangutan because it was not responsive enough to man or versatile enough in its activities. He felt that the chimpanzee, which was cheaper, had a more cheerful and sociable disposition, and appeared to be more motivated, might be better as a general-purpose experimental ape.

Dr. Yerkes approached the Rockefeller Foundation about the possibility of establishing an institute to house monkeys and apes and to provide facilities for experimentation with them. The Foundation provided $40,000 for a four-year test of the feasibility of housing and working with chimpanzees. At the same time he was offered by the university a vacant barn on Prospect Street on one of their estates. It was a brick barn and was fairly large and more or less suitable for Dr. Yerkes' needs. It needed a little remodeling and was eventually converted into satisfactory living quarters for the animals he had managed to acquire by that time.

The mortality of chimpanzees in captivity was at this time so great that many people doubted if it would ever be possible to establish and maintain a colony of chimpanzees that would permit continued research. Obviously one of Dr. Yerkes' first tasks was to show that this was in fact possible. He knew of John L. Buck of Camden, New Jersey, an animal collector, and when Buck arrived in the spring of 1925 from Africa with several young chimpanzees for zoological gardens, Dr. Yerkes had the opportunity of selecting a male and female from them, neither of which was more than five years old. He paid $400 for each one. They were named Bill and Dwina. Bill was named for the prosecutor in the Scopes evolution trial, William Jennings Bryan, and Dwina was short for Darwinia in honor of Charles Darwin.

Toward the end of the summer, just after news that the Rockefeller grant had gone through, and when he was sitting in a dental chair in the middle of an appointment, a telegram arrived from his wife. It said that a freighter from West Africa had just docked at east Boston and that it carried a pair of young chimpanzees for sale by the ship's officer, who was fed up with the strain of supervising them. Dr. Yerkes and his daughter Roberta made for the dock and found the animals still there and still un-

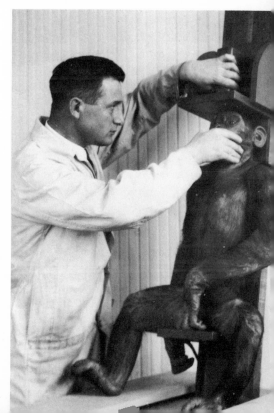

Wendy, now the world's oldest chimpanzee, being measured by Dr. Bingham—one of the first scientists to work at the Laboratories.

sold. There were a male and a smaller female, both young animals. The little female was an ugly-looking animal and appeared to be in poor physical condition. The owner decided eventually to sell the two for $500. The male he called Pan and the female he called Wendy. Wendy had come from Douala in the Cameroons and had originally been owned by missionaries. Wendy is still at the Yerkes Center and is forty-seven years old. She has had eleven babies and has five grandchildren and three great-grandchildren living. She behaves like an elderly person, moving around more slowly than the younger animals; she is much less aggressive and much less excitable than the other chimpanzees. At the same time she is more unpredictable and even erratic in her behavior than they are.

Dr. Yerkes introduced Pan and Wendy to Bill and Dwina. However, they never became very friendly, each pair tending to keep to itself. Because the barn presented to Dr. Yerkes was in Prospect Street, New Haven, it attracted many high school and college boys. Bill learned very early to fill his mouth with water and squirt it at them and also to throw sand in their faces, a technique which has been well developed by several chimpanzees in the current Yerkes colony.

The brick barn on Prospect Street remodeled to house Dr. Yerkes' four apes was the beginning of the organization which has now developed into the Yerkes Regional Primate Research Center. In this establishment Yerkes was able to show that with suitable care it was possible to maintain chimpanzees adequately and to use them for scientific research.

Before the term of the Rockefeller grant was up, Yerkes felt he ought to look for a site for a more permanent laboratory, which should be in a tropical or semitropical climate. He enlisted the help of a number of leading biologists to choose the site and plan the extension. Eventually the Rockefeller Foundation purchased a 200-acre tract of land for him in Orange Park, Florida, erected buildings, got him equipment, and met the operating expenses for the laboratory for the next ten years. The buildings that were built under these funds were completed in 1930. On June 9 of that year the architect turned them over to Yale University. On June 10 Dwina, Bill, Pan, and Wendy all arrived from New

Haven. At this time Dwina was pregnant. Everyone looked forward with great anticipation to the first birth in the colony. It occurred on September 11, and a little baby girl chimpanzee, appropriately named Alpha, was delivered. Unfortunately, as a result of this pregnancy, Dwina contracted puerperal septicemia (childbed fever). She lingered on for two weeks but finally died. This was the first time that childbirth fever had ever been recorded in anthropoid apes. The fact that she had become pregnant had given Dr. Yerkes the opportunity to make detailed studies of reproductive processes from conception to the birth of the animal. It was found that the gestation period was 245 days as compared to 280 days for the human mother. Then a great stroke of good fortune followed the unfortunate demise of Madame Abreu in 1930. Her son Pierre and daughter Adalita did not want to maintain the mother's group of primates, and they gave Dr. Yerkes the opportunity to select whatever animals he wanted. He chose thirteen animals; most of them were mature or nearly mature females. One of these animals was Patti. Patti remained with the laboratories for many years, and when she died about three years ago her age was estimated to be forty-five years. In 1930 Dr. Yerkes was also offered a group of sixteen young chimpanzees by the Pasteur Institute in Paris. The animals had been collected together at Pastoria in French Guinea by Dr. Henry Nissen, who was destined to be the third director of the Yerkes Primate Laboratory. These gifts placed the laboratory on its feet, provided chimpanzees for breeding, and enabled research to get under way. By 1932 Dr. Yerkes was well established at Orange Park in his laboratories for the study of apes. In his article in *Comparative Psychology Monographs* published by the Johns Hopkins Press in 1932, he described what had been achieved at that time.

The laboratories were called the Laboratories of Comparative Psychobiology of Yale University, and they were made up of three geographically separate Centers: the new laboratory and primate quarters in conjunction with the laboratories of neurophysiology of the Yale School of Medicine in New Haven;* the

* The primate laboratory at Yale University existed from 1925 to 1930. The Orange Park laboratories were called Yale Laboratories for Primate Biology from 1930 to 1942, the Yerkes Laboratories of Primate Biology from 1942 to 1950. The Primate Laboratory

anthropoid breeding and observation station at Orange Park, Florida; and arrangements for the cooperative use of temporary and permanent scientific stations in Africa, where the chimpanzee, gorilla, and other primates could be studied in their native habitat.

To decide on the whole question of whether the colony of chimpanzees could be used successfully for scientific research, President James R. Angell of Yale appointed a committee to advise him. This committee was formed of very distinguished people of the day, and Dr. Angell was, of course, a member. The chairman of the committee was a distinguished biologist, Edwin G. Conklin. Others equally distinguished were Milton J. Greenman, John C. Merrian, Theobald Smith, H. Gideon Wells, and Clark Wissler. Dr. Yerkes acted as secretary to the group. Eventually this became the first scientific advisory board of the new laboratories. After some deliberation the committee indicated that it was favorably disposed toward the idea of initiating research in anthropoid apes, and Yerkes was given the green light to go ahead. The Orange Park site was a 200-acre tract of wooded land in Clay County, Florida, fifteen miles from Jacksonville. Orange Park at that time was a tiny village. The buildings constructed were a laboratory, a service building, an animal quarters building, and a roofless enclosure which was surrounded by a 14-foot wire fence. In addition there were some outlying buildings, a hospital or isolation unit, a garage, a general storage building, a pump house and an electrical distributing center, and a residence for the superintendent. All the facilities were within an 8-acre enclosure surrounded by a 7-foot chain link fence with an electrified wire at the top. The whole assemblage was completed by June, 1930.

Studies on the growth, development, physiological processes, and psychobiological traits of chimpanzees were initiated at the

of Yale University was established under the direction of Robert M. Yerkes in 1925 and was housed on 135 Prospect Street in New Haven, Connecticut. From 1930 to 1942 the Yale Laboratories of Primate Biology consisted of a northern division in the Sterling Hall of Medicine, New Haven, Connecticut, and a southern division at Orange Park, Florida. From 1942 the Yerkes Laboratories of Primate Biology were conducted jointly by Yale and Harvard universities at Orange Park, Florida. This terminated when the laboratories were presented to Emory University in 1956. They became the Yerkes Regional Primate Research Center in 1961.

Center. Dr. Harold C. Bingham, one of the staff, went to the Albert National Park in the Belgian Congo to study the gorilla, and Dr. Henry Nissen went to Pastoria in French Guinea to study chimpanzees. Dr. Otto L. Tinklepaugh, who looked after the nutrition, health, and reproduction of the chimpanzee colony, joined the staff at Orange Park. The whole group was administratively under the distinguished neurophysiologist John F. Fulton, who was a Sterling Professor of Physiology at Yale and who subsequently became associated in a number of interesting and important studies at the laboratories.

In the early stages of the organization, the people who worked with Dr. Yerkes were Dr. Harold C. Bingham, research associate; Dr. Donald K. Adams, research assistant and Sterling Fellow; Dr. Margaret Child Lewis, Dr. Chauncy M. Louttit, research assistant; Dr. Morgan Achten, research assistant; Dr. Joseph A. Generelli, National Research Council Fellow in Psychology; and Dr. Eilhart von Domarus, Fellow of the German Academy of Science. In 1931 Dr. Yerkes published the list of staff and visiting investigators employed on the project. Dr. Robert M. Yerkes, the director, was also professor of psychology at Yale. Dr. Otto L. Tinklepaugh, research associate; Dr. Henry W. Nissen, research associate; Dr. Carlyle F. Jacobsen, research assistant; Dr. Joseph G. Yoshioka, research assistant; Dr. James H. Elder, assistant; Dr. Kenneth W. Spence, assistant; Dr. Lewis W. Gelderman, National Research Council Fellow; Dr. C. Ray Carpenter, National Research Council Fellow; Dr. Winthrop N. Kellogg, Social Science Research Fellow; William C. Atwater, superintendent; and Helen S. Northord, secretary.

By 1941, when Yerkes retired as director, the laboratory population had reached 45 chimpanzees, and the ability of humans to keep chimpanzees in good health and to run a successful breeding program with them had been proved.

From this auspicious beginning the work at the laboratory soon placed it in a major position in scientific laboratories of the day. The conception was revolutionary, and the work that was done was revolutionary; it is difficult to give a direct estimate of the extent to which the work done here contributed and influenced the fields of psychology, psychiatry, and neurology, but it certainly had an impressive impact on these areas of knowledge. Dr. Carl Lashley, who became director after Dr. Yerkes, was once asked to name the one most important contribution that had come from the laboratory, and he named the work which Dr. Jacobsen and Dr. Fulton performed between 1930 and 1937. Dr. Jacobsen had always been interested in psychoneurology, and he had the opportunity of working with John F. Fulton, professor of physiology at Yale and a neurosurgeon.

A study was begun by Dr. Jacobsen in 1933 on two chimpanzees with widely differing temperaments. One of these, Lucy, was a six-year-old chimpanzee, very calm and even-tempered. The other, Becky, about four years old, was described as an excitable neurotic who fell into a rage whenever she made an error in a psychological test. Jacobsen studied the behavior of these two chimpanzees in considerable detail, and then he and Fulton operated on the animals and cut out about half of the prefrontal area of the brain from each of them. After this, testing was repeated and the animals reacted pretty much the same as before. Their intelligence and their rapidity in solving intelligence tests did not seem to have been affected. The experimenters then did a further operation; they removed the remaining half of the frontal part of each animal's brain. In Becky this produced a most remarkable change of personality. Now instead of getting annoyed when she made an error in a psychological test she more or less shrugged her shoulders and showed no reaction to her failure or to not getting a reward. She became calm and relaxed.

In 1953 there was an international medical conference in England, and Dr. Jacobsen and Dr. Fulton read a scientific paper on this work. It attracted considerable attention. In the audience was a Portuguese neurologist, Egas Moniz, who was a director of a mental hospital in Portugal. Dr. Moniz thought that a number of men and women in his hospital who suffered from acute anxiety might be helped by this operation. Together with a surgeon in Lisbon, Dr. Moniz severed the nerve pathways between the prefrontal part of the brain and the rest of the brain, and in half of the patients the intense fears and the anxieties were relieved. Dr. Lashley subsequently pointed out that the contribution of this single experiment at the Yerkes Laboratories to the knowledge of the functioning of the brain as well as its therapeutic value was so great that it was worth all the money that had been spent in the laboratory up to that time.

Another study carried out at the old Yerkes Laboratories was an attempt to see whether the associative cortex, a part of the brain located in the temporal area, was associated with memory. The experiments carried out at the Laboratories demonstrated that the so-called associative areas were not very correctly named. They certainly were not the areas where memory is stored, and did not appear, in fact, according to Dr. Lashley, to have any localized function at all. He pointed out that the studies at Yerkes had demonstrated that almost any part of the cortical region of the brain seems to be capable of carrying out the function of the whole. He noted that one of the workers at Yerkes had shown, for example, that some nerve cells in the primary visual cortex that have been found to retain visual memory were also active in other functions connected with seeing. These studies were of fundamental importance to the understanding of the functioning of the human brain.

In 1939 Dr. Henry Nissen, the third director, began a long-term study of the physical and behavioral development of chimpanzees. He early isolated a number of baby chimpanzees, including some brother-sister pairs. They were separated from their mothers a brief period after birth and brought up in a nursery where they were under continuous observation. He studied these animals in very great detail, not only their behavior but their physical development, the development of the skeleton, the pulse rate, the respiration rate, etc. His conclusion was that the physical growth curve for the chimpanzee was very similar to the human being. Nissen made a study of the sexual cycle of the chimpanzee, fixed the time of ovulation, and described the pattern of sexual physiology and behavior. He also studied the effects of sex hormones on the chimpanzee temperament.

As already noted, after Dr. Yerkes retired in 1941, his place was taken by Dr. Carl Lashley. Dr. Lashley was followed by Dr. Nissen, who was followed for a brief period by Dr. Lee Peacock as acting director, and then by Dr. Arthur Riopelle, and finally by the present author.

It was during Dr. Carl Lashley's period as director that Keith and Cathy Hayes carried out their classical experiment of nursing a baby chimpanzee, Vicki, in their home. The Hayeses chose Vicki for their studies when she was three days old. In her book Cathy Hayes has given an interesting description of how they were escorted around the Yerkes nursery by Dr. Lashley. There they met Annie Jones, who was in charge of the nursery at that time and played foster mother to innumerable baby apes. Annie was with the Yerkes Laboratories for many years and dedicated her life to the care and welfare of the baby chimpanzees born at the Laboratories. She prepared the food for those babies who had outgrown the bottle, nursed and fed the very young with bottles filled with baby formula, changed and washed diapers, and gave the babies the cuddling they needed as a substitute for their mothers. By the early 1960's Annie began to have trouble with her eyes and eventually had to have an operation for cataract. We would have liked to bring her with us when the Laboratories were shifted from Orange Park, Florida, to the campus of Emory University in Atlanta, Georgia, but she felt that the transition would be too much for her. She was a wonderful, dedicated person and was foster mother to a number of the chimpanzees now grown up and still in the Yerkes chimpanzee colony.

There are a number of reasons why the chimpanzee babies are taken away from their mothers and brought up in a nursery. One reason is that many chimpanzees under cage conditions do not make good mothers, and some indeed have no idea how to look after a baby. I have seen a mother chimpanzee dragging a newborn baby around her "cage" by one of its legs. This is in part because chimpanzees brought up in captivity have been taken away from their natural environment at an early age, or in some cases have been born in the laboratory, and have never had a chance to learn how to look after a baby. On the other hand, some chimpanzee mothers seem to have a strong mothering instinct and do the right thing from the beginning, and the same applies to orangutans. We have had fourteen orang births at the Yerkes Center, a world's record for any institution. We have a colony of fifteen gorillas, but we do not have a pair old enough to breed yet. If a baby ape is taken away from its mother soon after birth there is very nearly a 100 percent certainty of keeping it alive; if some mothers are allowed to retain their babies there is almost no chance of that baby's growing up. A second reason for the separation is that babies also need to be removed from the mothers for studies on their blood and their physical and mental growth and development.

There is no doubt, however, that the separation of mother and baby is a stressful experience for both. Psychiatrists at the Walter Reed Army Institute of Research have made studies with rhesus monkeys of the amount of stress involved in separating mother and baby. When the body is subjected to stress, whatever its nature, it excretes into the urine chemical compounds called hydroxysteroids which are derived from the adrenal glands. The adrenal glands are among those in the body which react strongly to stress by pouring their secretions into the bloodstream. The presence of varying levels of hydroxysteroids in the urine is thus an index of the reaction of the adrenal glands, which is itself an index of how stressful the animal, or the human, feels about the situation. Dr. Peter Bourne, in his book *Men and Stress in Vietnam,* describes how the hydroxysteroid excretion in the urine is used to indicate the amount of stress in soldiers fighting in Vietnam. The Walter Reed scientists found that when a baby rhesus monkey is separated from his mother the hydroxysteroids in the urine of both mother and baby are increased. In the mother the excretion falls to normal in a few days, but it persists much longer in the baby, indicating that the stress is relatively greater for it than for the mother. This method of measuring the hydroxysteroids in the urine is a most valuable tool for studying stress in animals, who cannot talk and confide their feelings to the investigator, so it can also be used to study what circumstances cause stress in a young human baby who also cannot talk.

Even though a baby is left with its mother, it may do all right for the first three months, but its health may then "go off." We had a chimpanzee called Banana who had a baby a few years ago. She was a good mother and looked after it extremely well. The baby thrived, but after a few months it began to deteriorate and then died of an acute infection following severe anemia. The answer to this puzzle is a simple one. In both humans and apes in the last stages of pregnancy iron is stored in the liver and the blood of the fetus. The milk of primates, and in fact all mammals, is virtually devoid of iron, and the reserve store in the newborn baby's tissues is meant to tide it over the period when it is existing exclusively on the mother's milk. Iron is a vital constituent of hemoglobin, which gives the red color to blood and is the compound which carries oxygen to all the tissues of the body. If it is produced in inadequate amounts anemia develops, the tissues are starved of oxygen and do not develop properly, the body's defenses against disease decrease, and the chimpanzee or human baby may be swept into oblivion by some acute infection, just as Banana's baby was. These facts have been known to doctors for many years, and this is why milk preparations for human babies usually are fortified with iron. In our ape nursery baby apes are fed on the same preparations as human babies, and also they soon receive orange juice and fruit and vegetables.

I spent some time watching Banana and her baby. Banana, for some reason, would not let the baby touch any of the food put into the cage. If the baby picked up something she would take it away and pop it into her own mouth. Even if we put something in the baby's hand Banana would remove it and eat it. So the baby received no supplement to its mother's milk, became progressively more anemic, and died. It might be asked why this does not happen in the wild. First, all chimpanzee mothers are not as pernickety as Banana; cage conditions may also have made her peculiar in this respect. An additional explanation is that probably in the wild the baby is surrounded by vegetation which it can grab and put into its mouth even if the mother is anxious to prevent it from doing so; under caged conditions with feeding twice a day it is easier for a mother chimpanzee to see that all the food is eaten by her and none by the baby. There is also the possibility that since the food at least on many occasions in the wild is *ad lib,* and the mother may stuff herself if she wants to, she may not be so particular about the baby's doing likewise, whereas in a caged situation she may regard the baby as a competitor for her food.

When baby apes are left with their mothers, therefore, the pair needs to be carefully watched from three or four months on (the time when the baby's store of iron commences to run low), and if any one of them is being stopped by the mother from supplementing the milk diet he should be removed. This problem of providing iron may be the reason why some zoos have had difficulty in raising apes left with their mothers.

We have not so far had this problem with our orangutans. Of the fourteen babies we have had in the last three and a half years, three have been left with their mothers and are doing extremely well. They are now on view with their mothers in the Atlanta Zoo. The other babies did extremely well on a nursery regime.

Chimpanzee babies when they are born at the Yerkes Center are usually given common European names or combinations of the father's and mother's names; the orangutans, of which we now have thirty-five, have Malayan names; and the gorillas (we have fifteen) have African (Swahili) names. The same Vera who was Vicki's mother had one of her babies left with her on one occasion some ten or twelve years later and showed little competence in raising it; it died after a few hours. Incidentally, names of animals are never repeated; even after 40 years. When the name of an animal is used all parties know the animal that is being referred to.

The baby chimpanzee selected by Cathy Hayes and her husband was the daughter of Vera and Bokar, two chimpanzees who had come into the Laboratories some years before from the African jungle. Vicki's name was derived, from a combination of the names of both the mother and father. The names of all the Yerkes apes end in vowels if they are females and in consonants if they are males. This is most valuable if an animal is being discussed, since all the parties know immediately whether the animal is male or female.

The Hayeses made a very interesting study of the development of function in Vicki. Cathy Hayes noted that even before one month Vicki made swimming movements; this had also been observed frequently in the Yerkes nursery with other baby chimpanzees. It is interesting to note also that Vicki was able to support her whole weight by one arm for more than a minute. This apelike character is also present in human newborn infants. Humans lose this capacity, however, after two or three weeks and do not regain it for some years. Many years ago a European professor named Bolk suggested that man was only a precocious fetal ape, and he made the point that the fetal ape resembles man much more than the adult ape. We will discuss this theory later, but for the moment the ability of the human baby to support its weight becomes interesting in the light of this theory.

The Hayeses found that Vicki was physically much stronger than a human baby of the same age and were relieved to find that she did not cry. This is one of the things which strikes anyone visiting the Yerkes nursery—there is no crying. Even a hungry baby ape does not cry. Cathy Hayes wondered if the crying of the human baby is a first step toward speech. She also made the pertinent observation that maybe a quiet baby is essential for survival in the jungle.

Once our nursery babies become a year or more old, however, things are different. There is much banging of cages and excited vocalizations of "ooh-ooh-ooh," particularly if some other animal in the same room is receiving attention. Later, the "ooh-ooh" could become a scream of excitement.

Vicki, in the first weeks of her existence, did what most human babies do, slept most of the time. If a chimpanzee baby is left with its mother—and this applies also to gorillas and orangutans —she exercises its limbs and teaches it to grasp and climb. This starts at quite an early age. The Hayes family had to take the mother's place in this respect and in many others. They noted that Vicki by twelve weeks had two teeth, and two weeks later she had two more. At twelve months she had twenty teeth. With these she bit the ear of Dr. Austin Riesen, who was working at the Laboratories, and drew blood. She had almost certainly not intended to harm him but probably was just feeling exuberant at that time.

At twelve months Vicki began her first "pleasure pants." This is a way of expressing pleasure that is used by chimpanzees. It is very commonly used when they are grooming a human or each other or when they themselves are being groomed. It consists of a series of short, rapidly repeated pants which produce a quite characteristic sound. I have not heard orangutans utter anything quite the same, but I have heard gorillas make a similar noise.

Vicki was frightened of herself when she first saw her reflection in the mirror and spent a good deal of time looking behind it to find the ape she was sure was there. It seems that she eventually came to recognize that image in the mirror as herself. She was later taught to sort pictures of humans and chimpanzees into two piles, humans in one, chimps in the other. The project was made more difficult by having full-length photos, photos of busts, and photos of heads of human men and women in different types of clothing. Vicki learned to segregate the humans and chimpanzees without fail. However, the really interesting thing about her activities was that she put her own picture with the humans. What went through that little brain we cannot tell, but there seems to be little doubt that an animal such as Vicki taken in the first hours or days from its mother identifies with the person it has close contact with from then on. The famous professor of anatomy Frederic Wood Jones, when he was prosector to the London Zoo, had a little monkey he had brought up in his home from infancy. Every now and then he walked with it through the zoo. The baby was terrified of the other monkeys and apes; it retreated inside his coat and from this vantage point would peer at the furry little monsters in the cages that made such a noise. In other animals close relationships between the just-born and those who take care of them have been recorded. The European scientist Konrad Lorenz describes how he became the first person that some baby ducklings laid eyes on when they hatched from their eggs. They became, in his words, imprinted with his image in the way they would normally have been imprinted with the image of their mother. They therefore accepted Lorenz in this capacity and followed him faithfully everywhere. In the light of all this, perhaps we can understand Vicki's reaction to her photo.

In many ways Vicki showed behavior very like a human child. For example, she would play peek-a-boo around cushions with Dr. Henry Nissen, who later became director of the Laboratories. Cathy Hayes describes an occasion when Vicki grazed her finger.

Cathy fussed over it, bound it up, and Vicki's reaction was to use the finger as a sympathy catcher. There were continuous attempts to toilet-train the ape child, and Vicki would sit on the potty for long periods just as a human child does. It did not take Vicki long to learn to use a key to open doors and locks, and as a result of this she created a near-disaster on one occasion when she got into the Hayes' car. The key had been left in the lock, and of course she turned it and started the engine; the car took off and was stopped before it crashed only as a result of a heroic chase by Cathy Hayes. Vicki had no problems in mastering the use of a light switch to produce light. She knew also how to switch on a table lamp, and if it did not light up she would look for the cord, follow it to the connection, and plug it in if it were unplugged. She became an accomplished scribbler, and after going through a stage exactly like a human child in which a pile of blocks had immediately to be swept away, she learned to build towers of blocks, dice, and glassware.

Cathy Hayes describes a fascinating event which suggests that chimpanzees can have imaginary play like human children; if in fact this is what it was, it certainly indicates highly complex mental processes. Vicki had a number of pull toys which she used to pull around on a string. One day Cathy saw her walking around trailing one hand behind as she did when it held the string of a pull toy. Every now and then, Vicki would turn around, grasp the imaginary string, and appear to tug it much as she would have had her pull toy caught on something. She was especially pleased when Cathy entered into this imaginary game with her. This imaginary play behavior did not persist, but that it occurred at all is fascinating.

The Hayeses had Vicki doing a variety of problems, and in Cathy's book she expresses the view that some people might accuse them of "pushing" Vicki, but she goes on to point out that it is by solving problems that both animals and humans progress, solving each problem from the experience gained with earlier problems. In fact, in human education, the worst thing one can do to a child is not to push him to his capacity. The danger comes when attempts are made to push him beyond this point. Intelligent children are frustrated if they are not kept mentally occupied, and even mentally deficient children perform much better if what mental capacities they have are fully utilized. There is in fact evidence from animal experiments that young animals which are kept busy solving problems finish up with bigger brains and higher mental capacity than those not so employed. Many human brains are wasted by the assumption that one cannot start teaching and explaining things to very young children. At all stages in development children have a fundamental urge to learn which is often discouraged and aborted by unsympathetic or ignorant parents or teachers. When I was eleven and twelve years of age I attended a convent school, where I was put into a special class. The teaching hours extended from 8 A.M. to 6 P.M. with three-quarters of an hour for lunch, during which we were also expected to draw a number of maps. Each evening we had to write a three-page essay and learn by heart a chapter from each of ten books of history and geography. On top of this we had to work out a number of arithmetical exercises. Between January 1 and November 1 each year we had only one week's vacation. This is a pretty heavy program for eleven- and twelve-year-old children, but I have no evidence that it did me any harm, and it enabled me to obtain the scholarship which was the reason behind these two years of concentrated work.

Not many people would put up with the disturbance of their life and the damage to their furniture and house which results from the presence of a growing chimpanzee in the family, but the Hayeses have presented a fascinating account of what it was like to have had such an adventure. They struggled also to teach Vicki to talk, which will be described later in this book. One of the problems of having a baby ape in the house is that at some time or other it grows up and becomes so strong as to be physically dangerous and to be so destructive of its environment that it has to be put in some kind of restricted situation. Usually this is a cage in a zoo or an institution. To a young ape brought up in a human household this must resemble prison for a human. The Hayeses attempted to cope with this problem by having a little chimp house built for Vicki in which she could live after she left their household; unfortunately, she caught pneumonia and died before she could accept it.

The following comment was published about Vicki by Dr. Winthrop Kellogg:

A chimpanzee lady named Vicki
Had fingers and thumbs which were tricky.
  She opened some glue
  And sat in it, too,
So in the end became sticky.

Another chimpanzee brought up in a human household was Gua. Gua was also a Yerkes inmate, and Dr. Robert Yerkes himself was responsible for making her available to Dr. and Mrs. Winthrop Kellogg, who brought her up. In this case the Kelloggs' young child Donald, who was of comparable age with Gua, was brought up simultaneously with her, and the two were treated and tested in an identical fashion. Dr. Kellogg, in his book *The Ape and the Child*, talks about the stories of human children being brought up by animals, the reverse of what he had done. In 1921 two young girls were found in India living in a cave inhabited by wolves. When they were discovered they were cuddled up with wolf cubs. After they were brought back into civilization they ran about on all fours for several years. They were eventually trained to stand up. The older child learned to talk and lived to be only a little more than six years of age; her mentality remained that of a normal child two and a half years old. The younger child never learned to talk and could only grunt or growl. There is, of course, also the fable of Romulus and Remus, who were suckled by a she-wolf and founded Rome. There is also the more modern fable of Tarzan, a human child who was brought up in the jungle by apes.

Dr. Kellogg discusses the influence of environment on young animals; in his view, to really understand the extent to which a young human could be converted into a beast it would be necessary to place him in a wild environment and study his reactions in detail as he grew up. This is impossible to do at the moment, but at the rate the law of the jungle is encroaching on university campuses the time may not be too distant when such a study can be made in depth. Dr. Kellogg and his wife chose, naturally, to do the reverse experiment and bring up an inmate of the jungle in their home and study its reactions in the human environment.

Dr. Kellogg put it this way, "Why not give one of the higher primates exactly the environmental advantages which a young child enjoys and then study the development of the resulting organism?"

The Kelloggs decided that in such an experiment they could not take half-measures and that their baby ape had to be bathed like a human baby, given the love and cuddling that a human baby gets, trained to eat in the fashion of a human, and given human children the same age to play with. They tried to duplicate for the ape both the psychological and the physical features of the human environment. In this way Dr. Kellogg hoped to show that the heredity of the ape and child were so similar that the ape would respond in a human fashion to at least some of the same stimulations. Without such an experiment such likenesses would never be discovered.

Gua, the chimpanzee selected for this experiment, was seven and a half months old when she was separated from her mother, who had been in Cuba at the estate of Madame Abreu in 1930. At the time of the experiment the Kelloggs' son Donald was two and a half months older than Gua, and the two were kept together for nine months, during which time a series of tests and experiments, comparisons and observations, were made on them.

A number of interesting facts emerged from this study. For example, Gua drank more water than her human companion; she had a higher blood pressure and a lower pulse rate. She avoided bright lights and strange humans and developed a strong attachment to one person. Like apes and monkeys in general, Gua had a great tendency to chew or bite, and she could focus her attention on an object for only a short time. Although older chimps are expert at scratching off scabs from human and ape skin, finding and extracting splinters with great speed and dexterity, Gua was not able to pick up small objects with her fingers —this seems to be characteristic of apes. Yet only today, while letting my hand be groomed by Bobby, he removed a hair by isolating the hair with his fingers, bringing the nails of the index fingers of the two hands together until they caught the hair between them, and then pulling the hair out with them. So the fingers of chimpanzees are a curious mixture of clumsiness and dexterity.

How do the baby chimpanzee and the baby human compare in other things? The ape is ahead in some things and the child in others. Gua was able to coordinate her muscles better than Donald; her involuntary movements were faster, and she was stronger. She could localize the direction of noise better than the human child and had a better memory. Because of her better muscular coordination (faster physical development), Gua learned to skip with a rope like a much older child. For the same reason she could use a spoon better to eat with, and a glass better to drink from. In general, because she developed faster than a human child she was able to respond better than the child to objects and situations.

Donald was superior in his greater emotional stability, his lack of a tendency to bite and test everything with his teeth, and his ability to pick up small objects with his fingers—that is, he had greater manual dexterity. He was also less dependent on one person than the ape.

Although there were differences, there were also some likenesses, and these perhaps are more significant than the differences.

The two reacted in an identical fashion to drowsiness, nodding their heads and rubbing their eyes. They responded with wriggling and grinning to the process of being tickled. Their play reactions were also the same; they loved shoes, human faces, typewriters, and telephones; each could point to his nose and each could scribble.

One of the unusual capacities of Gua was her fantastic hearing ability—noises made by a raindrop, a motorcar in the distance, or a muffled footstep caused an immediate reaction in her, as demonstrated by an increase in her pulse and breathing rates and even of her blood pressure. The amazing hearing ability of Mrs. Hoyt's gorilla Toto has already been mentioned. This sensitivity of hearing, and almost certainly of other senses as well, led Dr. Kellogg to express his concern for what must be very disturbing handling of these animals by humans for testing and other purposes. He makes the following statement in his book:

> To test a captive anthropoid seized by force in the jungle, later kept in a cage, and motivated by hunger in some particular experiment is one thing. To test a human child who is kindly and gently talked to and who is never under any circumstances caged or starved is certainly a very different thing. We treat one organism in ways we would never think of treating the other. Yet there are specialists in the separate fields of animal and child study who seem prone to ignore the fundamental variations which ordinarily inhere in the two fields.

This passage should not be taken to imply that animals under test are treated inhumanely in any way, simply that scientists do not always realize the sensitivity of their anthropoid subjects compared with the human subject and that test results with the two are not necessarily compatible. In our Center all our animals are handled and tested with care and affection, and although we have never had anyone in our Center who has mistreated an animal, anyone who might would not survive at the Center longer than the time it takes to get him out of the front door.

Dr. Kellogg found that Gua rapidly learned various commands. Typical of the instructions to which she would respond were, "No, come here," "Close the door," "Blow the horn," "Don't put that in your mouth," "Go to Daddy," etc. In the first four months of the nine months that Gua was with the Kelloggs she was ahead of their son Donald in many things; this may have been partly because of the chimpanzee's highly developed ability to get around and to climb. In the last five months of the experimental period Donald surpassed Gua in the comprehension of commands. For the nine-month period of the experiment Donald had learned to respond to 68 commands and Gua had learned to respond to 58 commands.

Both the Hayeses and Dr. Kellogg found that their respective chimpanzee children would take hold of their hands and place them on objects they wanted them to handle or to manipulate.

A photo of some historic animals having a tea party. From left to right Pan, Wendy, Dwina, and Billy. All are early acquisitions by Dr. Yerkes.

Both, of course, would also take them by hand and lead them where they desired to go. It is interesting that our pet ocelot, Cleo, will sometimes take my wife's hand in her mouth and lead her to a part of the house (the bedrooms) where she is always anxious to go, but which she is not normally permitted to visit.

Dr. Kellogg, like the Hayeses, went to considerable trouble to teach his baby chimpanzee toilet training. One of the problems in doing this is that the chimpanzee is very prone to emotional defecation and urination. Both Gua and Donald were placed on nursery chairs at regular intervals during the day. After six weeks both of them utilized the opportunities presented to relieve themselves. It was, however, much more difficult to teach them not to defecate or urinate when they were not in the chairs; in fact, at the conclusion of the nine-month experimental period neither the chimpanzee nor the child had achieved complete control of the bladder or the bowel, but in Gua's case the number of daily errors had decreased from ten per day (twice that of Donald's) to an average of one and a half per day. I was recently told about a chimpanzee whose toilet training was so perfect that she had accidents only when she got excited.

The conclusion reached by Dr. Kellogg was that home-raised chimpanzees adapt to the physical features of a home quite rapidly. Even without being trained formally to do so they turn light switches and faucets off, open oven doors, turn keys in locks, and so on. They rapidly learn to scribble with pencil and paper and will do finger painting. The strength of a chimpanzee is out of proportion to his age compared with a human child of the same age. In one of his publications Dr. Kellogg said of Gua, "She possesses the learning and mental capacity of a one-year-old child, the agility of a four-year-old, and strength which in some ways probably surpasses that of an eight-year-old."

5. The Yerkes Laboratories Transfer from Yale to Emory

THE Laboratories at Orange Park remained under administrative control of Yale University until 1956. At that time Yale decided that its interest in this area was no longer active, and it felt that this important resource should be made available to one of the Southern universities. A number of possibilities were considered, and it was finally settled that Emory

University in Atlanta, Georgia, would be the recipient of the Yerkes complex. Therefore, the land, the buildings, the animals, and the staff were deeded over to Emory University, which accepted control of them in 1956.

I came to Emory University in September, 1967, to become chairman of the Department of Anatomy and shortly after that time was appointed to the Board of Scientific Advisors of the Laboratories. The other members of the Board at that time consisted of Dr. Leonard Carmichael, secretary of the Smithsonian Institution in Washington; Dr. Hugh Long, who had taken Dr. Fulton's place as Sterling Professor of Physiology at Yale; Dr. Fred Hisaw of Harvard, a distinguished zoologist; Dr. George Corner, leading anatomist of the Carnegie Institute of Washington; Dr. William Talliaferro, outstanding in the area of immunology; Dr. Arthur Richardson, dean of the Medical School at Emory University. At that time the director of the Laboratories was Dr. Henry Nissen, but in 1958 he died and Dr. Lee Peacock was made acting director while a search was made for a permanent director of the Laboratories. The Laboratories thus entered into a new phase as a satellite of Emory University.

In 1956, the year that Emory University took over the Yerkes Laboratories, Dr. Karl F. Meyer of California paid a visit to the Soviet Union and visited the Russian primate colony at Sukhumi in the Republic of Abkhazia (formerly the kingdom of Georgia), whose director is Boris Lapin. In August, 1956, Dr. Meyer wrote a letter to the National Heart Institute giving an account of his visit. The same month the director of the National Heart Institute, Dr. James Watt, also paid a visit to the Russian primate colony. The Sukhumi Primate Center, as already mentioned, was established in 1927. It marked the beginning of a new period in experimental primatology in the Soviet Union.

At the Sukhumi Center the biology, the maintenance, and the breeding of the monkeys have been primary problems for study, and there are also studies on the morphology and biochemistry of blood of monkeys and apes. The Center has had considerable success in acclimatizing monkeys to captivity, including both rhesus and green monkeys, and has developed a new nursery for them. Sukhumi now has the seventh successive generation of hamadryas baboons. Further studies have been made on the basal metabolism of monkeys, the regulation of temperature, and the diurnal periodicity of physiological function. There have been intensive investigations into the higher nervous activity and psychology of monkeys.

After Dr. Meyer and Dr. Watt had visited Sukhumi, they were more than ever convinced that the United States should do something about the establishment of Primate Centers. In September, 1956, it was recommended that the United States government should support colonies of monkeys for biomedical research. There was some doubt as to whether one single national center should be established or whether a variety of regional centers should be built. Dr. James Shannon, who was then chief of the National Institutes of Health, favored the regional centers rather than one single national station.

Further planning and consultation took place all through 1959, and in March, 1960, the Council of the National Heart Institute recommended funding of a Primate Center in Portland, Oregon. A year later, in March, 1961, the Council recommended that a Primate Center be established in Seattle, Washington, and one in Madison, Wisconsin; and in June of 1961 it recommended

The photo that went around the world on the wire services. Benito helps the author turn a sod at the groundbreaking for the new Yerkes Center.

that additional centers be established in Atlanta, Georgia, with Emory University and based on the Yerkes Primate Center; in New Orleans in association with Louisiana State University and Tulane University; and in Boston in association with Harvard and other institutions of that area. This meant that six Primate Centers were already established. In March, 1962, the seventh Primate Center at the Davis campus of the University of California was approved by the Council of the National Heart Institute. This Center was to be concerned mainly with the problems of conditioning primates, in other words, finding out exactly what their requirements were from every point of view and how these conditions could best be provided.

The award of funds to Emory University for the construction of a Primate Center based on the Yerkes Laboratories was probably the most logical award of all, and the surprising thing is that it was not the first to be awarded. There was a modest laboratory for primate research in Oregon which had been operating for a few years when it was awarded funds to build a Primate Center, but all the others had to start with nothing. The Yerkes Laboratories had, however, already been in existence for over thirty years, it already had a great deal of experience in primate husbandry, it was already world-famous for its primate research, and all the other Centers were able to take advantage of their accumulated know-how. Even those who built up the chimpanzee colony which was established by the Air Force at Alamogordo, New Mexico, had to draw on the accumulated experience of the Yerkes Laboratories to build and run their facility.

After having been informed in March, 1961, that it had been granted the funds to start a Primate Center, Emory University decided to try to find a director, since the existing director, Dr. Arthur Riopelle (who succeeded Dr. Peacock), had been appointed to head the Delta Primate Center in New Orleans. A number of people were considered, but no decision was made on either side. Finally, the present author, who was still a member of the Advisory Board of the Yerkes Laboratories, was invited to become the director, accepted, and took over the post in 1962. I was still chairman of the Department of Anatomy, and the building up of the operation at the Emory campus was headquartered in the Anatomy Department for the first few years. Since the main operation was still at Orange Park, Florida, I found myself in the position of having to commute between Jacksonville, 350 miles away, and Atlanta, which proved to be a not too unpleasant chore—it gave a welcome change of scenery and contacts.

This was an extremely busy period, and a great deal of time and effort was put into preparing schemes and plans for the new building to house the Center and of course selecting a site. Several sites around Emory University and some sites well outside of Atlanta were studied. One of the problems that the university Board of Trustees was concerned about was the possibility of noise and smell from such a large group of big animals being introduced into a select residential area represented by the Druid Hills sub-division in which the Emory campus was situated. For a time it was doubtful whether the Board of Trustees would approve the building of the Center on the campus itself, and it seemed that it might insist that it be built some distance out in the country. Eventually approval to build on the Emory campus was given, and the Carr property adjoining the Candler property, which bore the house of the university's president, was chosen. This was an area of about 26 acres, of which 18 or 20 acres were immediately available and another 5 or 6 would become available after the termination of the occupancy of a house still on the grounds. The next problem was to be sure that if we built the Center on the property we would not be disturbing the neighboring residential area. We had no worries about the smell and the waste materials because this had been for many years under very good control at Orange Park and we saw no reason why, in the new modern building, it should not be even more under control. The noise, however, was of distinct concern, since seventy or eighty chimpanzees screaming together can be heard for quite a considerable distance.

The site chosen was very wooded and hilly, and it was obvious that it would be necessary to build the Center up against the side of the hill. The building was therefore designed so that entry to the building would be on the ground floor; then on the second floor there would be access to a small animal wing, which would be a little farther up the side of the hill. The large ape wing would be built higher up the hill and would open up onto the third floor of the research building.

A group of sound experts was brought down from Boston to study the sound problems of the area. They made a survey of the local noise level and advised us that if we had any problem of sound from the animals, we should raise the level of the little dam that extended across Peachtree Creek running along one boundary of the property. This would raise the basic noise level, which would make any added noise less noticeable. They also recommended that the building be designed so that the animal runs were facing the ascending side of the hill and that the roof of these cages project upward and outward from the cages so that they would reflect the chimpanzee noises back against the hillside. Their predictions that this would cope with the situation have proved to be extremely accurate, and the animals cannot be heard, even when they are very noisy, to any significant degree in any of the residential areas. The noise that does get through runs along the side of the hill and appears to be funneled toward the house of the Emory president. But there have not been any complaints yet.

The firm of architects which built the Atlanta airport was given the job of working with the director to put his design ideas into architectural form. Both the director and the architects were faced with the fact that the amount of money for construction, in the neighborhood of $1,800,000, would not be quite adequate for what was needed. This was not realized until very extensive work had been done on the architectural plans, and to avoid having to redesign the whole building it was decided simply to cut the size of all the rooms by one-third. The plans also included a very fine modern quarantine or isolation area which would be a separate building from the main Center, but this unfortunately had to be cut out when it became necessary to reduce the cost of the building still further because the contractors' bids were so far in excess of the money available.

In addition to the main Center, there is a Field Station. Emory University purchased about 110 acres of land in Gwinnett County, about 25 miles away from the university, and a few chimpanzee cages were installed together with some office buildings, an animal kitchen, and a number of compounds. It was intended that this area be developed for the study of animals in social groups. Subsequently, many more compounds were erected for this purpose, and more recently the U.S. Army has built four compounds for rhesus monkeys, to study the effects of stress. The Space Agency has provided funds for a compound to breed rhesus monkeys for space studies. The superintendent of the Field Station is Clyde Wright, who came up with us from Orange Park and who has done a fine job.

Groundbreaking for the main Center was in November, 1963, and it was planned that we would move in sometime around June, 1965. The operation of moving from Orange Park was no small one, since it involved the transport of staff and animals and the provision of animal food and cleaning equipment at both places. The fact that the animal caretakers had to be transferred at the same time as the animals and that the caretakers also had to transfer their families and household goods complicated the situation. In addition, all the babies in the nursery and all the animal records dating back to before 1930 had to be transported. The whole operation was very carefully planned.

The building of the Center went ahead more or less without any serious problems but began to slow down as the deadline approached. We had to set a time for bringing up the animals (July 15) because in the summertime it is essential to book the transporting companies months ahead. They are so heavily involved in moving people during this time of year that otherwise it is impossible to secure their services. At one time both the Air Force and the Navy had offered to fly our animals up, but in the end we decided it would be less traumatic to bring them up by road. We had to warn the contractors, therefore, that come what may, whether the buildings were ready or not, the animals would be descending on them in the middle of July and that we would have to move in the beginning of June in order to get the place ready for them.

The time came, and of course the building was nowhere near finished, but nevertheless we had to move in and set up our headquarters there. Most of the laboratories still had no benches, the workmen were still in and out of the place, the director's office had not yet received its final coat of paint, and I would work in it for a while and then move out while the painters covered everything up and gave it the next coat of paint; after that was done at least I was able to stay in there. Nevertheless, there were still odd things that had to be done around the room, fixtures to be finished and so on. It was a time of many problems, and then a truck arrived from Orange Park laden with the records and papers and materials and books for the library, and there was an immense unpacking and stacking job to be carried on in the Center. During this period, of course, it was impossible for the director or anybody else to really do much in the way of scientific work; all the time available was involved in doing physical things to help the settling-in process and in solving the million and one ad hoc problems that came up from day to day. These included beating on the heads of the construction people to get one person's lab or another ready and trying to allot some kind of priority to the myriads of jobs—and then, before we really had everything under control, the animals and the animal caretakers moved from Orange Park.

I went down to Orange Park on the night the animals were due to start coming up. It was arranged that the truck should arrive in the early evening at Orange Park, where it would be loaded with as many animals as it could take, and would then set out on an overnight drive up to Atlanta, equipped with one of the doctors or the staff "riding shotgun"—in other words, carrying a gun in case there was an accident and an animal got out and hurt a human being or damaged property. It was also helpful to the animals for them to have somebody that they knew with them during this potentially traumatic period. After seeing the truck off in a tropical deluge, I caught a plane back to Atlanta. At half past three in the morning I got a call to say that the truck was just an hour away from Atlanta and would be arriving at the Center not long after 4:00 A.M.

A group of us were there ready to receive the animals. They were unloaded, the truck was hosed down and cleaned out, and the driver of the truck went off to have breakfast. It took the day to drive the truck back to Orange Park, and that night the same procedure was repeated. Four trips served to bring all the animals up, and the last trip was a nursery trip with all the young gorillas, chimpanzees, and orangs coming up together with a nursery attendant.

The actual moving of the animals proved to be no great problem. As soon as they were bedded down in the truck, they went to sleep and remained that way until the early morning when they arrived at the Center. They were immediately put into their new cages and confronted with their old caretakers, who fed them as soon as the animals had finished exploring their new quarters. They settled down extremely well without any problem at all. One of the truck journeys had to bring our monkeys, of which we had about a hundred at that time. These likewise created no problem. So the whole thing went through very well with no animal escaping and no animal even getting sick or distressed by the move. The same applied to the human beings. Altogether it was a fine bit of logistics, and everyone who helped with the planning and operating of it deserves great credit.

After the animals came in July as planned, we set about trying to get settled in and get the whole operation working. The finalizing of the construction dragged on and on, and it was very difficult to get much of the laboratory work finished; even at the year's end one of the laboratories still did not have its benches up and the scientific equipment was still standing in the middle of the floor. We were due to receive a visit known as a "site visit" from the National Institutes of Health in February.

The method by means of which the Center is operated might be of interest to the reader. The funds that were appropriated in Washington for each Center had to be budgeted for by the director and his staff. All the funds applied for were not automatically available; each director had to make a case for all parts of his budget down to the last dollar. This had to be presented not only in written form but also had to be defended orally before the money was finally allotted. However, to be sure that this money was properly used and that the Centers were not wasting government money and time, a group of independent scientists (not in government service) was selected by the National Institutes of Health. This group is sent to each Center on what is called a project site visit, and they spend two or three days going over in detail all the scientific work being done. They also have an accountant with them, usually a university controller, and he investigates the methods of handling the funds. The project site visitors then make a report back to the National Institutes of Health in Washington indicating whether they believe that a particular Center is being run as a satisfactory operation, whether the taxpayers' money is being well spent, and whether the scientific programs being carried out at the Center are worthwhile. Not only is the taxpayers' money carefully controlled in this way, but in addition government auditors drop in unexpectedly from time to time and do spot checks to make sure that the procedure of handling these funds is proper and in keeping with government requirements. Then the General Accounting Office of Washington, which is responsible for auditing all government accounts, may send a team of accountants to a Center. In our case the three auditors who were involved in a survey of our Center spent three to four months actually working in the Center full time and studying every account and all our administrative procedures again to be sure that the funds involved were adequately spent. I doubt if any public funds have been better controlled than the funds used for Primate Center studies. If anything, the control is too strict; there was too much of it, and it actually handicapped the scientific work in the beginning. The procedures outlined above apply to all the Primate Centers, and one thing the taxpaying public can be sure of is that there is no waste of public money in any of the Primate Centers. Every penny is well and seriously spent and gives a maximum return in new information that is important to human health and welfare. Recently we appointed as assistant director for administration Major General George T. Duncan, former deputy commander of the Third U.S. Army and commander of Fort McPherson. He has done a fine job, although he complains that it is easier to move an army across Europe than to look after all the prima donnas in the Primate Center. I am not sure whether it is the human people or ape people that he is referring to.

We were able to put in supplementary requests for additional funding to the National Institutes of Health. We had only one animal compound out at the field station, and we needed many more for the types of studies which were being carried out there; we requested matching building funds to erect four more 100-foot-square compounds and eight 50-foot-square compounds. After some considerable delay this money was made available; construction was started, and eventually all these compounds went up. Subsequent to that five more compounds were built, four for some studies which have been carried out jointly by the

Yerkes Center and the Walter Reed Army Institute of Research, which is concerned with studies of stress. Another compound has recently been completed on behalf of NASA to enable rhesus monkeys to be bred and made available for space-oriented research.

Dr. Yerkes had worked with a mountain gorilla and had enjoyed some experience with orangutans, but he had concentrated for experimental purposes almost completely on chimpanzees. Some of the other members of the staff at the Yerkes Center had subsequently brought in monkeys, and a number of monkey projects were proceeding during this time. When I became director, I was anxious to include further apes for study in the colony and succeeded in purchasing quite a number of young gorillas, finally building up the gorilla colony to fifteen. Prior to the move from Orange Park to Atlanta, my son, Dr. Peter Bourne, who at that time was interning in Seattle, noticed quite a number of orangutans at the Seattle Zoo and wondered if any of these might be available for us to purchase. After hearing the news from him, I wrote to the zoo and found that they were simply holding these animals for a dealer. On contacting him, I found that he had nearly thirty orangutans for sale. We arranged to purchase these over a period of two years, with the result that we were able to collect the largest group of orangutans that has ever been brought together in captivity in the history of the world. It certainly is the biggest collection that exists now, and it is very likely that there will never be another group like it because export of the animals from their places of origin (Borneo and Sumatra) is forbidden, and many countries, including the United States, now will not import them. It is estimated that there are only about 3,000 orangutans left in the wild.

Our fifteen gorillas also constitute a world record, and we hope when these animals become sexually mature, which should be soon, we will be able to start breeding gorillas. We have at the time of writing eighty-five chimpanzees, and five to ten baby chimpanzees are born each year. Furthermore, we have now about seven hundred monkeys and seven gibbons.

124

HELEN M. COUSAR

6. The New Yerkes Primate Center

Now that we had settled down in our new quarters, it was obvious that we had an organization which was unique. Nowhere in the world is there such a fantastic collection of apes and such a remarkable organization for caring for them. Our Ape City has been likened to something out of science fiction.

The building itself is of three floors and is situated on 20 acres of woodlands surrounded by an 8-foot chain link fence which has three strands of barbed wire at the top. The top strand is electrified to keep human primates out and to act as the last barrier in case some of our non-human primates should escape from the very rigid security arrangements which we have in the main building to contain them. The entrance to the whole complex is through a small entrance hall, and although strangers can enter through the main door into the entrance hall with no difficulty, they find themselves barred by a small door through which they can pass only if they have a key or if it is released by pressing an electrical switch in the reception room.

On the ground floor are situated the administrative section of the Center and certain laboratories which we will refer to later. Farther along in an attached building is the workshop.

On the second floor are some of our psychobiologists and sociobiologists who study the behavior of primates. The veterinary department is also there and has two qualified veterinarians, veterinary technicians to aid them, and a veterinary pathologist. On this floor is also situated a laboratory which is virtually identical to the clinical laboratory in most hospitals. This laboratory can do studies of the various chemical substances in the blood, the number of red and white corpuscles in the blood, the amount of hemoglobin, and so on. It also has facilities for studying bacteria and other microorganisms which can cause disease processes in the apes and monkeys, and parasitic infestations such as those caused by intestinal worms. It is an excellent diagnostic laboratory.

On the second floor too there is a postmortem room or autopsy room, just as in a hospital, and every animal that dies in the Center from whatever cause is subjected to a detailed autopsy, and tissues are taken for subsequent microscopic investigation.

This floor also houses our library, which contains many of the historical books and publications produced by the Laboratory over the years and a complete set of reprints of scientific papers which have been published over the last forty years. The library contains many books from the libraries of the former directors, including Dr. Yerkes' library. It is called the Carl S. Lashley Memorial Library after Dr. Yerkes' successor, the second director.

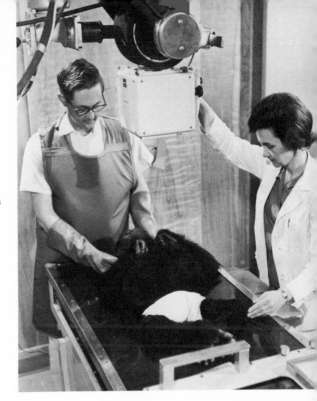

Bandam, a gorilla with polio, gets an X ray.

Many of Dr. Lashley's books are also in the library by courtesy of his widow, Mrs. Claire Lashley.

We also have an animal records department. Every animal, when it enters the Center, whether from the outside world or its mother's womb, is immediately given a name, a number, and a diary. From that time on, everything that happens to that animal is recorded until it dies. If it has any type of illness, receives any type of treatment, has any type of operative treatment, has any particular type of experiment done on it or is tested in various ways, the details go down in its diary. When its blood counts and blood examinations are done, the details are kept; when it has X rays, the details are recorded. This is just like a registry of patients in a big hospital. For some of our animals, especially in the case of Wendy, who is now forty-seven, the records go back before the 1930's.

I mentioned the X rays of the animals. All our great apes and all the staff working with them have a chest X ray once a year. This is carried out in our own X-ray department, and we have a full-time radiological technician who takes these photographs of the animals and the human members of the Center. In the case of the big apes, taking an X ray of the chest involves putting the animal to sleep because it would be too difficult and in some cases impossible to restrain them if awake, and even if some kind of restraint could be imposed, the animal would not keep still long enough for an effective X-ray picture to be taken. The reason for this meticulous taking of chest X rays is that great apes, just like human beings, are susceptible to tuberculosis, and an outbreak of tuberculosis in our animals could be disastrous.

All human beings working in the Center, before they are accepted for work, are given a skin test for tuberculosis, and if this is positive they are then given a chest X ray to see if there is in fact any active tuberculosis in the lungs. If anyone has a positive skin test we try to avoid having him work with the animals, or if he is with the animals, we take him off this work until it is absolutely certain that he has not picked up the disease itself. People can give a positive tuberculosis skin test and not have the disease.

Near the X-ray room is the pharmacy, where we keep a complete stock of drugs for treating the animals. If an animal is sick, it is studied by the veterinarians (Dr. Michale Keeling and Dr. Wesley Bonner), who in fact act in the role of family doctors to the Center. They may decide to collect feces for bacterial examination from the animal, or if the situation warrants it, the animal will be anesthetized, its temperature taken, and blood may be drawn for microscopic or chemical examination. If it is thought to be not desirable to subject him to anesthesia, the animal will be put in a special restrictive cage known as a "squeeze cage" which has movable walls; when they are squeezed together, he can be confined into a corner, and it is then possible to make some kind of clinical examination or inject him. Obviously in some infectious diseases it would be undesirable to anesthetize the animal because such a procedure would weaken his resistance to the infection.

The reader may be interested in the way our big animals are got into the squeeze cages for anesthesia and so on. They normally live in cages which are part of the permanent structure of the building and are situated on the third floor. The cages have an inside section and an outside section with a connecting door which can be locked to keep the animal on one side or the other. There is an exit door to the cage both outside and inside. Normally the animal is captured from the inside—a collecting box is bolted to the supports on the frame of the cage door, which is then opened; our apes have been trained from infancy to go into such boxes when they are presented, and in most cases they go straight in without trouble. The guillotine door on the collecting box is then shut and locked. Occasionally animals are recalcitrant, but they can usually be encouraged to go in with aid of a well-directed stream of water from a hose. Very rarely the animal has to be put to sleep in his cage by letting him drink Coca-Cola containing a heavy dose of sedative, and even more rarely he is shot with an anesthetic dart from a gun invented and manufactured in Atlanta by Mr. "Red" Palmer.

On the second floor we have a conference room where seminars and meetings and conferences are held. From this floor runs a glassed-in corridor to a neighboring building which is a wing

A baby orang from the nursery gets an X ray.

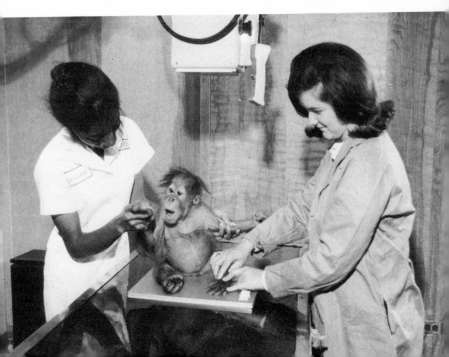

for small primates. In this wing there is a superintendent who occupies an office with a large glass window facing onto the entrance so he can observe who comes in and out of the animal facility. This is Tom Burke, whose knowledge of the handling and welfare of small subhuman primates has been of great benefit to the Center. There is a special kitchen for preparing the meals for these animals, which include both monkeys and lemurs. There is also a large room more than 80 feet long and about 30 feet wide in which there are a large number of monkeys. Most of the monkeys present are of the rhesus variety, and many of them were exposed to radiation from an atomic bomb back in the 1950's, before the test ban treaty. These animals are very closely monitored and will be held until they die (if funds can be found to maintain them) so that it will be possible to make a study of the blood changes, the possible development of blood diseases like leukemia, the effect of irradiation on the length of life, the possibility of developing cancer, and the possibility that the genetic material of the monkeys has been damaged. If this has occurred then baby monkeys born to this group could have some congenital structural defect. We have not actually found any genetic defects to date, but we have found a great increase in the number of stillbirths, and we believe there is evidence of an increased incidence of cancer; there is no doubt that the irradiation has caused a reduction in the length of life of a number of the animals. In this large room live a number of the rhesus monkeys and some green monkeys which belong to the neurophysiology laboratory at the Center. I will be writing a little later about this laboratory.

In another room are a large number of squirrel monkeys from South America. These are the smallest of the true monkey group, and they are being used at our Center for the study of the development of cancer of the reproductive organs.

I have mentioned that we have some lemurs in this wing. Lemurs could be described, in a sense, as animals who have not quite "made it" as monkeys; they are in fact described by the Germans as "half-apes." They have many of the characters of the true primates, but they are obviously not quite monkeys. Most of them come from the island of Madagascar, but some come from Africa. In Madagascar there are many varieties of lemurs: black

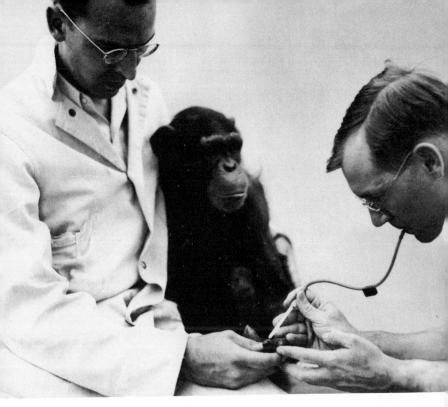

A chimpanzee has a blood sample taken.

lemurs, lemurs with circular bands around the tail, lemurs that move very slowly and are called slow lorises, flying lemurs with flaps of skin between the arm and the leg which act as a parachute when they jump from branch to branch; there are many other varieties of lemurs.

In this wing a room is set up rather like an outpatient examination room in a hospital. There are a couple of tables on which animals can be laid out for examination, for withdrawing of blood, to receive injections, and so on.

Outside the small primate wing are a number of structures resembling trailers. They are not really trailers in the accepted sense of the term; in fact they look rather like house trailers, but they are not. They have no wheels and are supported by cement blocks. Two of these trailers are used for the purposes of isolation and quarantine. All animals that come into the Center must go through a period of quarantine in which they are isolated from all the other primates in the Center for at least one month. Only the veterinarians and the veterinary technicians are permitted to enter the quarantine area during this time, and they take elaborate precautions against spreading any disease the animals might have, whether the animals show any signs of it or not. If the animal survives the quarantine period without showing any sign of disease, it is released into the general colony. During the quarantine period the animals are given tests for tuberculosis and other diseases, and an opportunity is taken to observe whether spontaneous diseases develop in them and so on. These trailers have floors made of plywood thickly painted with water-resistant epoxy paint which enables the floor to be kept clean and hygienic all the time. There is a companion trailer to that used for quarantine. This is to isolate animals which have developed an infectious disease which could spread to other animals in the colony.

There are also three other larger trailers, or "labmobiles" as they are sometimes called, at one side of the small primate wing. Two of these trailers are simply to house experimental monkeys for which there is no space in the permanent structure. The third trailer is designated as a NASA trailer and is reserved especially for monkeys involved in research related to space activities. We have two programs going on in the Center which are related to space activities. One of them is to study general problems connected with the nervous sytem which have a direct relationship to space. The other project, for which the director is particularly concerned together with his wife, is a joint study with the Navy, the University of Illinois, and the Space Agency to place two monkeys in orbit for a year. This is known as the Orbiting Primate Experiment, and we will discuss it a little later.

On the top floor of the Center are situated most of the members of the staff who engage in research in psychobiology. These scientists study the behavior and the mental processes of primates. On that floor also there is a group of neurophysiologists who are studying the behavior of the brain from a more basic, scientific point of view.

Two scientists also work partly with us and partly with Duke University on the problems of immunology and the transplantation of organs such as kidneys and hearts. Two other scientists are concerned with the localization of enzymes in different parts of the brain. In another part of the third floor are an operating room and a preparation room, where an animal is prepared for an operation. It is usually anesthetized out in the animal wing and brought into the preparation room in the anesthetized condition. Most of the operations carried out in this operating theater are of a minor nature—for example, the passing of probes into the brain of the animal, which causes no pain whatsoever but enables a very detailed study of the functioning of the brain to be carried out. Some kidney transplants have taken place in this operating theater too, and it has been a very valuable place for the

Lada. An orang that developed a cyst on the lung that had to be removed surgically relaxes during convalescence.

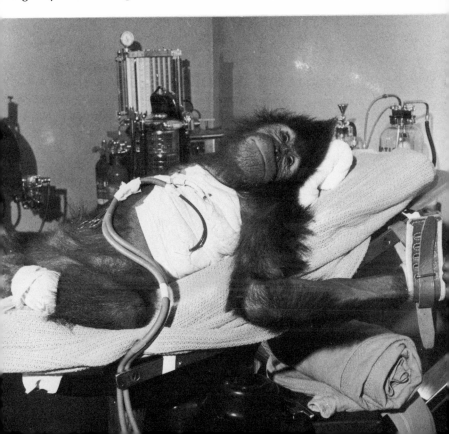

treatment of the animals. Some of the biggest operations have been for the treatment of sick or hurt animals.

There is one particular case which is most interesting and demonstrates very well the use of our operating theater to help a sick animal. I mentioned earlier that every ape person in the place gets a chest X ray every year. On one occasion when the chest X-ray films of a large female orangutan called Lada were examined, it was found that one lung had collapsed, and that the tissues between the lungs had been pulled over toward the other side. The function of the intact lung had been affected, and Lada was actually using only about a third of the air space of one lung, but she gave no clinical symptoms of being sick. However, it was obvious that this condition could not be allowed to continue because it was only a matter of time before the animal got an infection of the intact lung and she would then suddenly die—before we could save her. It was obvious that something had to be done to try to bring her back to a normal state. She was given tranquilizers and strapped down lightly on an operating table. A tube was passed into the space between the body wall and the lung, and air was sucked out. In this way the lung slowly reflated itself. However, it was not long before it was down again, and it was obvious that something more serious than we suspected was the problem.

Further studies of the X rays demonstrated a small spot on the top of the lung, and it was decided to ask Dr. John Skandalakis, a leading surgeon in Atlanta who was surgical consultant to our Center, to come in and operate on this animal. This of course meant opening up the rib cage and getting into the space in which the lungs are situated, the pleural cavity. When Dr. Skandalakis did this he found that the spot on the lung was actually a little cyst which was leaking air from the lung into the space between it and the body wall, and as the pressure built up in that space it gradually squeezed the lung flat. The surgeon cut off the top of the lung with the cyst in it and sewed up the cut end of the lung. He then sewed the chest of the animal back in place. Lada was kept on the operating table and tranquilized for some days after this; she was fed by tube and by bottle and carefully looked after. It was quite remarkable that she appeared to

Mary Lou (gorilla). Partly paralyzed from an accident when she was a baby.

realize that all this was being done for her welfare, and she did not behave like a big, dangerous animal at all, but was extremely sweet and gentle and responded very well to the affection and kindness and attention which everyone was giving her. In some respects I guess she was probably thoroughly spoiled during this period. She made a very happy and uneventful recovery, and she has since had three babies, shows no ill effects from her operation, and is a great credit to our surgeon.

Another case of interest was that of Mary Lou, a young female gorilla bought for us some years ago when the Laboratories were still in Orange Park. When she arrived she had what is known as a hemiplegia—she was almost completely paralyzed down one side of the body. This was attributed to the fact that when she was very young in Florida she had been injured by a hurricane and the damage had affected her brain. She was an extremely amiable animal when I first knew her and she formed a very close relationship with me. She had relationships with other members of the staff as well, particularly with her handler, Roger Townsend, who was very fond of her and she of him. It was possible to go in with her even when she was quite large and be affectionate with her; however, after a while she would get emotional and eventually start beating her chest with her good arm, and this was the time to leave the cage.

After some years with us Mary Lou began to get epileptic fits. These were relatively infrequent in occurrence, and they were treated by giving her antiepileptic drugs, which controlled the fits to some extent. After we got her up to Atlanta, Mary Lou's epileptic fits got worse and worse, and it was obvious that she would not last long. It was felt that her skull should be opened up and her brain inspected to see whether it might be possible to perform some kind of operation that might relieve the incessant fits. Our consulting neurosurgeon, Dr. Ellis Keener, was called in. He had already taken a great interest in her, and he advised that she be operated on. At the appropriate moment he and a team of surgeons assisted by the staff of the Center operated on the animal, took off the top of the skull, and found considerable atrophy, that is, wasting away, of the brain on one side. It was found impossible to do anything for the animal because the brain was so badly affected. So the top of the skull was replaced and the animal's scalp was sewn up again. She subsequently died. The brain was retrieved and cut into slices. When the slices were examined it was found that there was a great area on one side where there was just space and no brain substance whatsoever. It was perfectly obvious that Mary Lou had no future, and death was a happy release for her.

Near the operating theater is the entrance to the nursery. The nursery is a separate area on the third floor which is opened by two doors. One of the doors opens opposite a utility room where we have our washers and driers for the laundering of towels, diapers, and the special clean overalls and foot coverings which are used in this part of the Center. Next door to the utility room is a kitchen, where the various diet formulas are prepared for feeding the baby animals. All the babies in this part of the Center are

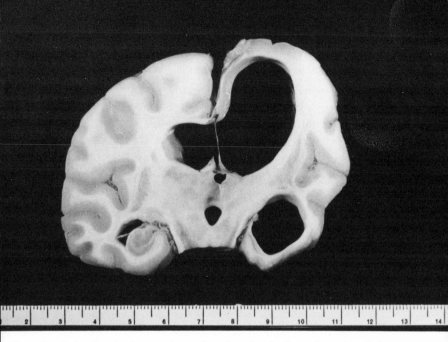

Mary Lou's brain. A photo taken after her death showed gaping holes where brain tissue should have been.

baby apes—that is, baby chimpanzees, baby gorillas, and baby orangutans. The baby chimpanzees and the baby orangutans are all born at the Center itself, whereas the baby gorillas are mostly purchased or obtained by exchange. Next door to the kitchen are three nurseries where the small animals are located. Next door to those is a room called the nursery playroom, in which all the young apes spend up to an hour a day playing with their friends or with the nursery staff. We regard this early relationship with humans as extremely important. If such a relationship is not established early in the ape's life, it grows up more or less as a wild animal and is difficult to really make a relationship and work with. Playing with the babies is regarded as an essential part of the duty of the nursery staff, and I believe they enjoy it very much themselves.

Next door to the nursery playroom is a little isolation room where any baby apes that get sick are isolated for special care and treatment and to prevent them from communicating their illness to the other babies in the nursery. Next door to that is a room for newborn reception. This is where a just-born baby who is taken from his mother is placed in an incubator and kept warm and sterile just as in a maternity hospital. One of the nursery staff nurses him periodically during the day by giving him his bottles; at night a night attendant takes over.

These animals are worth very large sums of money. A young chimpanzee can be purchased only for the sum of $600, and a young orangutan (if you can find one for sale) will cost from $2,500 to $10,000. Young gorillas are $4,500 to $5,000 each. Sometimes the babies are taken away from the mothers because they are required for some particular type of experimentation. I have already mentioned a group of baby chimpanzees who some years ago were withdrawn from their mothers immediately after birth and brought up for about the first twenty months of their lives in total isolation. Animals are sometimes required for a study of chromosomes. Some of them are fed milk from leukemic cows to see if the leukemia factor which is believed to be in this milk can be transmitted to the young. This will have very important repercussions for humans, whether a positive or a negative reaction is obtained. It will have important implications not only for human welfare but for dairy production.

In the nursery there are at the moment perhaps a dozen or more young chimpanzees. There are five or six young orangutans and one young gorilla. The young gorilla is now about three years old; her name is Inaki, and she came to us from the National Zoo in Washington, D.C. The Director of the Zoo agreed to swap her for our firstborn orangutan, Seriba. Inaki was taken from her mother at birth and was kept in the household of one of the keepers at the National Zoo. When she was sent to us she was one year old and she was brought down clad in a diaper and sitting on the lap of the keeper on a first-class seat in an Eastern Airlines plane. The extraordinary thing was that the man sitting next to the keeper and this strange black baby did not even feel sufficient interest in our baby even to make a comment. One passenger across the aisle asked in an interested kind of way, "What is that?" and the keeper told him it was a baby gorilla. He said, "Really," and went back to reading his paper. Nobody else in this first-class section expressed any interest in the animal or even addressed any remarks to the keeper. But the baby was, of course, the pet of the air hostesses during the voyage down to Atlanta.

The young orangutans in the nursery are extremely interesting animals. The chimpanzees are noisy if you come into the room; they jump up and down, beat on the doors of the cages, and call out. The orangutans just look at you quietly with very little, if anything, to say. The same thing applies to the young gorillas. At one time when we were building up our gorilla colony we had eight or nine young gorillas in one of those nursery rooms at the same time. When they were taken for their romp in the nursery playroom, it was really amusing to observe. The way the animals brought each other down while running was reminiscent of the wildest of American college football games. They were, needless to say, rather destructive to the room itself, but were indeed an entertaining group to be with. They were a bit exhausting after a

Gahgah. A young orangutan employs a stick to obtain a reward of candy. This is an example of tool using.

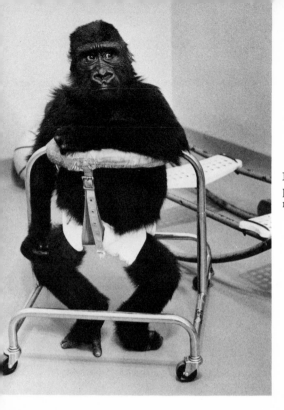

Bandam, a gorilla that caught poliomyelitis, moves around the nursery in his "walker."

while, because even at the young age of, say, eighteen months or two years, they were already extremely strong.

There were many characters in the nursery, and one I remember was an orangutan called Gahgah. He was being tested in the nursery on one occasion by Dr. Richard Davenport. Dr. Davenport was using a long clear plastic tube with a hole in the middle. In the hole he would drop an M & M sweet or some other inducement to work. The only way the baby ape could get it was to pick up a stick, insert it in one end of the plastic tube and push the sweet out the other end; then he could pick it up and eat it. Gahgah could of course see the bait, if it could be described as such, lying in the clear plastic tube. So he knew the sweet was there and could see when the stick he had inserted was effective in pushing it out. On one occasion while I was watching this, the young orangutan "goofed off"—went to one side of the room and sulked, wouldn't play the game anymore. I then picked up the stick, poked it in the plastic tube, pushed the M & M out, and pretended to eat it. The young orangutan was very upset by this behavior of mine and demonstrated in no uncertain terms that he was not in favor of it. About an hour or two later as I passed him in the passage when he was being carried back to his nursery cage, he took a swipe at me as if to try and get his own back for my interfering with the situation in the nursery room.

Another animal of great interest in the nursery who is not now with us was a young gorilla called Bandam. Bandam was purchased by us some years ago when we were still in Orange Park. A few days after he was brought into the nursery, he developed a high temperature and very shortly after that showed signs of paralysis. We were highly suspicious of the circumstances and decided that this might be poliomyelitis. We got in contact with the National Communicable Disease Center in Atlanta, and a team of experts in this disease came to the Center within twelve hours to survey the situation for us. By this time it was evident that another gorilla had the disease and also one of the orangutans. As soon as the disease was completely diagnosed, all the other animals of the colony were hastily given polio vaccine. This was in 1964; it represented a small epidemic of poliomyelitis, and it is of interest that the only epidemic of poliomyelitis that occurred in the United States in that year was the one that occurred in the Yerkes Laboratories.

This, incidentally, was the first time it had been shown that this disease occurred spontaneously in great apes and that it could be transmitted from one to the other. One of the gorillas that got infected with poliomyelitis died. Bandam survived, but with very severe paralysis. Both his legs were partly paralyzed, one arm was completely paralyzed, and there was some slight paralysis in the other arm. He was kept continuously clad in a diaper. Later, when we came up to Atlanta from Orange Park, he was put in one of those little carts in which young babies are placed in an attempt to teach them to walk. He could move around the nursery in this cart, which had three small, well-oiled, easily running wheels, by moving his feet against the floor. He was of course a great favorite with everybody, and enjoyed himself. He was usually put in the cart in early morning and allowed to run around the nursery as he liked. He followed the nursery workers from room to room and was specially fed by them. As he got older, of course, it was obvious that it was going to be impossible for us to keep him alive, since a big gorilla that was paralyzed to the extent that he was would have an impossible life. So he was used in a kidney transplant experiment which was unsuccessful; mercifully for himself, the animal subsequently died.

Upon leaving the nursery, a visitor goes out through a large corridor and swing doors into the main large ape wing. In the entrance hall to this building are three large magnetic boards containing the names of every one of our great apes. His birthdate is shown, if it is known, his official Primate Center number, what experiment he is being used for, and the name of the experimenter. There is a special column for health. If an animal has deviated at all from the normal, whether it be pregnancy, diarrhea, or some kind of infectious or functional disease, this is put up against his name on the board, and it is possible to see at a glance the condition of all the members of the colony.

Opposite the control board is the office of the superintendent of the large primates, who monitors through his large window people coming in and out of that wing. A little farther along on the opposite side beyond the control boards is a large primate kitchen with steam kettles, hot plates, a large storeroom, and a walk-in cold room. The superintendent of the large primates was till recently Jesse Townsend, who was also superintendent of the whole Center. Mr. Townsend is part of the history of the Yerkes Center, having been associated with it for more than thirty years, and he worked for some years with Dr. Yerkes. His knowledge of the handling, care, and maintenance of great apes was encyclopedic, and his death this year was a great blow to all of us. We are fortunate to have his protégé, Jimmy Roberts, to whom he imparted much of his great ape lore, as our new superintendent of large primates. He is competently assisted by the new assistant superintendent, Robert Pollard. Mr. Townsend's widow, Murray Townsend, has also been with the Yerkes Center for many years and has been a tower of strength in the administrative section of the Center.

Proceeding from the kitchen, one comes to the inside of the galleries which lead to the cages. The cages are all part of the structure of the building, and there are 50 of them. Each one has an indoor area about 8 feet by 8 feet square with a wire front to it to the corridor. All the cages are lined up alongside each other, and each opens into the corridor. There is a door for each cage with a double lock on it. Inside is a perch consisting of a slab of concrete stuck halfway up the wall onto which the animal can climb to sleep at night. A guillotine door which can be raised or lowered from the corridor communicates with an outside run which is 10 feet by 8 feet. The outside runs are also lined up alongside one another.

Our system of security for the animals, since we are situated in a residential area, is important. We do not want any of the neighbors around the Primate Center to wake up one day with a chimpanzee in their bathroom or a gorilla in their automobile. Consequently the doors to the pens have not only a built-in lock but a padlock. If an animal escapes on the inside he still has to get out of the inside corridor. If he escapes from the outside door, he still is contained by the outside corridor. Both these corridors are also broken up into short stretches by gates, so that if any member of the staff is caught in a corridor with an escaped over-excited animal, he does not have far to run to safety. If the animal escapes out of the corridors he is still restrained within a 20-acre wooded area by the 8-foot-high electrified fence. We feel that our security conditions are almost foolproof.

However, we did not count on two escape experts, two chimpanzee Houdinis known as Maxine and Gina. These two found a way of breaking the chain link wire which enclosed their pen. Chain link fencing of this size mesh and this thickness of wire has always been used at the Yerkes Primate Center; it was erected by the Anchor Post Company, way back in 1930, at Orange Park, and the same company installed the same material in the Primate Center in Atlanta. No animal ever escaped in Orange Park during a period of forty years by breaking the fencing. Nevertheless, Maxine and Gina found some way in which they could break the chain links in the fencing. The wire from which the links are made is extremely thick, and there appears to be no obvious way it could be broken by either human or animal hands. The interesting thing was that the two apes learned to break the wire in the roof; this was the weak link in our security precautions, because once they broke through the roof there was no corridor to restrain them and they were immediately out into the area surrounded by the electrified fence. These animals broke out of their cages no fewer than five times. On almost all these occasions it was a break through the roof. Apparently they would work on the two wires where they crossed each other until they were able to fracture the wire, and then they would unlace it until they got a hole big enough to climb up through and get out. They would never actually perform this activity or give any indication of performing it whenever there were any human beings around to observe them. When they were left on their own, their first and most urgent object was to work on these wires until they were able to break them. They were so successful at this that we found we could not contain them in the ordinary cages anymore. At about that time we had decided to strengthen some of the cages anyway, particularly against the great strength of the gorillas and orangutans, by fortifying them with one-and-a-quarter-inch-thick aluminum bars. Maxine and her friend were not able to break through the bars, and to everyone's relief they were restrained at last.

In these runs there are many interesting animals. Bobby, the animal who introduced the reader to this book, is there. Wendy, the oldest known living chimpanzee, is there. Suzetta, who came to us from Circus Circus in Las Vegas, and Jent, a large strong male whose special activity is throwing feces at visitors, also inhabit the large animal wing. A story is told that when the Laboratories were at Orange Park one of the animal welfare societies began to take great interest in them because they knew that monkeys and apes were kept there, because they were surrounded by an electrified fence, and because visitors were restricted. They must have pictured to themselves all kinds of diabolical activities going on inside the electrified wire, and they made representation to the Laboratories for a visit to see what was in fact happening. As the story goes, one April morning two beautifully dressed ladies in Easter bonnets turned up to tour the Center, and as they walked past Jent's cage he picked up a handful of feces and plastered the two of them from head to foot. It took an hour or so to clean them up and put them back on the road, and from then on their organization lost all interest in what was going on at the Yerkes Laboratories.

Alpha, the first chimpanzee to be born in the Yerkes Laboratories in 1932 used to grace these cages until she died from a tumor of the reproductive tract in 1966. In the early days at Orange Park, she formed a good relationship with Dr. Leonard Carmichael, at that time secretary of the Smithsonian Institution in Washington, who was a member of the Yerkes Scientific Advisory Board for some twenty-five years. She would complete drawings given her by Dr. Carmichael and under his tutelage she became a great cigarette smoker and would puff away very happily on any cigarette given to her, holding it deftly between finger and thumb. I have also seen her stub out a cigarette and try to put it back into the package from which she had extracted it, but not too successfully, because her big fingers seemed a little clumsy for this particular task. Yet even though one might think the clumsiness of the fingers would necessarily be characteristic of these animals, they do show remarkable precision on occasion with their hands—for example, the use of the fingernails to extract a splinter from the skin of another animal. They also are very expert in picking off small scabs and even freckles from the skin of humans if they are given the opportunity.

Out on the animal runs and also on the three floors of the main building are series of buttons labeled ANIMAL ESCAPE ALARMS. The idea of these is that when an animal escapes, one of the buttons is pressed and a buzzer goes off throughout the building. This is a signal for everyone to remain in his room while a team of people who know what they are doing go out and capture the animal or herd it back into its pen. However, this is only theory. In practice we found that when the animal alarm was pressed everybody would run up to the animal area to see what was going on, so we found it better not to press it at all, and then in most cases by the time anyone knew an animal had escaped it had been caught and returned to its cage. The reason for taking precautions when an animal escapes, and I am thinking especially of great apes, is not that it would set out in a malignant way to attack anyone, but once an animal is out it gets very excited, and since it has the strength of two or three men, it can do damage to a human without intending to.

We have had only one complete escape from the Center; this was a small monkey who managed to get out and apparently decided to seek sanctuary at the Georgia Mental Health Institute, where he was found in the basement a few days later.

With the financing of the Yerkes Primate Center by public funds from Washington, it became necessary to define very explicitly what the function or mission of the Center was to be. Since it had a large collection of great apes, it was obvious that the study of the great apes—the gorilla, the orangutan, and the chimpanzee—and also the lesser ape—the gibbon—was to become the most important activity of the new Primate Center. This did not, of course, eliminate the possibility of some studies with monkeys, but the work with the apes was to be the major work.

The mere study of the great apes themselves was likely to provide information that was valuable to human welfare simply because of their close relation to man. For instance, studies on the aorta, the large blood vessel that carries blood from the heart to the lower part of the body, have shown that it is identical from the point of view of both structure and chemistry with that of man. A human being under apparently "normal" circumstances may develop a disease of this vessel called atherosclerosis; an identical disease develops spontaneously in chimpanzees. This finding indicates that the chimpanzee is an ideal animal in which to study in detail this human disease. Studies of chimpanzee kidneys demonstrate that they are also identical chemically and structurally with those of man and therefore could provide, if the problems of rejection could be overcome, a perfectly satisfactory kidney for transplantation into man. In fact this has already been done, and one person has lived nine months with a chimpanzee kidney. Also the psychosocial and the neurophysiological complexity of great apes approaches very closely that of man and makes the use of these animals of very great value for the study of such areas in human beings. Orangutans are rapidly approaching extinction in the wild. One of our functions therefore is to perpetuate the species so that it will be available for use and study by posterity.

Although our studies and our veterinary care are directed exclusively toward our own animals, we do study some animals in other zoos and institutions and of course also in the wild; occasionally in an emergency with an animal outside our group our veterinary staff lends its help. The case of Judy, a chimpanzee, is worth relating here.

There is a company based in Alabama which keeps a variety of animals for demonstrating to schools in the southeastern area. One of these was a chimpanzee called Judy, who was a guest of honor at the Second International Congress of Primatology hosted by the Yerkes Primate Center and held in Atlanta in July, 1968. She attended a reception sponsored by "Red" Palmer of the Palmer Chemical Company, who invented and manufactures tranquilizing guns. At the reception Judy, dressed in a long dress, sat very properly at a table drinking Coca-Cola from a glass and daintily eating savories. This chimpanzee could understand more than forty spoken commands and would smile and laugh, stand up and sit down, etc., on request. She was a very even-minded animal, and there appeared to be no danger that she would ever attack anyone. I sat next to her for some time talking to her, and she gave the appearance of paying great attention to what I said. My drink was Coca-Cola and vodka, and when I put it down on the table Judy picked it up and enjoyed the taste better than her straight Coca-Cola. She was told by her human lady companion to put it down, which she did. However, as soon as our attention was diverted elsewhere, she picked it up again and began to sip it. If she really liked it better than her own drink because of the taste, she differs from the chimpanzees in the Yerkes Colony, who will not choose fruit juice mixed with vodka in preference to straight juice. However, when they are offered the vodka and fruit juice without choice they will drink until they become inebriated. Whether they find the inebriated condition pleasant or not is hard to say.

Judy was a delightful chimpanzee. It was thus with distress that I received a telephone call late one night from the lady who looked after her. She said Judy was desperately ill. I arranged for her to be motored at once to Atlanta from the Georgia countryside and alerted our veterinarians Dr. Michale Keeling and Dr. Garry Moore (who has since left us), our veterinary pathologist, Dr. Harold McClure, and our senior immunology technician, Charles Guthrie. Judy arrived at the Center near midnight. She was unconscious, was very pale, and had a very weak pulse. She was given oxygen, which revived her a bit. In the meantime a study of her blood revealed an anemia so extreme that it was a miracle she was still alive. She was treated, just as if she were a human patient, with infusions of glucose and electrolytes into her veins. Her blood group was established, and three of us went to the large primate wing at Yerkes (where all the great apes are kept) and placed a chimpanzee with the same blood group in a transport cage so that she could be used for a blood transfusion.

Just as we started to move the chimpanzee into our operating room, we had a call that Judy had stopped breathing. We ran into the building, and Dr. Keeling tried artificial respiration and injection of drugs, but it proved impossible to revive her. We heard that she had been passing black feces for some days, and this indicated that she had some kind of internal hemorrhage. Autopsy showed that a cluster of worms in her intestines had been responsible for this hemorrhage. The worms had of course been drinking Judy's blood themselves and had caused a leakage of blood into the intestines. This is not uncommon. Only the other day I had a letter from a lady who owned a chimpanzee and who complained that her animal was constantly getting anemic and had to be given periodical injections of vitamin B_{12}. It is

148

my guess that this chimpanzee has the same kind of worm infestation as Judy. Infestation by various worms is extremely common in apes and monkeys. Almost all those coming from the wild are affected in varying degrees. Most of these worms can be passed on to human beings, and it is most important if anyone is planning to obtain a baby ape for a pet or if it is to be used in a situation involving personal contact that it be well dewormed. Even so, some varieties of worms are very difficult indeed to eliminate. Regular deworming is a routine at the Yerkes Center, and there is a rigid rule that anyone who handles an animal must wash his hands carefully with an antiseptic solution immediately afterward.

Judy had been seen a few times by a veterinarian or M.D., but M.D.'s are not aware of the special problems which beset chimpanzees, nor in fact are many veterinarians—only someone with experience of great apes is really able to help in a case like Judy's.

A rhesus mother and baby at the new center.

7. Some Observations on Behavior and Mentality of Ape and Monkey People

Dr. C. Lloyd Morgan has warned against the acceptance of anecdotal reports of animal feats as an indication of their level of intelligence. Many types of behavior which seem intelligent are in fact a result of a genetic imprinting or coding which makes their expression in the animal purely automatic and not related to an intelligent appraisal of the problem and the development of a solution. For instance, a baby quail crouches when a hawk flies over not because the baby has learned that the hawk is dangerous and crouching makes it less conspicuous, but simply because the shadow of a hawk passing overhead produces a purely automatic crouching reaction. You can produce this crouch reaction in the quail by simply passing over it a cut-out object which causes a shadow similar to that of a hawk. Many of the actions of insects which seem to be intelligent are purely automatic and are built into the genetic constitution of the animal.

In the higher apes such as the chimpanzee and in ourselves there is a good deal of learned behavior. According to Dr. Henry Nissen, there is considerable evidence that in the chimpanzee, as in man, the principal learning going on during the extended period of helpless infancy and in childhood is really a formation of what he describes as "perception," which he explains as the building up of a knowledge of the world and making sense out of what is at first an undifferentiated confusion. Nissen, a former director of the Yerkes Laboratories, has also suggested that play behavior, which is very common among the most intelligent animals, provides a type of experience which leads to perceptions and knowledge of the world about them—as a matter of interest one might note the playfulness of porpoises. This is why primates are very active in play but you never see an insect ready to play. Dr. Nissen in 1954 described one of the types of experiments which he carried out in chimpanzees to test their mental level. A chimpanzee being tested found if he chose the larger of two square white blocks he was rewarded with a small piece of food such as a slice of banana. If he chose the smaller one he did not get any reward. He quickly learned that the larger one was the one to select in order to get the reward and picked it almost every time. He was then taught that if the two squares were black, it was important that he select the smaller one because this became the one that provided the reward. Then he had to reverse the size relationship if the squares were white instead of black. Then it was found that if the shapes were altered so that the blocks were triangular instead of square, all the previous relations were reversed; the smaller of the white triangles and the larger of the black triangles were positive and produced the reward. The problem continued to be made more complicated until the chimpanzee had to take into account five different factors or cues in order to make the right choice and get a food reward. A problem of this complexity actually is somewhat of a strain even on a human subject, but it was mastered by the chimpanzee.

Dr. Harry Harlow and his colleagues in Wisconsin have shown that rhesus monkeys can respond to at least four cues but rodents and carnivores have great difficulty when the number of cues is more than two. The chimpanzee experiments that I mentioned above show that a chimpanzee can be taught a concept of form. Chimpanzees can, in fact, multiply their conceptions enormously by training or by individual experience. In many animals, for instance, mating behavior is a highly instinctive activity, but for the chimpanzee it is a matter of trial and error. Many of them never learn a proper mating behavior under caged conditions.

What appears to be an instinctive behavior in apes and other primates is the more or less automatic tendency to groom or part the hair on another animal or even on a human, or to try to pick out irregularities in the skin. Of course they may learn this behavior from the mother.

Dr. Yerkes made a remarkable observation about problem solving in chimpanzees. Chimps would learn by imitation from a high-ranking member of their group but not from a low-ranking member. He quotes an example of how a low-ranking chimpanzee was removed from the group and taught how to manipulate a complicated feeding apparatus so that it would deliver bananas to him. This ape was put back with the group with this feeding apparatus, but the high-ranking chimpanzees, although they saw the low-ranking animal at work and getting bananas, did not make any attempt to imitate him; they simply tried to take the bananas away from him after he had earned them. When, on the other hand, the top-ranking chimpanzee was taught to use the equipment and then put back into the group, all the other members of the group lower than he refrained from taking away his bananas but looked at his activities with great interest and eventually learned to imitate him and get bananas for themselves. I feel sure this has interesting connotations in human society.

Interest in animal intelligence and especially in primate intelligence goes back a long way and attracted a good deal of attention during the nineteenth century. Dr. G. F. Romanes, writing in a book called *Animal Intelligence,* in 1888 quoted many examples of animal intelligence. He gave an account of an animal which was probably a chimpanzee, described in a letter which was written by Professor Robertson:

> I witnessed the following incident in the Jardin des Plantes now many years ago; but it struck me greatly at the time, and I have narrated it repeatedly in the interval. A large ape—I believe anthropoid but cannot tell the species—was in the great iron cage with a number of smaller monkeys, and was lording it over them with many wild gambols, to the amusement of a crowd of spectators. Many things— fruits and the like—had been thrown between the bars into the cage which the ape was always forward to seize. At last someone threw in a small hand looking glass, with a strongly made frame of wood. This the ape at once laid hold of and began to brandish like a hammer. Suddenly he was arrested by a reflection of himself in the glass, and looked puzzled for a moment; then he darted his head behind the glass to find the other of his kind as he had evidently supposed to be there. Astonished to find nothing, he apparently bethought himself that he had not been quick enough with his movement. He now proceeded to raise and draw the glass nearer to him with great caution, and then with a swifter dart look behind. Again finding nothing he repeated the attempt once more. He now passed from astonishment to anger and began to beat with the frame violently on the floor of the cage. Soon the glass was shattered and pieces fell out. Continuing to beat, he was in the course of one blow again arrested by his image in the piece of glass still remaining in the frame. Then, as it seemed, he determined to make one trial more. More circumspectly than ever the whole first part of the process was gone through with; more violently than ever the final dart was made. His fury over this last failure knew no bounds. He crunched the frame and glass together with his teeth, he beat on the floor and he crunched again till nothing but splinters was left.

Charles Darwin recorded with interest a story that in Paraguay when eggs were first given to monkeys they smashed them and lost much of their contents. Afterward, they very quickly learned to hit one end against some hard body and pick off the bits of shell with their fingers and pour the contents of the egg into their mouths. If these animals cut themselves with any sharp tool they would not touch it again, or if they did, would handle it very cautiously. They would also unwrap lumps of sugar given to them in paper, and their owner would sometimes put a live wasp in the paper so if they unfolded it hastily they got stung. This had to happen only once to them, and afterward they would always hold the packet to their ears before they tried to open it to see if they could detect any movement inside. It is not certain what these animals were, but there seems some evidence that they were organ-grinder monkeys called cebus.

Much earlier than Darwin's time the great naturalist Baron Georges Cuvier once kept an orangutan and noted that it used to draw a chair from one end of a room to another, so it could stand on it and reach a latch it wanted to open. Dr. G. F. Romanes described this as a rationally adaptive action which no dog has equaled. Monkeys have also been noted employing a stick to pry up the lid of a chest which was too heavy for the animal to raise by any other means, thus discovering the principle of the lever. No animal other than the monkey has ever been known to do this, although of course the monkey has the advantage in having hands which can grasp, a big advantage over many other animals. Monkeys have also discovered independently for themselves the mechanical principle of the screw. Many of them have used stones as hammers. Stories are told of monkeys thrusting stones into the open valves of oysters so the animal within could be pulled out with their fingers, the alternative being to smash the shell. In addition to monkeys it is of interest that animals such as birds are also very ingenious in methods of getting at the contents of molluscs. They have been known for instance to pick them up in their beaks, fly to a great height and drop them onto rocks so that they will be smashed and they will be able to pick the animal out from the shattered remains of the shell. The mongoose also has a very ingenious method of getting at eggs; its mouth is not big enough for it to bite through the shell, so it stands with its back to a stone or, in the case of a captive mongoose to a wall, picks the egg up in its front paws and then throws it between its hind legs, so that it hits against the wall or stone and breaks; the mongoose then sucks up the juice. The method of some sea otters in California of opening shells is also of interest. They bring up a shell and a stone, lie on their backs and hit the shell against the stone which they put on their stomachs while they are swimming upside down.

Dr. Romanes also describes certain sacred monkeys in India as being very clever at catching snakes and being able to distinguish poisonous and nonpoisonous snakes; in the case of the poisonous animals they would destroy the poisoned fangs by breaking them against stones. He also quotes some memoirs written by a Lieutenant Shipp which I quote:

A Cape baboon, having taken off some clothes from the barracks, I formed a party to recover them. With twenty men I made a circuit to cut them off from the caverns, to which they always fled for shelter. They observed my movements, and detached about 50 to guard the entrance, the others kept to their post. We could see them collecting large stones and other missiles. One old grey headed one, who had often paid us a visit at the barracks, was seen distributing his orders, as if a general. We rushed on to the attack. When at a scream from him, they rolled down enormous stones on us, so that we were forced to give up the contest.

There are quite a number of records in the literature of monkeys rolling stones down on people who were trying to catch them. It has never been authenticated that the animals are doing this deliberately, and there is some possibility that the stones might have been disturbed by the scuffling about associated with their attempt to escape. However, the possibility that they rolled the stones deliberately cannot be ignored.

It is remarkable what some primates can be trained to do. There was an authenticated report from Australia of a farmer who had trained a rhesus monkey to drive a tractor. Apparently once the motor was set and the tractor put into gear the monkey could steer it extremely well. The matter came into prominence because the owner of the rhesus claimed the cost of support of the animal from his income tax, and revenuers being what they are, they did not, of course, believe it, so they went out to inspect the rhesus for themselves. That the claim was correct was evidenced by the fact that the income tax authorities in Australia agreed after this visit that the cost of keeping the animal could be deducted from the owner's income tax. On at least two occasions in the last ten years in the United States individuals have been fined for letting chimpanzees drive their automobiles on the highway; one of them, in California, was actually steering his owners through expressway traffic.

At Brooks Air Force Base rhesus monkeys have been trained to sit in a cockpit located in a movable platform. In front, and a little to the side, is a joy stick by means of which the animal can tilt the platform-cockpit combination backward or forward or side to side at any angle. This cockpit can also be tilted in the same way by the experimenter by remote control. The rhesus monkeys have learned, as the experimenter tilts the cockpit-platform combination in any particular direction, that by moving the joy stick they can keep the platform "flying" in "level flight." They are rapidly becoming extremely expert in this and so presumably they could fly an airplane without too much problem if anyone would be prepared to go up with them.

Desmond Morris, in the first edition of his *Animal Life,* described a baboon in South Africa who had been trained by a signalman to pull the levers controlling the points for the trains. There were six lever points which could be moved. A picture shows a baboon actually pulling one of these levers. Apparently the signalman had certain words and signs to denote to the animals which lever they were to pull.

Many Siamese farmers keep pigtail monkeys which they use to collect coconuts. The monkeys run up coconut trees and twist a nut with their hands until it falls to the ground and is collected by the humans. Several of the pigtail monkeys which we imported from Bangkok, Thailand, were trained coconut pickers. Monkeys are also used in the East for picking tea and for picking peppers. Some Thailand banks use monkeys to detect false coins and sort them from good coins. It takes about two years to train a bank ape for this purpose, and they are then valued at $5,000 each. In Malaya monkeys have been used by botanists to collect species of plants. One has been known to have collected specimens from 350 species of trees in a six-month period. The monkeys run up these trees with a rope attached to them; sometimes this rope becomes tangled, but they are extremely good at untangling it. This reminds me of a story about Benito, the little capuchin monkey I once owned. On one occasion he was tethered out in the grass at the back of the house. He was attached by a fairly long lead to a stake driven into the ground. Apparently he chewed through or broke the lead and ran up a tree. When he got to the top, the end of the lead got tangled in the branches. When I came home he was sitting up there rather perturbed that he was stuck. It was a tree about 40 feet high with the first branches starting a long way up. I could not leave him up there; it was getting dark, and the weather forecast predicted the temperature would fall below freezing that night. I put a ladder against the tree but still could not get up high enough to reach the top branches. So I decided to cut the tree down, and just trust to luck that Benito would survive the fall. It was better to do that than to leave him out with the certainty of freezing that night. I cut the tree down, and there was no problem at all. Benito rode it down like a champion, moving onto the upper side of the tree as it fell. I was able simply to go up and untangle the rope and take him back inside into the warmth. Maybe if he had been left there long enough, he would have been able to untangle the rope, but he did not look as though he were going to do it at that time.

Gelada baboons, which come from Ethiopia, have been used for centuries to perform various jobs. They have been recorded as bearers of torches at banquets and have been taught various other exotic tasks.

They are interesting animals and are known as bleeding-heart baboons because of the heart-shaped, bare red patch of skin on its chest, which according to Desmond Morris is the representation of the sex skin of the backside of some monkeys. In gelada groups each male forms a small harem instead of one male becoming the dominant animal and having the prior right to certain females in the group. Geladas also seem to be a very agree-

157

able type of person. In the compound where we keep our group the animals will often come to the side of the fence where a human is standing and mumble away, using all kinds of vocalizations for quite a long period of time. We hope to have someone very shortly who will be studying their vocalizations; perhaps the geladas have a message for us.

In this discussion of the abilities and behavior of monkeys it seems appropriate at this point to refer to the work of Dr. Joseph Brady of the Walter Reed Army Institute of Research. He produced what might be described as an "executive monkey." In his experiments he had two monkeys seated side by side restrained in chairs. The animals were allowed to move their heads and their arms and legs, but their bodies were restrained. At regular intervals they received short electrical shocks which made them uncomfortable but which were not painful. One of the monkeys could prevent the shocks to both of the animals if it pulled a lever at the right time. The other monkey also had a lever, but when he pulled it nothing happened at all. The monkey with the working lever soon found out that when a red light came on, he and the other monkey could avoid getting a shock if he pulled his lever once every 20 seconds. He had to do this six hours a day, and he was then allowed six hours of rest. He died after 23 days, and when an autopsy was performed on him it was found he had developed a large ulcer. His companion, who had had the dummy lever but had not been faced with the same problem, did not have the same anxiety or the same responsibility, did not die, and seemed perfectly healthy. This work may be of interest in view also of the studies of Dr. Peter Bourne in Vietnam, in which he studied under conditions of stress, the excretion of certain hormones from the adrenal gland in the urine. On one occasion when he was with the Special Forces in Vietnam they received a warning that there was to be a mass attack by North Vietnamese and Vietcong within a specified three- or four-day period. The receipt of this information caused rises in the excretion of these hormones which were related to stress in the urine. In the enlisted men these compounds rapidly fell to normal, indicating that the men had responded and reacted to cope with this stress situation, but in the officer and the radio operator, the increased excretion of these hormones continued, indicating that in their executive positions the anxiety and worry had continued.

There are at present a number of groups at the Yerkes Center who are extremely interested in the problems of behavior in the great apes. These include Dr. Richard Davenport and Dr. Charles Rogers, who are concerned with the effects of early deprivation upon subsequent mental development of ape persons. This is a continuation of a study which was begun by Dr. Henry Nissen in the late 1950's in Orange Park. In this study a number of baby chimpanzees were removed from their mothers at birth and were brought up in total isolation. They were kept in little cribs with enough room for them to move around and exercise. The cribs were in a dark room, and on top of each crib was a light which was on for twelve hours every day and off for twelve hours. The cribs were in a room in which noise was suppressed; people were requested not to talk when they were in it and to make as little noise as possible. Some of these animals had no form of visual or other stimulation; they saw no human being or any other animal, for a period of twenty months. They wore diapers, and Annie Jones looked after them. She put her hands through into the cage once or twice a day, changed their diapers, and saw that the animals had food and water. They were unable to see Annie Jones herself, of course; only her arms were visible as they went into the cage to perform these necessary hygienic missions. Some of the baby chimpanzees could see the animal in the next cage; some were given geometrical shapes and colors to see. All the animals were kept in this condition for a period of twenty months. After that time they were taken outside and were then introduced to the rest of the world, which of course they found extremely frightening to begin with. However, they rapidly adapted to it. But during the period in which they had been in this isolation they had developed a variety of repetitive movements which can be seen in many types of mentally deficient children. The movements consisted, in some animals, of sticking their fingers in their eyes or ears. One animal would lie on its back and by kicking the sides of the cage spin itself at high speeds

159

on its back. Another one would stand on one leg, put its arm above its head, and pirouette like a ballerina for long periods. Many of them would shake their heads, make strange movements with their hands and arms, and so on. These aberrations have persisted into subadult life. The animals are now seven or eight years old and are still showing many of these strange changes, some of which are reminiscent of mental deficiency and others of schizophrenia. This experiment, more than anything else, demonstrated the profound effect which infant experience or lack of it can have on behavior later in life.

Dr. Harry Harlow in Wisconsin has demonstrated similar kinds of effects in baby rhesus monkeys who have been isolated in this way. There is, however, a big difference between the baby monkeys and the great apes. Dr. Harlow found that once these aberrations had been instilled into the baby monkeys as a result of early treatment, they were fixed for life. While this is true to some extent in the great apes also, if these animals are placed with normal animals they do improve. Since the apes are so much closer to humans than the monkeys it is perfectly obvious how important the great ape, and in this particular instance the chimpanzee, is in the study of the factors that are concerned with human mental development. These isolated animals are now in a large 100-foot-square compound at our field station; they are able to run loose during the day, and they come inside to sleep in heated quarters at night and during the winter. In one corner of this compound a tower has been built which overhangs the compound, and the front and bottom of the tower were once composed of a thick plate of specially tempered hardened glass about 16 feet away from the animals on the ground. However, they are able to see from the ground the people up in the tower observing them, and this has obviously provided a temptation to them. They were not able to get up to touch the glass because it was beyond their reach. After a while they developed the habit of grabbing stones or sand in their hands and rushing at the corner of the compound, jumping and levering themselves as high up as they could in one movement. At the apex of their leap they would throw with all the force in their command the stones or sand they held in their hands. They did this many times, and forunately nothing happened. But eventually one of them threw a stone big enough and hard enough to smash through the specially tempered glass. This glass then had to be replaced by thick plexiglass which to date has resisted their onslaughts.

Dr. Harlow and his colleagues in mid-1970 announced a fascinating additional discovery concerning their isolated monkeys which were apparently irrevocably abnormal as a result of their isolation in early life. These animals when placed among normal rhesus monkeys would spend all day sitting huddled in a corner and rocking aimlessly, making no attempt to contact the other animals. In fact the latter reacted aggressively toward them, which did not help matters at all. No kind of conditioning or experimental treatment caused any improvement in these animals, and of course they did not have and would not permit any mating behavior. However, some of them, when they came of age, were made pregnant by artificial insemination and produced babies. Although the mothers tried to reject them, however much they were punished and abused by her, they continued to try to make physical contact and to cling. After four months of attempted rejection, the mothers showed signs of giving in and then progressively improved psychologically. Being forced to accept from their own babies the affection of which they had been deprived when babies themselves, seemed to be the therapy they needed.

The Yerkes Center has been responsible for a number of outstanding studies on the mentality of chimpanzees and great apes in general. One of the earliest and simplest was the study demonstrating the ability of the chimpanzees to work together. For example, if you take an ordinary wooden box, put a number of weights in it, attach a rope to it, and place a bit of banana on it as a reward, then even though the box is quite heavy, the chimpanzee will pull it up to his cage and enjoy the reward. If extra weights are put in the box and an extra rope attached to it, cooperation between chimpanzees can be demonstrated. When the second rope together with the second chimpanzee is put in the cage, there is a period in which both of the animals pull at different times; they will eventually learn that if they pull together they can move the box up to the cage and can in this way obtain the reward. An animal that is not anxious to work in this way will be coached by the animal who knows what he is doing and wants to get the reward. He will put his arm around the disaffected animal and bring him over to the rope or lead him by the arm or the hand to the rope, and sometimes get very concerned if the animal will not assist. On one occasion our investigators found that an animal got so furious when his cage mate refused to pull the rope that with one superhuman, or shall I say superchimpanzee, pull he did actually pull the box close enough to the cage on his own to enable him to get the reward. Characteristically, however, he reached for the reward that was in the position where the other chimpanzee should have received it before he reached for his own. He was determined that, having done all the work himself, the other chimpanzee was not going to benefit from it.

The Yerkes Laboratories eventually developed a device known as a Chimpomat. This Chimpomat would receive either metal or plastic disks and would dispense some form of food reward in return for the insertion of a disk. Animals were eventually taught to pull the box of weights up to the cage in return for plastic or metal disks which they could then take and put in the Chimpomat to get their reward. By the process of lengthening the time between which they could earn the reward and when they could actually receive it by using the Chimpomat (by making the Chimpomat available only certain times of the day), the animals could be trained to collect plastic disks, in other words, to work for money. They would store up this money until the time came for them to spend it. Eventually they were trained to earn the money one day and spend it in the Chimpomat the following day. On these occasions the animals used to walk around clutching their earnings to their breasts, sleeping on them at night so they would not be stolen, and getting very hysterical if any other animal came near their earnings or tried to take any of them away—a very human side of their activity and the dawn of ownership of private property and capitalism, a thought that has intriguing implications.

162

A most extreme case of chimpanzee cooperation was carried out by putting two chimpanzees in adjacent cages and in each cage putting little machines with four colored buttons. To gain a good reward the chimpanzees were required to press four buttons in succession. For example, one animal had to press the green button, the other the blue button, the first one the yellow button, the second the red button. Only if those colors were pressed in that order would the automatic food device unlock and permit them to obtain the food. Two intelligent chimpanzees would work well together in this procedure, but how frantic one animal would get if a dull animal were placed in the next cage! The intelligent chimpanzee would gesticulate wildly and signal to the other animal in an attempt to persuade it to get to work and press the right key in the right succession.

Dr. O. L. Tinklepaugh, who worked in the Yerkes labs for many years, described in 1928 a series of experiments in which the ability of chimpanzees to complete an experiment after a delay was studied. He mentions that Dr. Wolfgang Köhler had found that when food was buried in the sand outside the cages of some chimpanzees they had no difficulty in locating it; in fact they located it immediately after a delay of $16\frac{1}{2}\sqrt{}$ hours. Yerkes found that the gorilla Congo, with whom he worked, was able to locate buried food very quickly and accurately 48 hours after a delay. When he also buried four boxes similar except in color and placed them to either side and in front of and behind the subject, Congo was still able to find the right box even after delays of 3 hours. Chimpanzees will locate buried food after delays of 48 hours and were also able to select the right one out of four boxes after a delay of 3 or 4 hours.

The chimpanzee Joni, whom Dr. N. N. Ladygin Kohts in Russia trained, was able to match objects from a sample very accurately, but if a delay of 15 seconds was introduced between the showing of the sample and the choice of the similar object, he was not able to do it. This is obviously a more difficult task.

At Holloman Air Force Base, where scientists have been working with quite a large number of chimpanzees, some of their ape people have been trained to recognize numbers. Some animals in fact were able to recognize numbers as high as nine. An animal was placed in a cage where there was a screen which lighted up with a number, say, 7; the chimpanzee then took a lever and pressed a lever 7 times. He then hit a second lever to demonstrate that he had finished counting. Similarly, the chimpanzee could be shown any number from 1 to 9 and would tap the lever the correct number of times. Another activity the chimpanzees have been trained to do at Holloman has been to use two hand levers to keep a small cross inside a circle on an illuminated panel board. The two hand levers control vertical and horizontal movements of the cross. As the circle is made by the experimenter to wander over the panel, the chimpanzees with the aid of these two levers keep the cross continuously inside it. They have become so expert at this that they could use this mechanism for navigating; they could, in fact, fly a space machine or some kind of an aircraft using this type of navigational system.

One of our problems in assessing animal intelligence is in the methods we use for this purpose. We estimate the animal's intelligence upon his ability to solve the particular tests that we design for him. In the wild with his own problems to solve, he may show himself in fact, in some respects at any rate, more intelligent than we are. Dr. Vernon Reynolds, an English primatologist, believes that the main advantage in giving intelligence tests to apes lies in the fact that it gives an opportunity to study humanoid thought processes on a relatively simple level.

Some of the earliest works on the intelligence of apes was carried out by Dr. Wolfgang Köhler who worked in the anthropoid station at Tenerife in the Canary Islands from 1912 onward. The first resident investigator at Tenerife was Dr. E. Teuber, who was a psychologist; he was followed by Dr. Köhler, who was also a psychologist. Dr. Köhler had a group of eight young and one adult female chimpanzees. He was one of the first to set up a series of problem-solving tests for these ape people. He applied the tests also to a number of other animals. One of his earliest experiments was to have a straight wire fence with an animal on one side of it and a food reward—in the case of the chimpanzee, a banana—on the other side. The chimpanzees, when they saw the banana through the fence, almost immediately attempted to find a way around the fence so that they could pick it up. The same kind of test was given to a dog. If the meat was placed very close to the dog on the other side of the fence, he simply rushed at the fence and did not try to go around it; however, if the food was not too close to the fence the dog would eventually find his way around. Hens were unable to solve the problem at all; they simply rushed continuously at the wire fence and never learned to go around it.

Dr. Köhler also studied a baby girl in the same situation. Though she was only fifteen months old, she immediately "got the idea" and went around the fence.

I have mentioned Yerkes' chimpanzees pulling a box of weights with a slice of banana up to the cage by means of a rope. This type of study was also one of those made by Köhler. He also tried it with dogs; however, they showed no real understanding of the solution, although they could be taught in a mechanical way to pull a string with a box attached and would then snatch up the attached food award. The dog, however, did this as a kind of a learned trick; he did not really work out any stage of the significance of what he was doing.

Raking in out-of-reach food with a stick was a fairly simple procedure for chimpanzees. But if the stick was too short and there were two sections of stick which could be fitted together to make it long enough to pull in the food, this problem was fairly promptly solved. Even fitting three pieces of stick together to pull in a food reward was not beyond a chimpanzee's ability. It was interesting that the chimpanzee would use the stick to rake in the food not only if the stick was lying in place and if the food was between the stick and the cage, but also if one end of the stick was in front of the food and not behind it. This piece of deduction was one of the tests that, as Yerkes pointed out, makes apes so different in their behavior from the monkeys. Many monkeys will move the stick to rake the food in if the latter is between the cage and the stick, but they are never able to solve the problem if the food is on the other side of the stick. Yerkes also had some problems in getting a mountain gorilla to perform this task.

Some years ago Dr. Yerkes worked out a very complex series of procedures in which a piece of food had to be pushed along a kind of a maze and even in some part of the operation pushed away from the cage to get around an obstruction before it could finally be pulled into the cage. This is a very complex piece of reasoning for a chimpanzee to carry out, but at the Center there are moving picture films showing chimpanzees performing this task.

Dr. Köhler carried out an experiment which has become very famous and is frequently illustrated in psychological books. He suspended a banana well above a chimpanzee's head so that he could not get at it by reaching or jumping, but he also provided a series of boxes for the chimpanzee to stand on. No individual box was big enough to enable the animal to get hold of the banana, but he eventually worked out that by putting the boxes one on top of the other he was able to get high enough to grab the banana. There are no animals other than apes that are known to be able to reach this solution. Whether the porpoise could solve this problem if he had any limbs is anyone's guess. My guess would be that the porpoise would solve such a problem very easily.

In the food and stick problem the monkey failed to grasp the conception that even if the food lay on the other side of the stick, it was still possible to rake it in. This indicated a great difference in the type of thought and problem-solving ability which exists between a monkey and a chimpanzee or other ape. A group of Gestalt psychologists has emphasized the tendency of the mind to organize and integrate so it perceives problems as a whole rather than as a sum of their parts. Dr. Köhler, one of the founders of this type of psychology, claimed that the ability of chimpanzees to solve problems depended upon this ability and that this was what distinguishes them from monkeys. He found that they did not gradually come to the solution of a problem as a result of calculated trial and error, but that the animal eventually conceived the nature of the entire problem and proceeded to solve it. This indicates how valuable chimpanzees and other apes are in studying problems related to the human mind and how much more valuable these animals are for this purpose than monkeys.

These studies also indicate that chimpanzees and other apes would probably be very mechanically minded, and they are. They are able to manipulate locks, doors, and keys in a variety of ways, both for opening and for closing cages, boxes, and so on. I have seen a group of chimpanzees at the London Zoo open a complicated box system with locks and bolts in a remarkably short space of time. Very few monkeys have this specific type of mechanical ability. Probably one of the most outstanding in this respect is the little organ-grinder monkey, the capuchin, who could be described as a mechanical genius; in fact he approaches the chimpanzee very closely in his ability to perform mechanical activities.

I have mentioned our little capuchin Benito. He lived in a cage at the university at one time. The cage had a latch that could be lifted to open the door, but only if a vertically hanging bar was pulled out of the way first. The solution to this particular problem was nothing at all for Benito. He mastered it in a matter of minutes. Then we took some thick heavy wire and twisted it many times around one bar of the door and one bar of the cage. However, Benito first undid the latch and then undid the wire and was out, playing about in no time. We found that really the

Benito rolling on his back enjoying a game with the author.

only way to keep him in these cages was to put a chain with a lock around the door, and to keep the key out of reach. On two occasions previous to this when Benito got out he created absolute chaos. The first time, he got into a neighboring mouse room where hundreds of mice were being used for medical experimentation. They were kept in small plastic cages with loose tops, each cage carefully labeled. Benito tipped all the cages upside down on the floor, and when the scientists working with the mice arrived to inject them they found a great seething heap of wriggling mice on the floor, all the animals inextricably mixed up, and with no hope of distinguishing the experimental animals from the controls. On another occasion when Benito got out he opened a can of aluminum paint. He painted his cage, the floor, the walls, everything else in the room, and himself. He became the first silver-colored capuchin in history, and it was months before the paint wore off.

Benito was a very interesting animal from many points of view. I used to take him on a rubber raft and swim out into a lake probably 300 yards. Benito would sit on the raft, and when he saw the bank of the lake disappearing as we got farther and farther out, he would get very agitated and finally was not able to stand it any longer. At this stage he would leap off the rubber raft and strike out for the shore. He was able to swim with such remarkable rapidity that I would not have been able to keep up with him had I not been wearing a pair of frogman's flippers. With these, however, I was able to keep abreast of him, and as he arrived at the shore I would pick him up and carry him the last few feet onto dry land.

One of Benito's interesting reactions was to fish. I sometimes used to take him fishing and would tie him on a long rope attached to a tree alongside the lake in which I was fishing. On one occasion I caught a little bluegill bream. When I turned around toward Benito with the fish dangling on the end of the line, Benito sparred with it and tried to grab it from the line. Frightened that he might get hurt by the hook, I pulled the whole thing away from him, disengaged the fish from the hook, and thinking that he just wanted to play with the little flopping fish, I threw it toward him. He picked it up and held it flat between two hands and began to eat it, starting at the face and finishing up at the tail. He ate the entire fish right through from the face down to the tail, bones, innards, and all. Another of Benito's interesting food habits was spider eating. He was so closely attached to us that if we took him out, say, on a picnic and let him go in the trees he would always come back after a little bit of encouragement to be attached to a leash and taken back to the car for the trip home. As soon as I let Benito out in a place like this in any wild country at all, he would hop from tree to tree looking for spider webs. He would pick the spider out of the center of each web, pop it in his mouth, and chew it up with what was evidently a great deal of relish.

Benito was subsequently placed in a mixed species group of monkeys at the field station at Lawrenceville. He rapidly found some friends for himself. However, he made several mistakes in the beginning. As is well known, whenever a group of monkeys is kept in an enclosure, or in the wild, one of the males becomes the dominant animal. The dominant male in this particular group was Penrod, a very powerful, very antihuman, nasty type of rhesus monkey who had in fact been brought up in a human family. This was the family of Dr. Irwin Bernstein, who was working with this particular group. Penrod had been banished from the family because as he began to grow up he slashed Dr. Bernstein's wife with his teeth. Benito made the mistake, since he had been brought up with humans and had only just left a human family, of thinking that he was more human than monkey, and of course he was not going to take any nonsense from a mere rhesus. When the rhesus threatened him he threatened back, with the result that he got very badly beaten and cut in the first few months of his stay in this group. It was interesting that two quite unrelated and different animals came to his aid. One was a small female capuchin monkey, the same breed as himself, and the other was a large, very mild animal called Red who was a hybrid between a rhesus and some other brand of monkey unknown to us. We will talk more about this group later, but there is an incident I would like to mention here. On one occasion I went into this enclosure to talk to Benito. Needless to say, this was after Penrod, the big rhesus, had ceased to be the principal animal in the

169

group and had been removed. Benito could hear me from a considerable distance away if I was in the vicinity of the field station; he would call me if he heard me and would show great pleasure, including shaking his head and grinning, which is a recognition sign in such monkeys. Very often he would try to encourage me to come into the compound by coming close to the wire to be petted, and then before I could actually pet him retreat back into the compound to try to entice me in. On this particular occasion I did go in and picked him up in my arms and patted him a little bit and then put him on his back on the ground to rub his tummy.

In this group of monkeys was a very young, tiny little monkey of a species called a "mustache monkey." She was very timid and tended to retreat into the far corner of the compound whenever any human beings were around. But it so happened that this little animal was a friend of Benito's, and when she saw me bending over him on the ground, she obviously misinterpreted the situation and thought I was hurting her friend, so she launched a high-speed attack at me. She rushed right across the compound and endeavored to bite my arm. It was a very touching and very gallant performance by this little animal.

A question very frequently asked is: "Which is most intelligent, the chimpanzee, the gorilla, or the orangutan?" Dr. Yerkes seemed to favor the chimpanzee as the most intelligent of the three, being influenced partly by the fact that the chimpanzee is very much the extrovert among these animals, and also by the fact that he had carried out some quite extensive intelligence tests with a mountain gorilla and had found it surprisingly deficient in its proficiency to perform certain tests which caused the chimpanzee little trouble.

Dr. W. T. Shepherd, writing in 1943, described some tests he carried out in an attempt to demonstrate the difference between the chimpanzee and the orangutan. He had first of all a piece of apple suspended by a string in front of the cage, but it was beyond the reach of the animals. Attached to the string was a stick which was within reach of the animal; the problem was to see if it would reach out, seize the end of the stick, pull in the string with the apple on it, and thereby secure the apple. In this experiment, the chimpanzee performed the first trial in 5 seconds and the second trial in 4 seconds. The orangutan took 8 seconds the first time and 6 seconds on the second occasion. The experiment was repeated the next day, and both animals performed the act, as might be expected, in shorter time. Dr. Shepherd then placed a board about 30 inches long with one end inside the cage and the other end sticking out of the cage; at the far end of the board was a piece of banana. The animals pulled the board in without much difficulty and secured the banana. The chimpanzee took 20 seconds to do it the first time, 15 seconds the second time. The orangutan took 25 seconds the first time and 16 seconds the second time. Dr. Shepherd mentions that the orang appeared somewhat fearful and cautious in carrying out these experiments. I think that the longer period that the orang takes to perform this type of experiment does not suggest a lower intelligence, but indicates simply that it is slower in doing anything than the chimpanzee; the latter is much more inclined to rush at things. This experiment deals also with only one chimpanzee and one orangutan. Chimpanzees and orangutans have a range of intelligence comparable to the range found in human beings. In other words, chimpanzees range from mental deficiency up to the genius level, and the same is true for orangutans. So to get a reasonable average estimate of intelligence, many animals should be tested.

More recent studies done at Yerkes using orangutans have shown that they are at least as intelligent as chimpanzees, and in some cases orangutans have been found better than some chimpanzees. Dr. Charles Rogers and Dr. Richard Davenport at the Yerkes Center have found that both the chimpanzees and the orangutans are able to perform what is described as cross-modal transfer of information. For example, animals are shown a geometrical shape and are subsequently able to select that shape by feel. This is a procedure which was thought to be beyond the ability of great apes, and some authorities claim that these animals do not even possess the neural structures necessary for such a transfer of information to take place. However, both chimpanzees and orangs were found who could perform this remarkable ape feat; in fact some could actually be shown a photograph of a geometrical shape and were then able to select the identical object by feel only.

A chimpanzee from France named Joni has been said to be able to distinguish thirteen different geometrical figures—a circle, an ellipse, a dodecagon, a decagon, a hexagon, an octagon, a pentagon, a square, a rectangle, a rhombus, a trapezoid, a sector, a semicircle—and various forms of triangles. He was also able to distinguish ten solids: a sphere, a cylinder, a cone, a pyramid, and prisms with various bases. The method of testing whether animals can detect these structures is relatively simple. You simply present the animal with two or more of these shapes, and under one particular shape there is food. The animal finally learns to associate food with that particular shape. If you put a decagon in with a hexagon and an octagon and put food only under the decagon but move it in each test so that it is not in the same position with relation to the other figures, the animal will show, by consistently selecting the shape associated with the food, whether he can distinguish the decagon from the hexagon or the octagon or any of the other different geometrical figures or solid figures mentioned.

There is no doubt that the three great apes vary greatly in their overall reaction to people and things. I have mentioned that the chimpanzee is a very extroverted animal who gets emotional and excited with strangers. Chimpanzees are also excessively vocal. The gorillas and orangutans are very much less vocal, have much less to say, and do not get excited easily. The only time I have ever heard an orangutan make a loud noise was when we separated two partly grown orangutans who had been together for two or three years. The female who was left when the male was removed became vociferous and made a noise quite as loud as any chimpanzee. But under normal circumstances the orangutans make a low, whimpering sort of noise and very little else. Gorillas are also capable of making a roaring noise, but under normal circumstances in captivity they do not do so.

The differences in reaction among these three animals to a single event is shown very well by something I did with them. I had a child's color picture book of animals, opened it at an alligator,

172

and showed it to a number of chimpanzees. The chimpanzees rushed up immediately to the wire, put their fingers through, and tried to touch the alligator; some of them tried to trace its outline with their finger. The gorillas, when shown this picture, came close, peered at it, and then retreated and stood some eight or ten feet away from it with all the appearance of being nervous. Some of the orangutans took one look at it and retreated from their outside cages altogether and went into their inside dens. Other orangutans just backed well away from it. I do not know how this reaction may be interpreted, but it certainly does show a very profound difference in reaction of these three species to something unusual which they do not understand.

One of the problems in deciding whether one ape is more intelligent than the other is to query what is intelligence. In certain respects the ability of some of these apes to survive in the jungles shows that in this environment they have some factors of intelligence which are probably a great deal better developed than those of humans. During the last war, when I was responsible for the survival of Special Forces being sent into the jungle for sabotage and subversive operations, I had to give these agents a great deal of instruction on how to survive in the jungle, how to test jungle plants for edibility, how to tell which were poisonous, and so on. There was no natural instinct among these men on how to survive such an environment. The gorillas and orangutans of course have been brought up in the jungle and are expert and intelligent, if you like to use that word, in regard to surviving in this environment.

Dr. Duane Rumbaugh, who has worked extensively with great apes and is now associate director of the Yerkes Primate Center, has used what he describes as "learning set" measurements in an attempt to compare the mental age of the animals with their chronological age so as to give an IQ score. Dr. Rumbaugh and a number of other authors have concluded that the way an animal performs on these "learning set" tasks is a reflection of basic intelligence which is found in both humans and apes. In such a procedure the animal is first trained to learn a simple discrimination, for example to distinguish a red square from a red circle, and he has to associate a food reward with either one or the

173

other. In 25 tests he is expected to get 20 correct responses. If he does this an extensive series of trial problems follows, and from these it is possible to calculate some index of the ape's intelligence. Dr. Rumbaugh found that certain orangutans, gorillas, and chimpanzees all performed equally well, giving very high levels of accuracy, in fact almost 90 percent, and so it could be concluded that these three types of ape were approximately the same in intelligence. In addition to those who gave a high level of performance, all three types of ape also produced some specimens who did very poorly. So, generally speaking, we can say there is very little difference in basic intelligence between any member of the three great apes. More recent studies at the Center by Dr. Rumbaugh have, however, indicated that orangs may be superior to chimpanzees.

The fourth ape who is not normally described as a great ape, is the gibbon. He acts at a lower level of intelligence than the three great apes, but is superb in the jungle where he lives, moving with a delightful swinging rhythm, hand over hand, at surprising speed through the branches.

The reaction of all the apes to clothing is quite interesting. One of our chimpanzees, Beleka, has always shown great interest in the clothing I wear whenever I am in contact with her. She is intrigued by the layers of clothing, and I find that she explores through the clothes very quickly; by pulling and shoving, she eventually finds her way through to the skin.

Many of the animals are also intrigued by eyeglasses. One of our baby gorillas, Inaki, who came to us from the National Zoo in Washington, enjoys touching my face when I am with her, particularly the various features of the face, the nose, the eyes, and so on, and she also touches my eyeglasses. The apes seem to regard eyeglasses as part of the body; even the monkeys seem to do this. They very rarely try to remove the glasses. On occasion I have had a monkey snatch at the glasses and actually get them off. On the one or two occasions when this has happened, the animal has shown considerable confusion, just as if it had grabbed at your arm and the arm had come away in its hands. I have had one or two monkeys grab my glasses and simply try to mangle them. But apes, especially chimpanzees, who grab glasses show considerable confusion when they find that they have the glasses in their hands.

One of our orangs, Jala, has an interest in removing people's clothes. Whenever I go into her cage she attempts to remove my garments, so I have taken to wearing a disposable but quite strong paper suit composed of a shirt and pants when I go in to see her. Unfortunately, this outfit does not last very long; her first activity is to try to tear it off and she is usually successful. Jala incidentally is a highly intelligent animal and one of the orangutans who has been able to perform the cross-modal transfer of information that I mentioned earlier.

Orangutans are interesting in the way they like to put things on their heads. I have mentioned Lada, who had part of her lung removed and who has had three children since then. I have seen her put her newborn baby on her head. After a birth I have seen her take the cloth on which her baby had been born some time before, place it over her head, and wear it for many hours afterward. This tendency of orangutans to put things on their heads or to climb into a sack if given one does not exist in chimpanzees or gorillas.

Some animals do a kind of dance. We have a chimpanzee known as Franz who is about twenty-two years of age and who, incidentally, is the father of a little Mongoloid chimpanzee born to our colony a couple of years ago. Franz dances up and down, bangs at the metal guillotine door, and then makes a run at the front of the cage, grabbing it with his hands and jumping up into the air. This is a formalized dance performance which he will do for almost all visitors. He also has a habit of sitting just behind the wire of his cage and sucking his lips to make a kind of raspinglike noise and delicately touching the tips of his forefingers together. Chimpanzees in the wild do dances also. Jane Goodall has described wild chimpanzees doing what she calls a rain dance. Many of our chimpanzees will bang on the guillotine door, and this is undoubtedly related to the fact that in the wild these animals beat on the buttresses of certain trees, producing a hollow wooden sound which can ring through the forest for quite a considerable distance. I don't know from how far the banging on the guillotine doors can be heard, but it certainly is deafening close up.

Chest beating is very common among our gorillas. I have never seen it done by the orangutans or by chimpanzees, but even very young gorillas when they are running around and feeling happy beat themselves two or three times on their chest. Quite a loud noise is produced by this method.

Many people who read this book will be familiar with the use of chimpanzees and other apes and monkeys in stage acts. I have seen chimpanzees carrying out all sorts of tricks, riding bicycles, riding seesaws, jumping on trampolines, and so on. Probably one of the outstanding primate acts at present is that of Professor Berosini, who for the last two years has been showing his act at the Circus Circus Casino in Las Vegas and is now showing at the Dunes. He has three chimpanzees, two gorillas, and one or two orangutans. In the act which I saw at Las Vegas, he had the gorillas and the chimpanzees doing acrobatics on the trampoline. In the final part of his act he has an orangutan spread-eagle itself on a large vertical wheel which it turns around by itself. He has his chimpanzees on swings with metal arms so that when they swing on them they revolve through 360 degrees. In another part of the act Professor Berosini has the orang dancing the hula on a big drum and the gorillas beating tom-toms on either side. It is a very impressive act, and Berosini must be one of the outstanding animal trainers in this country at the moment.

One of the animals who has come to us recently is Susie, who was renamed Suzetta since we already had a Susie. Suzetta was a reject from Professor Berosini's act. She had in fact become too large for his act, and when I went to see him in Las Vegas, he introduced me to her. He let her out of her cage, and her first reaction was to throw both arms around me and give me a big hug. Professor Berosini said the chimpanzees were much harder to work with than are orangs or gorillas. Once his orang and gorillas knew what they had to do they did it without any problem. The chimpanzees, however, even though they knew what to do, were constantly tempted to "goof off" and do something else or to play up, and they had to be watched and cuffed and kept in place during the act.

Part of the Berosini act in Las Vegas. Two orangs pose with a fine specimen of *Homo sapiens*, female (Professor Berosini's daughter).

Keller and Marion Breland have set up an organization called Animal Behavior Enterprises which trains all kinds of animals from chickens to monkeys and dolphins to perform all kinds of tricks. These are often performed in response to the insertion of a coin into a piece of equipment like a slot machine which triggers a cue (often lighting up an electric bulb) and so causes the animal to start his performance. This may consist of beating a drum, doing a little dance, turning a wheel and so on. At the end of the "act," the animal receives a food reward. The training procedure used for these animals is known as operant conditioning. One of the Breland acts was in Circus Circus at Las Vegas where a monkey would turn a wheel and bang on a cash register when a dollar bill was slipped into a slot. It is not surprising that a monkey can be trained to do this, but it is amazing what animals at a low level of intelligence can be trained to do using operant conditioning.

At the London Zoo for many years young chimpanzees have been trained to have a tea party each afternoon. They sit around a table drinking from cups and eating cakes and cookies while the general public looks on and applauds. Dr. Yerkes also trained young chimpanzees to eat around a table.

Dr. Julian Huxley, brother of the famous Aldous Huxley and grandson of the even more famous Thomas Henry Huxley, who was the nineteenth-century protagonist of evolution, has described an interesting incident with a London Zoo chimpanzee. Dr. Huxley is a highly distinguished zoologist who was at one time director general of UNESCO and has also been secretary of the London Zoo. This chimpanzee was one of those who had taken part in tea parties at the zoo. He was brought by one of the zoo personnel to a dinner party at his home one evening. The animal was very restrained and ate the food as it was presented to him, did not swing from the chandelier, sat demurely in a chair, and did all the things that a chimpanzee should do at a human dinner party. However, when the fruit was brought in, this was too much for him, and he reached out and grabbed a handful from the bowl, apparently without realizing what he was doing. The members of the party burst into amused laughter at his antics, but the poor animal apparently felt that he had committed some kind of a social blunder. He dropped the fruit and hung his head in great embarrassment.

It is interesting to watch chimpanzees and orangs and gorillas that have been trained to do a particular task. They work in a detached kind of way as if each of them is a kind of automaton working alone and not a living being at all. It is as if the whole thing has been ingrained into the subconscious mind and the animal is working from that level in his brain.

One characteristic the chimpanzees have demonstrated is the use of sticks as implements; gorillas apparently do this, too. Jane Goodall describes how a chimpanzee will take a stick or a long stalk of grass, put it down an anthole, pull it out covered with ants, and lick them off. The Dutch scientist Adriaan Kortlandt has described how chimpanzees will even pick up a stick and throw it at an effigy of a leopard or at a leopard which is being led past them. This suggests the beginning of spear throwing. Dr. Wolfgang Köhler also describes the way chimpanzees use sticks to try to knock down bananas that are suspended too high above their heads. I have already mentioned the use of sticks by chimpanzees to rake in food and even the fitting of a small stick inside a larger one to extend its length. The use of implements represents a very high stage in the development of these animals, it is something that they have initiated themselves and is not the result of instruction. Of course apes can be trained to manipulate a large variety of objects, to use a knife and fork at a party, to pour

Moos (chimpanzee) shows how to get multiple sticks he can fit together to retrieve a piece of apple.

wine from a bottle into a glass and drink it; they would use these implements correctly on their own, but they use them promptly after instruction.

Animals such as the chimpanzee and maybe some monkeys use tools to perform various jobs. The interpretation of this as indicating a higher intelligence has to be treated with discretion because some other animals normally regarded as belonging to a lower intellectual level also show this type of behavior. For example, the ordinary woodpecker excavating in a branch for an insect, according to K. R. L. Hall, writing in 1965, will put its long tongue in a crack so as to get the insect out. The Galapagos woodpecker finch, *Camarhyncus pallidus,* which also has a long tongue, will excavate a hole but will then pick up a cactus spine or twig, which may be one or even two inches long, hold it lengthwise in its beak, and then poke it up the crack. It thus pushes or probes or stimulates the insect to get out, and then drops the twig and grabs the insect as it appears. If the twig or spine is too short or if it is too soft and bends, the bird will reject it or will allow it to break off, then pick up another of a more suitable size. A bird has been seen to carry a spine or twig about with it, poking it into nooks and crannies as it searches in one tree after another. It has also been shown that the bird may use this spine not only to drive the insect out but even to stick it into the insect and pull it out impaled on the spine.

The supposed attempts of some primates to roll stones on human beings trying to catch them may, in a sense, be described as tool using. Hall points out in this connection that there have been reports of polar bears rolling or casting blocks of ice onto walruses to kill them. He also notes that elephants have been observed to scratch themselves with sticks held in their trunks.

Dr. Hall mentions that chimpanzees brandish sticks at each other for the purposes of intimidation. When they actually fight, however, they throw away such weapons and use their teeth and hands. Apes are known to throw branches or fruit at an intruder in their natural habitat. Wallace reported in the nineteenth century that orangutans do this. Dr. Davenport of this Center had the same experience a few years ago when he was studying orangutans in the wild in Borneo. In the Barro Colorado Island

In the Panama Canal area, according to Dr. C. R. Carpenter, capuchin monkeys have been seen to chase coatimundis from the trees they are occupying and then drop nuts and branches on them.

These primitive uses of tools and toollike objects by great apes have been of special interest to scientists because it is believed that, in the course of evolution, the animals that were directly on the human line were those most commonly involved in toolmaking and tool using. In fact, in Tanganyika in the Olduvai Gorge, the source of many fossils, there are many bones which obviously were modified to produce some kind of tool by the prehumans who lived there.

Dr. Gordon W. Hewes of Boulder, Colorado, has pointed out that even macaques will chew the end of a bone into unusual shapes and that possibly prehuman primate bone handlers also reshaped bones by gnawing the end of them. He suggests that perhaps the nervous habit that some humans have of chewing the ends of pens and other implements might be related to this early facial activity. Dr. Hewes wonders whether modern humans, if placed in an environment without formal tools and similar to that occupied by gorillas and chimpanzees, would do much better in the fashioning of tools than their ape cousins. The tendency by Yerkes' chimpanzees to throw feces at people might also be considered an example of tool using, if one stretched a point. At best the animals are using feces as a projectile. Dr. Harry J. Jerison of Yellow Springs, Ohio, has described studies he carried out with a Java monkey, in which this animal needed to press a lever to avoid being given an electrical shock after being presented with a signal. Dr. Jerison suggested that maybe the act of using a lever was a bit like using a tool. What surprised him was that whereas the animal could press this lever with great facility and speed on the given signal, if the lever was moved back only 2 centimeters, it completely disrupted the animal's reactions. He apparently was not able to compensate for the extra distance. This led Dr. Jerison to wonder whether in fact the monkey was using the lever in the sense that it would use a tool in the wild.

Goodall has described an emotional display in which chimpanzees break off branches, stand on their hind legs, and sweep with the branch in a vigorous fashion. The chimpanzee does not attempt to use it to strike the animal against which it is displaying, although of course it could do so accidentally. Dr. S. L Washburn of Berkeley, California, has suggested that the use of the stick for aggression or defense is much less effective than the ape's own teeth. Nevertheless, when he uses his teeth he brings himself in close proximity to the teeth of the other animals, so that even a poor stick is, in some respects, more likely to be effective particularly for defense.

Dr. Wolfgang Köhler was under the impression that apes suppressed their abilities because they were afraid of being put to work. He describes how one of his apes, Sultan, was persuaded to go around in the evening with a basket and to pick up and place in it the stones and skins from the food that had been eaten during the day and thrown around. He understood very quickly what to do and did it without any problems for a couple of days. But by the third day he had to be directed continuously, and by the fourth day he was even slower. On the fifth day he had to be forced to make every movement. Finally, it was decided not to persist with him. So while he would work during the first couple of days for something to do, he soon got bored with his job and pretended he did not know what to do.

The chimpanzees at the Holloman Air Force Base were trained to play ticktacktoe. The method of play was that the human entered one cubicle and the ape the other; there was a display panel in each cubicle. The crosses and noughts appeared on a screen when the appropriate buttons were pressed. The apes soon got the idea that to win all they had to do was to get three noughts or three crosses in a line. They learned to play the game very effectively. One item of interest about apes is that they seem to be able to understand the difference between right and left.

All apes have a reasonable dexterity in climbing, but they are rather clumsy when they try to walk bipedally. When on all fours they move with remarkable speed. They can, however, be trained to perform surprisingly difficult physical activities. One of the skaters in the show *Ice Capades*, Dave Pits, has a number of chimpanzees who are trained to perform on skates. Mr. Pits finds chimpanzees no more difficult to teach to skate than a child. In his experience chimpanzees are smarter at learning to perform physical feats than children up to the age of three. He spends about an hour a day four times a week to keep his chimpanzees up to the skating mark. One of his animals does 385 shows a year. Mr. Werner Muller of *Holiday on Ice* also has a fine chimpanzee ice hockey act which demonstrates his exceptional powers as an animal trainer.

Although apes have a lower intelligence than human beings, there are all levels of intelligence among them, including some that are subnormal for apes. On March 24, 1969, Cathy Belden, a technician employed in studying chromosomes at the Yerkes Center, had finished preparing, examining, and photographing the chromosomes of a chimpanzee we owned called Jama. Jama had been born on July 6, 1968; on that day there was a Japanese-American seminar meeting at the Center immediately following the International Congress of Primatology, and she was named Jama after this coincidence. Cathy drew the attention of the Center's pathologist, Dr. Harold McClure, to the fact that there appeared to be an extra chromosome in Jama's chromosomal pattern; there were 49 instead of the 48 normal for a chimpanzee. This chromosome picture appeared to Dr. McClure to be similar to that found in human infants with Mongolism. Jama was at this time about nine months old. Realizing that this was an interesting possibility, Dr. McClure decided to go and see Dr. Alan Pieper, to whom the animal had been allotted for psychological studies. He asked Dr. Pieper about the intelligence level of this animal. Dr. Pieper had been working with a test of postural development which he had adapted from the Gesell-Thompson schedule for children and had found that Jama was well below the normal range for chimpanzees of her age. At seven months, for instance, she could not sit up or move around in her cage, although other chimpanzees the same age had no difficulty in performing these activities. She seemed to Dr. Pieper to be developing at about half the rate for normal chimpanzees. She was also only half the normal weight. In general, she tested very poorly on psychological tests. A further study of Jama by Dr. Pieper and Dr. McClure showed that she had what are de-

Jama. A Mongoloid chimpanzee born at the Center.

scribed as epicanthic folds, little extra folds of skin in the lateral corners of the eye. These are the Mongoloid folds which give human infants who possess them an Oriental look. The fourth and fifth toes of both of Jama's feet were partly webbed; the doctors also noted that the joints of the limbs could be flexed to a much greater degree than normal, and that the muscle had very little tone. It seemed that the animal also had some kind of congenital heart defect which at that time had not been determined. All these characters are found in human Mongoloids. In addition, Jama was very prone to pick up infections of the intestine and the upper respiratory tract. Again, this is characteristic of the human Mongoloid.

The condition of human Mongolism was first described by Langdon-Down in 1866. He described it as a congenital idiocy of unknown ultimate cause. In 1959 Drs. Lejeune, Gauthier, and Turpin demonstrated that in human Mongoloids there was a

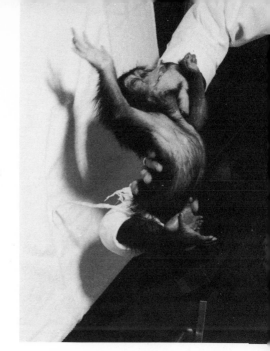

Jama giving a muscular reaction
common in Mongoloid babies.

small additional chromosome thought to be an extra chromosome number 21. There is no indication as to how this additional
chromosome causes all the congenital changes which are present
in an animal affected this way. Nor do we know exactly what are
the factors which cause the presence of this additional chromosome.

In human beings an older mother is in fact more likely to produce a Mongoloid child. Jama's mother was Wenka, who was
fifteen years old, and her father was Franz, who was twenty-two.
Neither of these is old for chimpanzees, who in our colony have
been found to live at least until the forties. Wenka's chromosomes
and Franz's chromosomes are normal. An earlier baby which
Wenka had was stillborn. Since chromosomal studies were not
done at that time, we don't know whether that animal was a
Mongoloid as well. In the meantime Wenka is pregnant again,
and we will see what the next baby is, although the odds against
its being Mongoloid are very large indeed.

Jama continued to be very difficult to raise and gave plenty of

185

trouble. One day the veterinarians came into the room where she was living and noticed she was extremely blue, which indicated that she was having some problems with her heart. With the slightest excitement it was possible to bring on this blueness, which was especially obvious in the gums and the mucous membrane lining the mouth. Her hands and feet were also blue. It was apparent that if something were not done, Jama would not live much longer. Since it was a cardiac problem and the X rays did not show us anything that would be helpful, Dr. Robert C. Schlant, head of the cardiology unit at Grady Hospital in Atlanta, was consulted. It was decided to attempt to pass a catheter into the blood system (as is done in some human patients) to try to find out what the problem was and then if possible to undertake some heart surgery to repair it.

Jama was put to sleep with a drug known as Sernylan, which we have found to be particularly useful in working with our great apes since it is a relatively nontoxic tranquilizing type of drug and the animals tolerate it very well. A catheter was put into a vein in Jama's groin, and a series of cinemagraphs were taken with radiopaque material being injected into different chambers of the heart. About an hour after the catheterization started, Jama seemed to wake suddenly and began vocalizing, and she was given a little more Sernylan; then she began to have mild seizures and an attempt was made to control these by injecting a little phenobarbital, but the convulsions continued and became more and more severe. She became blue (cyanosed); a resuscitator was used to help her breathe, and she was given oxygen. The seizures continued but were less severe. Her heartbeat rate began to slow down and became slower and slower. Even with the administration of drugs to keep it going, there was only a very slight improvement. Finally the heart stopped beating, and an attempt was made to get it to beat again by massage of the upper half of the body. Further heart stimulants were injected, and for another hour she was massaged continuously. A defibrillator, an electrical device which makes the heart beat normally in human patients, was tried. Jama did not respond to any of these treatments, and finally it was necessary to pronounce her dead. In the postmortem it was found that not only did she have brain damage, but she had what is known as a patent ductus arteriosus, a blood connection which bypasses the heart, at least in part, and is the cause of human "blue babies." This condition in humans is usually corrected by surgical operation. In addition to this condition, however, the animal had two perforations in the internal walls separating the heart into various chambers. So it seems highly improbable that she would have been able to survive for very much longer. All the tissues from this animal are being intensely studied, and this study may in itself produce information of very considerable value to our knowledge of the nature and causes of Mongolism. This is just one example of the importance of such a colony of great apes; it gives us the opportunity to study diseases which are characteristically human in a way which it would be impossible otherwise to study them. The fact that a Mongoloid chimpanzee which is apparently identical with a human Mongoloid can be produced shows how close the gene pools of the apes and humans really are.

Many authors have recorded imitative acts on the part of different primates. Some of these have probably been more accidental than intentional. However, Dr. and Mrs. Keith Hayes, whose work was mentioned earlier, found a good deal of imitation by the Yerkes chimpanzee Vicki. As early as sixteen months of age she would imitate household routine. For example, she would pretend to dust furniture and wash clothes and dishes. At a later stage she appropriated a lipstick, looked in the mirror, and applied the lipstick specifically to her mouth, not all over her face. She was then seen to press her lips together and smooth the color with her fingers, just as she had seen Mrs. Hayes do it. She dabbed on face powder, using the same technique as Mrs. Hayes. Having seen a wooden stake driven into the ground with a hammer, Vicki would try to do the same thing. When she was shown the process of sandpapering the stake with the abrasive side of the paper, she immediately copied it, turning the correct side of the paper in contact with the wood. There are also recorded examples of delayed imitation. She would see an experimenter sharpen pencils. She was not able to do it immediately, but as soon as she could get a pencil herself she would put it in the sharpener and turn the handle. Seeing, through the screen door of her room, windows being sprayed by a spray gun preparatory to cleaning, she went immediately to the spray bottle as soon as she was let out and sprayed it on the window. She also would flatten photographs between the pages of a book, having once been shown this procedure. She was once shown how to use a screwdriver for prying off the lids of several empty paint cans. One hour later she was brought back, and given the opportunity to do this she did it immediately and was eventually able to open the two cans. Hayes points out that these imitations were not done with the expectation of a reward. One very interesting item was mentioned by the Hayeses: their attempt to get Vicki to blink an eye in response to their eye blinking and to receive a reward for it. However, they were unsuccessful and felt that this movement was absent from her voluntary motor repertory. Her solution to the problem was to put a finger to her eye, which of course caused it to close automatically, but apparently she could not do it without this kind of stimulus.

One of the problems Vicki would solve after demonstration was to recover an object she wanted which was suspended from a magnetic device attached to the center of the ceiling. On the wall was a toggle switch, and when this was opened the object would fall to the floor. Vicki needed only three demonstrations of this to get the idea herself. In another experiment, a lure was put in a box; the front of the box was a transparent plastic door. The door could be opened only by displacing a short length of string which was stretched between two posts beyond the box. It was not possible to touch the string directly, but only with a stick. After one demonstration Vicki devoted 35 seconds to trying to pry open the door and then took the stick and pushed the string up with it; thus releasing the door, she was able to get the reward inside. In another case a door was kept shut by a string attached to a neighboring object, and the only way the door could be opened was to burn through the string with a candle. After three demonstrations Vicki had still not got the idea, but on the fourth occasion the experimenter picked up the candle and thrust it a little bit toward the string. She then took the candle and immediately put it under the string and solved the problem. From then on, she did it without any difficulty at all. Dr. Hayes felt that her delay at the solution of this problem was a result of her fascination with the flame of the candle. She would spend some of the periods during tests dancing around the lighted candle. She would jump over it and deliberately singe her hair with it. The experimenter then set up three levers which were attached to the box; only if they were pulled in the right sequence would the door open. Vicki understood immediately that she had to pull all three levers to get that door to open, but she did not appreciate the significance of pulling them in the right sequence, which was actually the left one first, middle one next and the right one last. It took her 32 trials, during which the experimenter helped her by guiding her hand or pointing to the successive levers. This was the hardest of the experiments which she was able to do.

In another test there was an object high up which could be obtained only by throwing a ball at it. Vicki had the idea of throwing the ball to knock it down before this was even demonstrated to her. She was a little more accurate after the demonstration had been made, but she had the idea first. All these activities took place between the ages of 17 months and 34 months. One other test I will mention is the stick and tunnel problem. The apparatus for this was a wire mesh in the form of a tunnel tacked down onto a piece of wood; an object in the tunnel could be pushed out only by a stick. She could see the object through the wire and had to insert a long stick in the tunnel and push the object out. She was able to solve this problem after the third demonstration.

Some human children were also tested with the same tests. The youngest child was 26 months but had a mental age of 28 months, and the oldest child was 36 months old with a mental age of 49 months. Of the four young children who were tested with the ball-throwing problem, none of them attempted to solve it spontaneously as Vicki had done. Three of them imitated the experimenter only after one or two demonstrations. The youngest child with a mental age of 28 months refused to try even after four demonstrations. All the younger children solved the stick and tunnel problem with one or two demonstrations. The problem of manipulation of the string to open the box was solved after one to four demonstrations. The children did not have the same fascination for the candle flame that Vicki demonstrated. Three of them solved the burning-the-string problem after one demonstration. The youngest child refused to try at all. Four of them solved the toggle switch problem which released the object magnetically held to the ceiling after one demonstration.

The three older children all solved the sequence of levers to release the box lid after one to four demonstrations, and after one demonstration were able to reverse the sequence. Also, the oldest child solved the third sequence, which was left, right, and middle, after seven demonstrations. The youngest child paid very little attention to the demonstration of the levers and did not succeed on the first sequence, even after ten trials and even when guidance and pointing were used.

The ability of Vicki to solve the problems described above may be attributed to her being brought up in a human environment, where maybe unconsciously this type of problem was being coped with. The Hayeses tried this procedure with the cage-reared chimpanzee Franz, quite an intelligent animal from the Yerkes Laboratories, who incidentally is still with us and was recently the father of our Mongoloid chimpanzee. Franz threw the ball at the lever after he had been shown only twice. He was unable to solve the light switch problem, even after he had been shown it ten times. He made no progress at all with the stick and the wire tunnel, even after being shown how to do it eleven times. Nor did he learn to manipulate the string with the stick after six demonstrations. He was not given the candle or the lever problem. Thus it was obvious that a chimpanzee raised in the home did not differ very much from human children around the same age in their ability to imitate and solve a variety of problems. Franz's failure to solve these problems is almost certainly owing to his lack of experience with the various materials to be used. The apparent difference in intelligence in human children in relation to the richness of the environment to which they have been exposed has been recognized in the Head Start program. It is obviously very unwise to make a judgment of the intelligence of an animal in comparison with the human-based experiments which depend upon prior acquaintance with the objects to be manipulated.

This is not to say, of course, that studies with caged animals do not contribute an enormous amount of information about the basic intelligence of the animal. Work at the Yerkes Laboratories over many years has demonstrated this without doubt. But the human interpretation of experiments has to be treated with discretion.

Apes have figured extensively in fiction. Probably the most famous is the story of Tarzan, a human boy who was brought up in a jungle by apes. The orangutan figured in a horror story by Edgar Allan Poe, "The Murders in the Rue Morgue," published in 1841. It was based on the fictional discovery of two ladies who had been killed with a razor. Gripped in the hands of the corpse of the older of the two ladies was a small quantity of reddish hair. As the story developed, it was discovered that the red hair belonged to an orangutan owned by a sailor and that the murders had actually been committed by this animal. The orang had seized the razor from the sailor—it was an old-fashioned straight razor—and had escaped with it. It had crawled into the room these two women occupied and had slit their throats. I am sure this kind of story did a great deal to make people nervous of the orang and did little for the animals' reputation. It was of course all fictional. There is no doubt that an orangutan loose with a razor would be a real menace, although I suspect he would be a bigger menace to himself than he would be to anybody else.

Subsequent to this story apes certainly achieved a reputation for violence and misdeeds or at least potential misdeeds. Some readers will remember the movie *King Kong*, in which a gigantic gorilla got loose in Manhattan, grabbed a woman in his hand, and climbed the Empire State Building. It is interesting that on this earth it would be impossible for a gorilla or an ape or a human or any other animal to achieve the vast size portrayed by King Kong in this film. This is because of the force of gravity exerted by the earth. The material composing the bones would not be strong enough to permit bones of the size required for such a big animal to exist. Nor would the bones be strong enough to support the weight of muscle necessary to move them. In other words, the mechanical properties of living tissues are such that nothing very much bigger than an elephant could exist on land with the existing force of gravity. However, on the moon, where the gravity is much less, it would be possible providing the appropriate gases for breathing were present.

Pierre Boulle, a French writer, has written a novel called *Planet of the Apes*, which has been described as having descended from Jonathan Swift on one side and Jules Verne on the other. In this novel the hero of the story takes part in a journey as an astronaut to another solar system. Upon arrival there he finds a planet, Soror, completely peopled by apes, chimpanzees, orangs, and gorillas. After crash-landing on the surface of this planet the hero of the novel is captured by a band of apes who turn out to be gorillas, is transported into the principal city, and is carried to a medical research institute where he finds himself put in a large cage in a room with many cages like his lined up in two rows facing a long passage. The hero finds eventually that the planet is ruled entirely by apes and that the beasts of the forest are in fact low-grade humans who live naked in the woods as our present-day apes do on this earth. They are hunted from time to time by groups of gorillas who capture them for zoos and for use in medical research.

The humans on this planet are unable to talk, whereas the apes have developed a civilization and a language to a very high degree. They are divided into three groups: the orangutans are aristocratic scholars; the gorillas are either the very top administrators or the physical workers; the chimpanzees are a rather suppressed and exploited group who do nearly all the work and make nearly all the discoveries, particularly in the intellectual sphere. They are the main body of working scientists. I do not have any record that Pierre Boulle has ever been in the Yerkes Primate Center, but what he describes in this research institute is uncannily similar to many of the things we do at this Center, particularly the intelligence tests. The chimpanzees in the institute in *Planet of the Apes* also carry out a series of tests similar to those originally used by Pavlov in Russia to demonstrate conditioned reflexes. In this type of test, either a bell is sounded or a whistle is blown immediately prior to giving food to the animal; as soon as the animal hears the whistle and sees the food he begins to salivate. If the time between giving the auditory signal and making the food available is progressively extended, the salivation can be seen to start as soon as the auditory signal sounds and before the food appears; this happens even though the food may not arrive until an hour or more later. In Soror these experiments are carried out on human beings. (Pavlov originally used dogs for this work.) The hero of the novel finds himself embarrassed in being treated like an animal in this type of experiment. In many of the psychological experiments the humans have to do they receive an electric shock if they do not promptly do what is required. This is the standard method in many laboratories for conditioning animals to carry out particular types of activity. The shock is not a painful one, but is unpleasant to the animal.

On a subsequent occasion the workers at the medical institute in Soror try to start a series of mating experiments and put all the male humans in with female humans in the various cages so they can study their courtship and copulatory behavior. The hero of the story finds himself in the cage with a wild young human girl, a resident of the planet who was captured at the same time he was captured, who cannot speak (none of the humans on Soror could speak), but who is quite beautiful. The hero of the story is deeply concerned that he is expected to have copulatory activities and courtship activities under the eagle eye of the experimenters, who are making notes about everything he does.

He is eventually able to convince the scientists experimenting with him that he is of exceptional mentality. They are of course astonished that he can speak when all the native humans of that planet are unable to speak. Finally he is given an opportunity to address the annual scientific meeting in Soror and explains that he is a being from outer space, in fact from the earth. He has arrived by spaceship, and on his planet the humans are the dominant creatures and the apes are in the position that the human fills in the planet of Soror. A complication develops when the girl with whom he has been caged becomes pregnant and is apparently going to produce a child by him. At about this time the apes also unearth a buried city containing artifacts and skeletons which are obviously human. It appears that at one time this planet was peopled and controlled by beings who were like humans, that they were overthrown and their remnants finally became wild animals, while the apes then took over control of the planet.

In Soror the scientists have devised an evolutionary tree which consists of a single trunk, the roots of which fade away into the unknown at the base. Various limbs branch out at various levels, indicating the stages of vegetables, plants of various sorts, unicellular organisms, and jellyfish; the arrival of invertebrates, fish, reptiles, and eventually mammals is shown. So far the tree is exactly the same as that drawn by scientists on earth. But in Soror when the mammal part of the tree is extended to include the Anthropoidea, a new limb branches out to the side, and this is human beings. The rest of the branch continues upward and is the main shoot which gives rise to various types of apes. The ultimate ape is called *Simius sapiens,* the culmination of evolution on Soror, represented by three varieties, the chimpanzee, the gorilla, and the orangutan. In these animals the brain has developed extremely well, but in man it has not developed to the same extent. Apes have the gift of speech, but man does not. The discovery of the buried former human city in Soror causes great dismay in many circles of Soror, since it goes against the scientific and philosophical concepts of the planet.

The apes on this planet have developed the technique of launching artificial satellites but have not been able to carry out any interplanetary travel. They use the human beings as experimental subjects to be sent up in these artificial satellites to study the effect of the space environment on living beings, just as monkeys and apes have been used on earth for this purpose.

On the planet of Soror there had apparently once been an ape of considerable authority. His name was Haristas, and he held a number of beliefs and dogmas. Haristas believed that only apes could have souls, that human beings on Soror did not have souls. Even on the planet of Soror there are critical minds who contest this dogma.

Eventually the hero of the book, the lady he has made pregnant, and his young son, who by now has been born, are rocketed into orbit and make connection with their main space vehicle which has been circling the strange planet. After a period of some years, they are able to make it back to earth. They land at Orly Airport in France, only to find that the world has been taken over by apes in their absence.

Ric—a chimpanzee isolated from the world for twenty months at birth—performs a stereotyped eye poke.

8. Control of the Brain

IN *Planet of the Apes* there is a description of a human being with the top of his skull removed and an ape scientist stimulating the surface of the brain with little electrical stimulators, causing the person to carry out movements indicating that certain parts of the brain are responsible for the control of certain parts of the body. This type of thing has actually been done on human beings on this planet. One of the pioneers in this area was Dr. Wilder Penfold of McGill University in Montreal,

Canada. He was a neurosurgeon and so on many occasions found it necessary to operate on the brains of human beings.

Most brain operations can be carried out under a local anesthetic because the brain has no pain organs and may be cut or manipulated without any sensation of pain. A local anesthetic, of course, is put into the scalp, and some anesthetic is applied to the surface of the bone, where there are some pain sense endings, but once the top of the skull is removed the brain itself is free from any sensation of pain. In some of these cases in which he was operating for a variety of reasons, Dr. Penfold took a small electrical probe and touched various parts of the surface of the brain with it. According to what particular part he touched, the patient would draw up his leg, raise his arm, move his body in some particular way, roll his eyes, or turn his head. He even found one spot which, when he stimulated it, caused the patient to start singing a series of songs. He had obviously found the spot in the brain which served as a trigger point for bringing back the memory of songs the patient had learned. The interesting thing about these studies is that when the patient is carrying out the actions that he has been induced to perform he has no conception that he is doing them in response to some external force, such as the surgeon is employing. After he had rolled his head or lifted his leg, when asked why he did it he said he just felt an urge to do so. He had not associated this desire with the electrical stimulation of his cerebral cortex.

For the sake of this discussion we can say that the brain is divided into two main parts. It is of course much more complicated than that statement might indicate. There is an upper or superficial part, the newer part of the brain, which develops later in evolution and is called the cerebral cortex. The deeper parts of the brain, which are very primitive, were the earliest parts of the brain to develop. These are the areas responsible for most of the emotions; for sex, hunger, thirst, violent rage, etc. It is of interest that the newer part of the brain is the part that has a controlling action; it is the part that thinks and reasons and uses logic to keep the more primitive parts of the brain suppressed up to a point, the point varying in different people. In addition to the voluntary control of the movements by the cerebral cortex which

Rhesus monkey with electrodes implanted in his brain and radio receiving set attached. Animal feels no pain and completely ignores the attachment.

can be demonstrated by electrical stimulation, it has been found that by pushing electrodes deep into primitive parts of the brain, the more elementary emotions can be stimulated.

Dr. Walter R. Hess, a Swiss neurophysiologist, first demonstrated this deep electrode implantation in 1932. He found that practically all the normal functions of man could be stimulated electrically if the electrode was placed in the right place.

Since then a number of laboratories have developed this type of technique. One of the most outstanding in this country is that of Dr. José M. R. Delgado, a professor in the Yale University Department of Physiology. Another is that of Dr. Adrian Perachio, whose laboratory is located in the Yerkes Primate Center.

This technique of implanting electrodes in the brain is now so well developed that it is possible, by selection of the right part of the brain, to stimulate sexual desires and activities, to stimulate a feeling of good will and happiness, to stimulate memory, to stimulate sleep, or even to have an anesthesia produced by electrical stimulation. In fact if enough electrodes are placed into the brain, practically all the main functions of the brain can be controlled by an outside person. The stimulation can be carried out by attaching wires to the electrodes implanted in the animal's brain, but more recently these wires have been attached to a small radio receiving set secured to the animal's skull by dental cement; the electrodes can then be stimulated remotely by radio. This is known as telestimulation, and it is the technique which both Dr. Perachio and Dr. Delgado have been using.

Dr. Perachio, Professor Harold Warner, Dr. Margery Murray, and a former colleague, Dr. Brian Robinson, developed techniques whereby they could implant up to twelve electrodes into the brain of a monkey or an ape, then transmit radio waves to these electrodes so that they stimulated the parts of the brain in which they were implanted. The monkey would perform the action which was controlled by that particular part of the brain.

Furthermore, they developed, mainly owing to the expert electronic knowledge and experience of Professor Warner, a mechanism whereby they could operate by radio a specially designed electronic switch to stimulate any one of these twelve probes. In this way they could have the animal change its behavior at the will of the investigator. These studies have been made on monkeys at the Yerkes Laboratory and on a chimpanzee. In case anyone should think that these activities are cruel or painful, I can assure him that they are certainly not. The operation involved in putting in the probes is surgically negligible and is completely painless, although it calls for considerable skill on the part of the operator to put the probes in just the right position. It is in fact carried out on some humans. The skin is anesthetized with a local anesthetic, or the animal is given a general anesthetic, because if apes and monkeys are awake they will not keep their heads still as a human will under the same circumstances, so the general anesthetic is preferable. A small hole is then drilled in the skull with a dental burr, and an extremely fine stainless steel electrode is pushed through the hole and into the brain itself. I have mentioned that the brain itself feels no pain. The outside parts of the electrodes which project outside the skull are cemented to the skull with dental cement. Then a small radio which is in a small box is cemented on the top of the skull. These radio receivers remain firmly in place; they do not worry the animal at all. He handles the structure a little bit when he first comes out of the anesthetic, but very rapidly gets used to it and pays no more attention to it. He even learns to compensate for it when he is moving around so that he does not knock it on the cage, just as a person wearing a hat will bend a little farther down than he would without the hat when he wants to pass through a door or other opening.

All these experiments do is to change the animal's behavior when the electrodes are stimulated. If human experience is any example, the animal feels he is performing voluntarily any action that he is forced to do by stimulation. He does not feel as though he is being forced; he even has the impression that he is acting at his own instigation. Eventually it is planned to let some of these animals run free in a compound. In such a case some more permanent source of electricity other than batteries is required to power the small radio receiving set on the animal's head. If the animals are out in the sun, solar cells are attached to the top of the radio receiver so that power can be obtained continuously from them.

Three main types of study using telestimulation are going on at the Center at the moment. One is a study related to dominance. In any group of monkeys if there is more than one male, one of the males will assert himself to become the dominant member of the group. The other males as a general rule do not challenge him unless they feel they have a chance of beating him and taking over the control of the group themselves. In the experiments carried out by Dr. Perachio, three monkeys were used. One was a dominant male, and there were a subordinate male and female. The subordinate male was the "out" member of the group. He was ignored by both the senior male and the female. However, a part of his brain was implanted with an electrode which when stimulated by pressing a button on the radio transmitter in the next room caused him to become aggressive. This animal would immediately spring at and attack the domi-

ant male with great ferocity, and force him to become a subser-
ient animal. It is of interest that the moment he took over as
number one, the female also changed her loyalty from the previous dominant animal to him, a type of behavior which is perhaps
not unfamiliar among humans on occasion. If the electrodes are
placed in another part of the brain, an animal who is normally
an aggressive, dominant animal can be made to become a benign
animal.

Dr. Delgado's experiments have shown that a dominant monkey can be made to become a benign, relatively subservient animal by stimulation of a particular section of the brain. A lever
can then be placed in the cage with the monkeys which when depressed "dedominates" the dominant monkey. If the other monkeys have access to the lever, it does not take them long to associate the process of pressing it with the process of demoting the
boss, and they would queue for the pleasure—a typical example
of how small persons like to pull down those in power.

One of Dr. Delgado's fascinating experiments was to insert
electrodes into certain parts of the brain of a bull. He then entered a bull ring with the bull. The latter, on seeing him on the
other side of the ring, immediately charged. When he was within
a few yards, Dr. Delgado pressed a button on his little transmit-
ting set, thus stimulating the electrodes which were connected to
the small receiving radio on the skull of the bull, and the bull
ground to a halt without touching him. This is the type of project
in which the experimenter needs to have plenty of confidence in
his experiment.

Dr. Delgado has recently made a fascinating development in
this area of research. He has implanted electrodes in the brain of
a chimpanzee and attached a small radio receiver/transmitter to
them. When certain types of electrical brain waves were picked
up by the electrodes in the brain, they were transmitted by the
radio to a computer. This computer had been programmed to respond to these particular waves by radioing a signal to the brain
electrodes to turn off that type of brain activity. Normally the
brain operates by receiving signals from the sense organs; the
eyes, ears, nose, sense of touch, etc., and on the basis of these,
issues its own orders to the body to respond appropriately to these

sensory messages. Dr. Delgado, however, bypasses the sense or gans, and he or his computer talks to the brain using radio waves

Dr. Delgado and his colleagues feel that these experiments will prove valuable in treating both mental and physical disorders in man, and, in fact, the new technique will be used on human beings within a year. It will probably have a special application in the control of epilepsy. If the computer is programmed to de tect the type of electrical waves which the brain produces imme diately prior to a seizure, it can radio a message to the part of the brain which inhibits such seizures and turn off the impending fit

There is a particular part of the brain which produces intense pleasure when stimulated electrically. An electrode can be placed in it and a lever for stimulating the electrode made avail able to the monkey with the implanted electrode. As soon as he finds out what pressing the lever does to him he will sit over it by the hour, pressing it sometimes three or four times a second and luxuriating in the pure pleasure that he receives from his brain Here is something else for hippies to try.

Dr. Perachio and Dr. Murray have shown that the stimulation of an electrode placed in another part of the brain in male mon keys produced an erection of the penis. In addition to functions already mentioned, implanted electrodes can also be used to con trol blood pressure and heartbeat.

Dr. Perachio is particularly interested in problems of sleep Some recent developments in the study of sleep have been of great interest because it has been found that there are two types of sleep. One is accompanied by what is called rapid eye move ment (REM), and there is also nonrapid eye movement sleep. The REM sleep is apparently the most important. It has been found that when a person who is sleeping makes rapid move ments of the eyes during this time, he is in the process of dream ing. There seems to be a good deal of evidence that dreaming is psychologically necessary for a healthy person. Individuals who have been prevented from REM sleep for any length of time show unusual psychological behavior and often have been found to become psychotic.

Dr. Perachio is carrying out his studies on REM sleep for NASA and has shown that it is possible to induce or inhibit

REM sleep with stimulation of the appropriate parts of the brain. He also finds this REM sleep is affected by variations in acceleration and also by gravity or lack of gravity. All these studies may seem kind of academic, but they have very important practical applications and they help us in our understanding of how the brain works and in space travel. Even in the case of the electrode that stimulates an erection, it has been suggested by one of our colleagues that if an electrode was inserted in this part of the brain of humans, it would then be possible to run a little wire from it, with a button attached, down inside the clothes, or the pajamas as the case might be, and an older person or one who was otherwise impotent would simply need to press the button when he wished to have an erection for the purposes of sexual intercourse.

In the Boston City Hospital and other hospitals some mental patients who have shown outbursts of violence have been treated by implantation of electrodes. Properly placed electrodes also can be used to produce some types of anesthesia and to prevent the feeling of pain.

David M. Rorvik, in an article about brain stimulation in *Esquire*, December, 1969, has considered what might happen if a small group of men who wanted to gain control over society were able to obtain the opportunity to implant electrodes in the other members of the community. He conceives of a society known as an Electroligarchy. This, he suggests, would be composed of about forty or fifty individuals in the society

whose brains would remain untouched. On their orders, however, everybody else would have varying numbers of electrodes implanted in his skull.

The Electrons, the second rank in such a society, might comprise ten percent of the population and would each have fifty electrodes implanted. These would be remotely controlled and programmed by the Electroligarchy and they would be designed to ensure the Electrons' unquestioning allegiance. The Electrons would be the society's most creative components—the Electroligarchy being clever enough, in a corporate way, to give them their heads so that they could come up with innovations and discoveries to enrich society. They would be the scientists, economists, scholars, cyberneticists, philosophers, poets and other thinkers of society. They would not be so controlled that they no longer would experience unhappiness or other emotions that often goad individuals on to do creative things. But their potential for hostility and rebellion would be considerably attenuated. And, of course, like all the members of this electro-society, they would not even realize that they have been partially robotized.

Positrons might be the name of the next caste within the system, directly under the command of the Electrons, thirty percent of the population and each possessing two hundred embedded electrodes. These would be the white-collar support contingent. They would help put the theories, plans and projects of the Electrons into practice. They would be less imaginative and less intelligent than the Electrons, hence more closely controlled and regimented. They would be characterized by dedication, driven by the desire to implement the goals set by the Electrons. They would be positive thinkers, enthusiastic components of the machine; the more they accomplish the more pleasure they would experience. They would have none of the Electrons' negativism, but they would maintain minimal personalities, if only to make them more palatable to the Electrons who would have to work with them.

At the lowest level might come the Neutrons, sixty percent of the population with five hundred electrodes each. These would be the blue-collar people, the factory workers, the soldiers, secretaries, bus drivers, all those engaged in repetitive, often menial tasks. They would be cheaper and more reliable than automatic equipment and mechanical robots. They would, in fact, be completely robotized. They could dig ditches all day and love every minute of it.

The ideal about such a society is that whatever work anyone performed he could be programmed to love what he was doing.

We have no evidence of any of the governments of the day using or trying to use this method of mind control for any purpose at all. There is a story going around which is probably apocryphal that the Chinese have a regiment of soldiers who have had their brains implanted with electrodes and that they can be directed from the rear to attack any position, however impregnable and irrespective of the losses which they receive. If this is true, it would be an extremely sobering situation and would be the first instance of government control of the people using this potentially incredibly valuable, but also highly dangerous tool. This is certainly a technique that the United States should take the lead in developing, although hopefully not for control of the population. Of all the techniques in biological sciences, it is at the moment probably the one in which we can least afford to fall behind because of its potential both for good and for evil.

It was also mentioned that parts of the brain can be stimulated electrically to produce memory. Some interesting theories about memory have been developed recently. One is that memory is actually stored in the brain cells in the form of ribonucleic acid (RNA). However, it has been known for some time that there are two types of memory: short-term memory, which may leave us fairly quickly; and long-term memory, which persists indefinitely. For instance, some of the memories which we have from our childhood are very deeply engraved into the brain and it seems that we would scarcely ever forget them; they are often remarkably vivid. Short-term memory can be as short as a few seconds, as when we look up a telephone number, or may last more than 24 hours or a few days or a few weeks and then fade away. This recent type of memory is probably electrical in nature and probably consists of activated electrical circuits which continue to circle around in certain parts of the brain until they fade out. Some evidence for this comes from the following.

It is very well known that potassium, sodium, and chloride are present both inside and outside the brain cell; they are extremely important for the transmission of the electrical activity of the brain. Not only does electrical stimulation affect the brain, but the brain itself generates an electric current as an essential part of its functioning. This becomes obvious by the demonstration of brain waves, electrical waves which may be recorded with the aid of an instrument known as the electroencephalograph. The electroencephalograph is made to work simply by placing electrodes on the outside of the skull. They are then affected by the electrical energy produced by the brain, and they pass the electrical pulses produced by it to the machine, which records them in the form of waves on paper. The electrical activity in the brain and its function are caused by the differential distribution of small units of potassium, sodium, and chloride in the nervous tissue in the form of ions. This was demonstrated in one laboratory by removing the top of the skull from monkeys who had been trained to do various tasks. Some of them had been trained for a year or two, so the information was very well tucked away into the brain; others had been trained to do tasks over the preceding few days or weeks. Once the brain was exposed, its surface was washed over with a solution of water containing potassium ions. The skull was then replaced and the animal brought back to normal. When the animal's memory was tested, all the short-term memories had been eliminated because the washing of the brain with the potassium ions had interfered with all the electrical circuits which had developed as a result of a memorizing process. However, long-term memory was left intact. Therefore it seems very likely that long-term memory is incorporated in RNA or in some protein produced by it. In some way which cannot be explained, this memory RNA or protein can alter the electrical activity of at least parts of the brain and bring back the memory of a particular long-term event. Some memories are so tucked away that they take a bit of digging out; other long-term memories may be instantly recalled.

There have been experiments in some more primitive animals and even in rats in which some degree of memory has been claimed to have been transferred from one animal to another by injecting ribonucleic acid from a trained animal into an animal which has been untrained. However, a great deal more work needs to carried out in this area before it can be accepted by the majority of scientists.

One of the extremely interesting possibilities which stem from the effects of stimulating electrodes passed into the brain is the possibility of enabling the blind to see. They would probably never see as clearly as with normal eyes, and at least in the beginning not in color. It is conceivable that a small object like a miniature television camera could be placed on the skull and connected with a very large number of electrodes implanted into that part of the brain at the back of the head which we know to be the area where we receive stimuli from the optic nerves; this might produce on the back of the brain some kind of an electrical image of what the eye actually sees. It would presumably be possible to project what the camera is seeing onto the visual portion of the brain. This is by no means a wild prediction of the future. In fact some laboratories in the United States are already working on this problem.

In connection with telestimulation we have talked about dominant animals in a group of monkeys. At our field station, 25 miles away from the main Center, there are some 400 monkeys running loose in a series of wire-enclosed compounds. Some very interesting aspects of the hierarchies which develop in various monkey groups are being studied there.

Dr. Irwin Bernstein of the Yerkes Laboratories has been making this kind of study for some years. Among one of his collections of monkeys is a group of pigtail monkeys, the type commonly used in Thailand to collect coconuts. Dr. Bernstein started with only two or three of these monkeys and began adding single individuals, fully or partly grown males or females and youngsters, and studying their acceptance by the group. An immense amount of valuable and interesting material has accrued from his studies which is not possible to detail here. One might note, however, that on occasions animals were introduced who appeared to be totally unacceptable to any member of the group. They would be treated as outsiders and would not be given the opportunity to join in any activities, and they were often partly or wholly deprived of food by the others, even by the young monkeys in the group. Sometimes a young monkey would come up to the newcomer and bite his tail or pull his ear or be unpleasant in some other way. On more than one occasion an animal introduced in this way and rejected by the group has been picked up one morning dead without any signs of injury—he could not accept indefinitely being treated as a complete outsider.

As this group grew bigger it showed a typical orientation into dominance groups. One animal was the most important animal in the group. He was the dominant male, and he would be the animal who would come to meet you if you came to inspect the compound; he would look you over and threaten you if necessary. In other words, he was not only the most important animal in the group, but he was also the one to whom all the others in the group deferred. He was responsible for the safety and the welfare of the group and had no fears about taking on this part of his duty. In addition to this animal there were obviously a number two and a number three male in the dominance hierarchy. There was also a series of females, some of whom were preferred by the principal male and others preferred by the other dominant males. In pigtail monkeys the dominant animal holds his tail curled stiffly backward. Numbers two and three hold the tail less tightly, and in the others, who don't rate, the tail hangs limply down. Although the dominant females stick with the dominant male, and although the other males tend not to interfere with the female who belongs to the dominant male, occasionally, as in any well-organized society, some individuals do not wish to go along with the rules. On some occasions a female belonging to a dominant male in this group has gone over to the farthest corner away from her lord and master and has indulged in quick sexual intercourse with another male; by the time the dominant male was aware of it the whole act was over and the two were apart again. Even though the dominant male may chase the other male and chastize him, he is not able to prevent the act from taking place.

In a group like this sexual intercourse or at least a representation of sexual intercourse is regarded as a form of demonstration of dominance or submission. For instance, if the dominant male approaches a particular female, she will stop, turn her back toward him, lower herself more or less onto her elbows, and stick her rear end toward him. This is known as "presenting," and usually the male will mount her, make a few thrusts with his pelvis, and go off. It is not sexual intercourse, but the female has shown that she regards him as a superior being and he has demonstrated his acceptance of their two roles. In fact even males will use this method of presentation to demonstrate to a dominant male animal that they are subservient to him.

The dominant animal in this field station group had been the dominant animal for five years. His name was Earl, and he was twelve years old. He had lost some teeth and was certainly in no condition to defend his position as the dominant male, and he held onto it mainly by tradition. He could have been beaten by

Onan. Powerful leader of a group of pigtail monkeys from Southeast Asia menaces the photographer.

the number two male, Daddy, who was bigger and heavier than he was. A young aspiring rebel number three male called Onan decided, however, to stake his claim to the number one position and started a series of attacks on "the boss." This went on for some weeks, and eventually Earl was killed. In the jungle Earl would probably have abdicated and got lost in the jungle, leaving Onan to it, but in a 100-foot-square compound there was nowhere to go. Having coped with number one, Onan found he had to deal with number two. Number two might have been quite happy to remain that way, but Onan had to show him who was boss and gave him a severe beating. When he recovered he was permitted to rejoin the group in his old position. However, it was not yet a bed of roses for Onan. He still had to beat the top two or three females into submission. Finally they accepted him as the leader and he became the established "head" of the whole group.

To a visitor looking at this group they are just a collection of monkeys. He can see no sign of the drama which underlies the appearance opposite him behind the wire of the arrogant Onan with his tail held stiffly backward. These interesting observations of this group of monkeys were made by Dr. Bernstein as part of an important program he is carrying out on a series of monkey groups supported by funds provided by the National Institutes of Mental Health. Many aspects of this work and that on the other groups have significant application to human social relationships.

Another group of monkeys at the field station proved to be most interesting as a study in the development of dominance. This was a group of mixed species of monkeys, and it had been formed with two main objects. One was to study whether any particular species was more likely to become dominant in this situation. Another was to find out whether the codes of communication between species of monkeys could be interpreted by other species of monkeys.

When the group was first put together the dominant animal, not surprisingly, turned out to be a rhesus monkey, since this species is normally very aggressive. This particular rhesus monkey was Penrod, who has been mentioned before and who had been banished from human company for slashing Mrs. Bernstein. He was put into this group of mixed primates and immediately became the dominant male. He was very aggressive if any human being came near the wire enclosure, coming up close to the wire and threatening and sometimes even grabbing at the wire. He discouraged other members of the group from having anything to do with humans. He fought very aggressively any male who tried to challenge him. Penrod had all the monkeys in the group thoroughly under his control and was a very strong, powerful, and vicious animal.

In addition to Benito and the little mustache monkey already mentioned, there were in this compound a little female capuchin monkey of a breed similar to Benito, and a number of others, including quite a large animal known as Red. Red had a sandy-colored kind of hair; he was a big animal, bigger than Penrod, the dominant male, but he was an extremely mild-mannered animal. On occasions Dr. Bernstein would go into this group and sit on a small folding chair in the compound, and Red would climb into his lap and would permit himself to be fondled and stroked. If a stranger or some person he was not used to came to the outside wire enclosure, Red would come up and inspect him. A visitor could put his hand through the wire and stroke Red, hold his hand, and so on. This mild and ordinary kind of animal for quite some time remained completely subservient to the dominant animal in the group.

Then one day it was obvious that some kind of change had taken place. There had been an attack by Red on Penrod; but he had apparently not operated on his own—he had worked with a red stump-tail macaque. This is a rather ugly-looking monkey with a blotchy red face, a short tail, and a red bottom. These two between them had appeared to have beaten up Penrod, and he seemed to be completely subdued. He now skulked in the background of the compound and did not try to boss the other animals. He would not eat, and he began to lose weight catastrophi-

Red. A deposed revolutionary. Having challenged the leadership of group, he was later deposed himself from the top position.

cally. He finally had to be taken out of the compound. Even then he ate only poorly. He continued to lose weight and eventually he died, apparently completely unable to take the demotion from the powerful position he had held before.

In the meantime Red assumed the role of unchallenged boss of the new colony, and wherever he went he was accompanied by the red stump-tail macaque, who apparently functioned as his hatchet man. Even when Red came up to the wire to talk to a visitor, the hatchet man would usually be quite close to him and would stand back from the wire and threaten even while the boss was fraternizing. As the weeks passed, an extremely interesting change came over Red. Apparently obsessed with the importance of his position he began to develop all the characteristics that went with a dominant male. After a month or two he no longer welcomed the attentions of human beings and would threaten them. He would come close to the wire, put his hand out, and grab through the wire at a visitor in a very aggressive way. A visitor who got too close was in danger of being savaged by his large and powerful teeth. He soon became completely in charge of the other animals, and they developed the same deference toward him that they had previously shown toward Penrod.

Then after several months there was trouble in the camp. The red stump-tail macaque was apparently dissatisfied with his role as hatchet man and had begun to threaten and challenge Red. They had a series of rather severe fights, and then there was a period in which the leadership of the group oscillated between Red on the one hand and the macaque on the other. Eventually, after one very serious fight, Red was finally evicted from the top position and the red stump-tail macaque moved in. Red was pushed into the background, and now animals who had previously been subservient to him cuffed him as they went past and similarly demonstrated to him that they no longer regarded him as a threat. Red too lost weight and did not eat. Partly this was because the other animals took food from him. He too had to be removed eventually from the group. Following this, he did pick up in strength and began to eat again. He was kept for breeding purposes in a private cage of his own with selected females as company. He did very well, but eventually he was found to give a positive TB skin test. It was feared that if he really had tuberculosis he might communicate it to other animals in the field station, so he was subjected to euthanasia. The rest of the group went on for some time with the red stump-tail macaque as the boss, and eventually it was broken up so the animals could be used for other scientific purposes.

One interesting example of animal recognition of dominance was given to me by Dr. Hans Kuhn of the University of Frankfurt, whose father in 1938, under political pressure, declined a Nobel Prize for his work in biochemistry. Dr. Kuhn had a small monkey—I believe it was a rhesus monkey—in his house, and the animal itself placed the members of the household into a dominance hierarchy. To the monkey the most important member of the household was Dr. Kuhn's mother. If, for example, the monkey was with Dr. Kuhn and his mother came into the room, then the monkey would leave Dr. Kuhn and go to his mother. On the other hand, if he was with Dr. Kuhn's sister and Dr. Kuhn came into the room, he would leave the sister and go to Dr. Kuhn. It is interesting that the Nobel Prize-winning father was not rated by the monkey anywhere in the hierarchy and was just ignored.

The social relationships which various monkey groups develop at the Yerkes Center are social groupings which simply represent procedures and behavior patterns characteristically found in the same groups in the wild. Probably one of the most detailed social groupings in the primate world is that of the baboon. There are several species of baboon. I have mentioned the geladas; two others are the chacma baboons and the savanna baboons of Kenya. The geladas are found in Ethiopia, where there are also hamadryas baboons.

The savanna troupe usually has a principal dominant animal and also subdominant males, very young bachelor males, and of course groups of females, infants, and the young. When such a group moves across the savanna, there are usually two or three leading males out in front as scouts. The fully grown males move on the periphery of the troupe. Within are the young males and females and the babies. Sometimes a mother baboon with a baby finds that she has to use one arm to hold the infant and so has to walk on three legs, causing her to move more slowly than the

Alpha, the first chimpanzee to be born in the Yerkes Laboratories. Her mother was Dwina. She is shown here at the age of one year.

group. If she has to drop back, an adult male usually drops back with her and sticks with her until the three of them regain the main group again.

Unlike the monkeys, who in most cases have a rigid social structure, chimpanzees have a very loose social structure. Even the groups that are formed are temporary groups, and there do not seem to be permanent leaders. There is a tendency, for example, for the mothers and babies to form a separate group known as a nursery group. There is evidence of so-called sexual groups, males and childless females running together. These latter groups also frequently contain adolescent animals. The sexual groups usually contain twenty or more members; the nursery groups usually have fewer than fifteen, and of these at least half are children-babies or youngsters. The nursery group is a rather shy type of group and does not move very far at any particular time, whereas the sexual groups are noisy and range widely over areas of the forest.

Chimpanzees build nests in the trees, but they never use the same nest twice. They usually build these nests toward nightfall and situate them 30 or 40 feet up in the trees. They scarcely ever build nests on the ground.

Among the apes the orangutan appears to be the least gregarious of all. In fact it appears that the male leads a solitary life except during the mating season. It is said that females retreat deep into the jungle on their own to bear their young. Groups of two or three females with young have been found together and also small family groups, male and female and child. But the social life of the orang in the wild has been very little studied in comparison with the chimpanzee.

The lowland gorilla families appear to consist of males, females, and young animals. There may be five or more families associated together in a single band. The individuals usually look for food in the same general area and then gather together at night. On these occasions, the nests that the individual family builds for itself are close to one another but may be separated by some distance from the next family group. All the animals build nests in trees to sleep in at night except the very large, heavy males, who tend to sleep on the ground near the foot of the tree where the others are nesting.

9. Ape Aesthetics

I HAVE mentioned elsewhere in this book that the firstborn chimpanzee of the Yerkes Colony was Alpha and that she had a desire to draw. Alpha also had a feeling for symmetry, and if she was given a piece of paper with a cross placed on three of the corners and a pencil, she would put a cross in the fourth corner. Alpha would also in her crude way try to complete designs and pictures which had been given to her deliberately unfinished or unbalanced.

An extensive study of the drawings of a chimpanzee was carried out over a number of years by Dr. Paul H. Schiller at the Yerkes Laboratories in Orange Park, and his results were published in the *Journal of Comparative and Physiological Psychology* in April, 1951. Dr. Schiller's work was confined largely to Alpha, who was eighteen years old when she was tested.

One of the interesting things which emerged concerning Alpha's drawing was that she developed a change of style over a period of time. This is exactly what Madame N. N. Ladygin Kohts found with her chimpanzee, Joni. But Alpha's drawings also showed a distinct sense of design and the ability to develop a pattern. Dr. Schiller believed that Alpha had as much interest in the action of drawing itself as in what she produced. He said, "There is certainly another factor at work. She does not draw with a pointed stick and discards or chews up her crayon when the point breaks and it no longer marks. Given paper and pencil with broken point, she retires to a corner, examines the point, makes a few tentative strokes, then returns to the front of the cage to beg. The fact of marking is thus an essential part out of the activity."

Visual composition in apes had not really been properly studied until Dr. Schiller's work with Alpha. It was Schiller who noticed that Alpha, when given a piece of paper and a pencil to scribble, always kept her scribblings within the confines of the paper and never went off the edge. She also liked to put a mark in each corner of the paper before scribbling in the center. It has been mentioned that if three corners were marked she would always put in the fourth. The tendency by Alpha to confine her scribbling to the sheet of paper suggested to Schiller that it might be interesting to see what would happen if Alpha were given papers already marked with simple shapes or containing some type of pattern. One of the problems he met with in these experiments was that she usually tore up her drawing after she had completed it. What he did then was to take a piece of wooden board 12 inches by 15 inches with a short handle, attach the paper to it, and then insert the whole thing in the space below the cage door; the experimenter was able to hold onto one end. On top of the piece of wood was a gray cardboard frame 2 inches wide, and sheets of paper could be slipped under the frame. The total area available for Alpha to work on was about 8 inches by 11 inches.

His test objects included various figures cut from colored paper and pasted onto sheets of contrasting color. Or he sometimes cut patterns in the sheets and pasted contrasting paper behind. Sometimes Alpha was given two pencils of different colors and allowed to draw from 10 to 180 seconds before the board was taken back. On occasions she would attempt to snatch the board or tear off the piece of paper, although during the test period she usually squatted before the board with her mind on her scribbling. Many of her drawings were in colored crayon on paper of the same color and would not photograph well. Dr. Schiller had to copy these with India ink at a reduced size so they could be reproduced in his article.

Alpha showed manual dexterity in other ways which she exhibited by undoing bootlaces if she got the chance. She was very expert at choosing the free end of a bow, and she knew that if she pulled this she could undo the bow; then she would endeavor to unlace the shoe. On occasions while she was trying to undo my shoelace, I have tried to pull my shoe back out of the way. Alpha

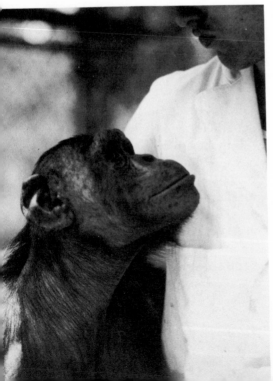

Alpha gives her keeper a look of confidence and affection.

would nearly always get angry and grab the lace and break it if I did this before she thought she was finished.

In his experiments with Alpha, Dr. Schiller had to use special types of wood-covered crayons. If he gave her colored chalk or paper-wrapped wax crayons, she simply chewed them up without attempting to use them for drawing. She would never attempt to draw on the cement walls of her cage or on the floor, which was gray in color.

Alpha made two types of strokes in drawing: short dashes which were made by flexing the wrists and moving her arm very little; and a series of parallel rather zigzag strokes which she made by flexing the elbow. She rarely made curved lines and rarely produced flourishes. On an ordinary unmarked sheet of paper Alpha would usually make a short stroke in each corner, then make scribbles along the margins, and finally she would fill in the middle of it with much coarser scribblings. She did this pattern whether she was drawing with black on white or white on black or even with black on black. She was tested almost daily for six months, and her drawings on blank paper showed considerable change. Toward the end of her period of testing she tended to make drawings consisting entirely of broad heavy strokes located more or less in the center of the paper. If the piece of paper was presented to her with a square or a circle or a regular polygon which was more than an inch across on the paper, she would confine her markings almost exclusively inside the figure. This again was irrespective of the color of the chalk and the background. If the figure presented on the paper was smaller than an inch in diameter, Alpha rarely made marks inside but tended to scribble all around it. When there were several small areas like this on the paper she would scribble between them and rarely inside them. If the figure was off center, Alpha would tend to make a mass of scribbling to one side of it to more or less give balance to the design. If the presented figure was in the middle of the sheet, she tended to scribble on top of it. If multiple figures were large, she treated each one of them as a separate figure and confined her scribblings within each one. If the figures were placed very close together, she just scribbled all over them as if they were a single large figure. If the small figures were arranged so that they enclosed a fairly regular space, this then became the field within which she did almost all her scribbling, but three or four small figures did not define a field for her; there had to be five or more figures regularly arranged before she would accept the area enclosed by them as constituting a field in which she would draw.

During the first four months of the six-month period in which Alpha was tested, she drew very well and was very well motivated. However, during the last two months it became increasingly difficult to persuade her to draw. Finally the whole experimental series had to be brought to an end because she had lost interest. Twenty months later, however, when she was tested once more, she was very happy to start drawing again.

There is no evidence that Alpha started to draw early in her life. She was given the Gesell tests when she was a baby, and the last of these was carried out at the age of forty weeks; at this time she made no endeavor to scribble when she was given a crayon and paper. For the ten years prior to her official testing her behavior when given a pencil and paper had been pretty much as had been described during these tests.

One of the many interesting facts emerging from these studies was that Alpha was never given any kind of a social or food reward for drawing, so whatever motivation she had, she got her reward either from what she produced or from the act of drawing. Dr. Schiller believed it was the latter motive. When given a pencil and paper by the experimenter without any plan for regaining the drawing, she would go to the far end of the cage, put her back to the observer, become completely preoccupied with her drawing, and when she was finished, tear up the paper. If another animal was with her she would push him to one side and turn away to work on her own in a corner. When she saw someone with a pencil and paper, she would lose interest even in food and would actually beg for them.

At the time Alpha was tested there were sixty chimpanzees in the Yerkes Laboratories, and only a very few of them showed interest in the mechanics of drawing in the way that she had. Alpha's drawings are actually at the level of the scribbling of a human infant aged a year to eighteen months. But she did not imitate a drawing by other people, even if the experimenter took the pencil and made a single stroke on the paper. In view of this, the observation by Mrs. Hoyt that her gorilla Toto was able to learn from her to draw a simple face is very important. The other extraordinary statement made by Mrs. Hoyt was that sometimes when Toto was walking toward her he would give her a greeting by drawing this miniature face in the air with his finger. We have no reason to doubt Mrs. Hoyt's observations, but it is far beyond what any other ape has been able to do; if it is in fact true she must have had an ape genius on her hands.

In children, according to Paul Schiller, "Scribbling has been interpreted as a stage in the development of representative drawing. The character and limitations of Alpha's drawing suggest, on the contrary, that scribbling is primarily a motor expression and that imitative and reproductive drawing derive from quite a different category of perception or of conceptual organization."

Desmond Morris, in his book *The Biology of Art,* discusses the results obtained with Alpha and gives also the details of many other ape and monkey studies. Morris mentioned one characteristic of Alpha's work, and that is that if the experimenter put a long band or a bold line across the page on which she was to work, she would make sweeping marks at right angles to it. In a very short time the lines would be crossed by scores of scribbled cross lines. These cross marks were always at an angle between 45 and 90 degrees. In Russia Madame Ladygin Kohts found that her chimpanzee, Joni, also had this tendency. Professor Bernhard Rensch, who incidentally with his colleagues recently spent a period at the Yerkes Primate Center studying young gorillas and orangutans, has pointed out that primates would all prefer to select cards that have regular patterns drawn on them and that Alpha gave better responses to regular figures than irregular ones. Professor Rensch also showed that birds would do the same thing. Alpha, when given a triangle, tended to make symmetrical markings on the outside of the triangle near each of its sides. This is another aspect of her sense of symmetry and picture balancing which we mentioned earlier.

The chimpanzee Gua, who was brought up with the Kellogg family, was also found to scribble if she was given the opportunity. When the Kelloggs' son Donald was $14\frac{1}{2}$ months old he was given the Gesell writing test, and Gua, at that time 12 months old, was also given the test. In this test a pencil is handed to the subject, the baby, and if the baby makes scribble marks of any type on paper he is considered to have scored. When Donald was given pencil and paper he scribbled spontaneously without having to be shown how to use the pencil. Gua also scribbled very well but had to be given a demonstration by Kellogg before she would do it. Six months later, when given the same test, Gua achieved it spontaneously just as Donald did, so at that time she was equal to the human infant. However, at the second monthly testing two tests later, when a straight line was drawn by the Kelloggs on a sheet of paper with a pencil, Donald took the pencil and immediately imitated it. Gua did not make any attempt at imitation at all; she simply continued to scribble when she was given the pencil and paper. Gua was recorded as performing an extraordinary childlike activity by making marks with her finger on a windowpane which had been fogged by the moisture in her breath. There is no evidence that she made the fogging on the windowpane on purpose. Nevertheless it is an extremely interesting observation.

In his book *Behavior Mechanisms in Monkeys,* published in 1933, Dr. H. Kluver records details of a capuchin monkey who drew lines on the floor of his cage when he was presented with colored chalks.

The only other instances of primates that were not apes scribbling or making some kind of picture is restricted also to two instances in which the capuchin was the drawer. This maybe is not surprising, since the capuchin is so mechanically talented.

Madame Ladygin Kohts in Russia started working with her chimpanzee, Joni, in 1913. In her publication of the results in 1935, she included photographs of scribbles by Joni and compared them with the type of scribble made by a child. Like the Kelloggs, Madame Kohts brought her chimpanzee up simultaneously with her child. Actually she studied the two of them together for a period of three years, compared with nine months for the Kellogg work. Although Joni would constantly fidget with a pencil he never succeeded in doing anything more complicated than a series of intersecting lines, while her son Rudi was very early able to make some elementary sketches of surrounding objects. Joni's first drawings were thus simple scribbles, as were Alpha's first drawings. Later Joni's drawings changed to the rather characteristic crisscrossing of lines. Concerning the tendency of both Alpha and Joni to intersect a single bold line with numerous small lines, Morris says that this "later stage of drawing clearly involves a deliberate intersection tendency and is therefore the first recorded example of visual control in ape drawing."

Although we have given Bobby only some fairly simple experiments in drawing, he did show some interesting color and figure combinations which we illustrate in this book. If shown a picture of an animal and allowed to come into contact with it he would trace the outline with his finger.

When Desmond Morris first read of Schiller's work he became intrigued with the possibility of doing the same sort of thing with other chimpanzees. He was at Oxford University at the time in the department of zoology and comparative anatomy but had no hope of obtaining experimental subjects there. From personal experience I know what kind of problems he faced.

However, in 1956 Morris got an opportunity to come to the London Zoo as head of the Granada Television and Film Unit which produced television programs on the zoo animals. One young chimpanzee known as Congo was selected for special treatment and as a kind of mascot for the program. Morris decided to teach him to draw, and at one and a half years he produced his first drawing. Morris describes this occasion as follows:

I held out the pencil, his curiosity led him towards it. Gently I placed his fingers around it and rested the point on the card. Then I let go. As I did so, he moved his arm a little and then stopped. He stared at the card. Something odd was coming out of the end of the pencil. It was Congo's first line. It wandered a short way and then stopped. Would it happen again? Yes, it did, and again, and again.

Still staring at the card Congo began to draw line after line, and as I watched, I noticed that he was beginning to concentrate the lines on one particular region, the part of the card where there was a small inkblot. This meant that even in this very first scribble, Congo's lines were not just random scratchings and like Alpha, he carried in him the germ, no matter how primitive, of visual patterning.

An ape known as Baltimore Betsy began to gain notoriety in the United States in 1956 from her finger paintings. Child psychiatrists use finger painting for human infants in order to give them some form of self-expression. Baltimore Betsy and two other apes were given the opportunity to try this method of painting. The finger paintings by these animals were shown to child psychiatrists in 1954. One of the psychiatrists interpreted them as coming from an aggressive seven- or eight-year-old boy who had paranoid tendencies. Baltimore Betsy's drawings were said to be from a fiercely belligerent ten-year-old schizoid girl. A second picture by the same animal was also said to be by a ten-year-old girl who was paranoid and showed a strong father identification. These comments do not show that the psychiatrists were stupid. It simply shows that children of these age groups if they are mentally affected will regress, and this regression is shown in their artistic work. Eventually a challenge developed between Baltimore Betsy on the one hand and Congo on the other. A special television program was given in England to demonstrate the paintings of Congo. He demonstrated his painting skill to an audience of 3,000,000, and at the end of the program it was decided to challenge any other ape to produce pictures of the same quality. It was not long before twelve paintings by Betsy were sent to London and were exhibited with twelve paintings by Congo.

Julian Huxley, for many years the secretary of the Zoological Society of London, opened the conference and made the following comments about the exhibition: "The results show conclusively that chimpanzees do have artistic potentialities which can be brought to light by providing suitable opportunities. One of the great mysteries of human evolution is the sudden outburst of art of a very high quality in the upper Palaeolithic period. This becomes more comprehensible if our ape-like ancestors had hese primitive aesthetic potentialities, to which was later added man's unique capacity for symbol making."

The first recorded primitive ancient paintings done by human primates were made on the walls of caves first discovered in 1879. In this year in the little village of Santillana del Mar, the Marquis Sautuola was engaged in a search for prehistoric implements and fossil bones. With his little daughter he had crawled into a cave near the village, and while he was digging in it for fossil bones the child wandered off down the cave with a candle. After she got a certain way in she happened to look up. Suddenly she saw a great red bull in full charge on the ceiling. She immediately shrieked out to her father, "Toros, toros." On that ceiling a whole zoo of animals was found to have been painted. There were bulls, ibex, horses, deer, elk, boars, and even bison. These paintings had apparently been unseen for 30,000 years. Although at that time it was not possible to date them that accurately, it was obvious that they were very ancient, and the Marquis Sautuola claimed that the art which he found in this Altamira cave was produced by prehistoric savages.

The savants of Europe, however, scoffed at such a possibility, and so the whole thing was forgotten for at least sixteen years. Then in 1895 Dr. Emile Rivière also discovered a cave in La Mouthe, France, with many wall paintings. Even his findings were scoffed at. However, it was not long before others were found. A series of paintings was found in caves at Les Combarelles and also one in Font de Gaume. It was obvious by now that the paintings originally discovered by the Marquis Sautuola were indeed the product of exceedingly ancient minds and hands. Dr. E. Lloyd du Brul records the acceptance of the ancient nature of these paintings, saying, "At last it became inescapable that, one by one, the roughest critics succumb, confounded in awe at the art of earth's first aesthetes."

In 1940 a fantastic cave was discovered in Lascaux by two French boys, Marsal and Ravidat. They were so excited by their find that they escorted their teacher to the spot. The first part of the cave was 100 feet long and 30 wide with the wall bulging outward. It led by a narrow passage into a gallery. From one wall of the cave a passage passed off at right angles to the main cave in a nave and from this by a very difficult, low, narrow tunnel to the Hall of Felines. In the great hall there were myriads of figures of horses, bulls, reindeer, bears, and cows. Four enormous bulls towered over all the other animals, and there was even a unicorn. Some figures were in black and white, some in color and some shaded, and their anatomy was excellent. They were obviously the work of more than one painter. Similar figures decorated the other parts of the cave complex. On one wall was a stencil of a child's arm. They were supplemented by pictures of ibex, mares and bison. In the Room of Felines were six beautifully painted lions.

Most of the cave paintings have been discovered in Spain and France. It may be that this is simply because these are the sites where the paintings which were done were preserved. There may have been other paintings done on stones and so on from the same era elsewhere which have not been discovered or which have been destroyed. The great Hall of Lascaux cave has at least twenty major figures which can be recognized, including those already mentioned. The painting was so good there was even contour shading present, and a variety of colors were used from gold/mocha to red/violet/sepia and blue/black. This is the evolutionary end product of the chimpanzee's primitive ability to scribble and make marks; in Lascaux it had been brought by humans to a reproduction of symbols. These cave paintings represent a high development of art. They were produced by the Cro Magnon men, the last stage of human evolution before modern man. The struggles of artistic expression of earlier men or man like apes have not been found to date. They were probably too ephemeral, and our only idea of any potential artistic striving they may have had can be derived so far only from the tool which they fashioned.

Dr. E. Lloyd du Brul, Professor of Anatomy of the University of Illinois in Chicago, has written a fascinating account of the "Biology of Artistic Behavior" which describes the discovery of these prehistoric cave paintings.

It must not be thought that our knowledge of ape art is restricted to the animals already mentioned. In Rotterdam a go rilla known as Sophie painted very successfully. Professor Heini Hediger, who was at that time the director of the zoo in Basel, had a gorilla who drew with a pencil and paper. Other American chimpanzee painters were J. Fred Muggs and Kokomo, Jr. In Washington there was a chimpanzee called Zippy who was making pictures during the 1957–58 period. Zippy tended to draw pictures in which all her lines were horizontal. This is rare among chimpanzees. Bella, a Dutch chimpanzee, was reported in 1958 to have been drawing pictures. So were Pablo, a capuchin monkey in Germany, and Jonny, a chimpanzee in the Vienna Zoo. Jonny tended to make very weak, rather wandering short lines over the page in a random fashion. According to Desmond Morris it is a fingertip type of drawing with no arm action that produced this style. Various primates have also developed characteristic styles.

For instance, Sophie, the gorilla in Rotterdam, drew with tight little zigzags, Zippy drew bold horizontal lines, and Alpha made characteristic markings in corners of papers. One of the interesting things about Jonny was that during the act of drawing and painting he appeared to get worked up sexually. He appears, according to Morris, to be the only sexually mature male who has been induced to draw.

Another chimpanzee in Holland, Bella, was studied by Miss M. Hylkema, who worked under Dr. Adriaan Kortlandt. When Bella was concentrating on her drawing she was likely to bite if she was interfered with, as Miss Hylkema found out on one occasion. Bella drew a type of fan pattern of similar nature to that produced by Desmond Morris' Congo.

Dr. Morris tested a group of six chimpanzees at the London Zoo for drawing ability. He found that three chimpanzees had to be shown what to do, but once they had drawn their first line on the paper they did not need further help. When he brought out the fourth chimpanzee she took the pencil from his hand and started to draw without having to be shown anything. He wondered if this was imitation, and when he looked around he saw a cluster of chimpanzees hanging from the wire wall of the cage at a point from which they had a clear view of the drawing which

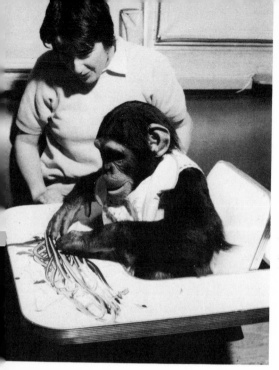

Washoe doing a little painting, aided and abetted by Dr. Beatrice Gardner.

Fifi was making. Presumably Fifi had already seen what was going on and knew exactly what to do.

Fifty years after Madame Ladygin Kohts did her first work, she was still getting drawings from chimpanzees, and her colleagues were also getting drawings from capuchin monkeys. Desmond Morris says that the phenomenon of ape art blossoming at the present time was no accident,

> for both the worlds of science and art were ripe for it. The former has arrived at a point where, in zoological spheres, objective experimental studies of animal behavior patterns are flourishing, thanks to the concerted efforts of the comparative ethnologists and the animal psychologists. The art world on the other hand has experienced wave after wave of increasingly extreme actions against the fading, traditional, communicatory functions of painting. As a result human painting today has become increasingly abstract and has returned

228

motivationally to a state similar to that found in primates, namely pure aesthetic experimentation. With Zoology and art in these phases, the stage was set.

This chapter on primate aesthetes might very well be concluded by a story from Dr. Adriaan Kortlandt. From personal experience he tells of a chimpanzee who had invaded a plantation of papayas to steal some of the fruit to eat and to take away. He ate several papayas and then, carrying two in his arm, began to leave the papaya grove. Just then he happened to look toward the west. At that time there was a particularly attractive and beautiful sunset with the most glorious colors in the sky. The chimpanzee looked, stopped, put down his papayas, sat, and looked fixedly at the western sky. He sat there for quite some time until the colors faded, and then, getting up, he softly stole away, leaving the stolen papayas behind him. Was he awed by the beauty of the natural phenomenon he had seen? Dr. Kortlandt likes to think that he was.

10. Communicating with Apes

ELIZABETH BORGESE has described how a long time ago there was a wise and powerful king, reputed to be the wisest and most powerful on earth. But his power, which was secret, was that he had the gift of understanding animals. The secret by which he was able to obtain this particular gift was that he ate a piece of a white snake so that he understood birds, he knew what dolphins were squealing about, and he could even hear fish whom other people thought to be completely without voice. Furthermore, he was able to give these animals orders in their language through their own king and was able thus to take advantage of the efforts of all their soldiers and workers, for instance in the ant and bee colony. So by his communication with these animals he was able to receive their cooperation, and it was this that made him so powerful.

One of the things that has always intrigued people who work with apes, and it certainly has intrigued many of the workers at the Yerkes Center, is why apes are not able to speak. Actually the vocalizations of the four types of ape are surprisingly dissimilar, considering the similarity of anatomical structure of the larynx which is mainly responsible for the noise. The gorilla, for example, grunts and occasionally roars; the orangutan's vocalization tends to be kind of a whimper with occasionally a roar. The gibbon has a series of long musical notes. Chimpanzees are able to scream and do a certain amount of chattering. Their vocal organs appear to be quite similar to those of man. Workers in the past have believed that the reason why the chimpanzee and the other apes were not able to speak was because of a lack of development of the brain.

More than a hundred years ago the vocal organ of primates aroused a great deal of interest. As long ago as 1835 Dr. W. Youatt was speculating why the chimpanzee was able to scream so loudly and yet was not able to mouth words. Dr. G. Kelemen has pointed out that the anatomical arrangement of the vocal system in the apes makes it impossible for them to reproduce the phonetic elements which are so characteristic of human speech. It will be remembered that Vicki, who was brought up by Cathy Hayes and her husband, Keith, even after considerable training not only by the Hayeses themselves but by speech therapists all over the country and by speech therapists particularly skilled in training backward children to speak, was never able to say more than three words: Mama, Papa, and cup. Altogether it took six years of patient training to get Vicki to say these words.

Dr. Philip Liebermann of the University of Connecticut studied gorillas and chimpanzees and rhesus monkeys under various conditions which included feeding them, withholding food, and other experimental situations which were expected to cause the animal stress or to provoke his aggression. He made tape recordings of the vocalizations of these animals and then analyzed them in what is known as a sound spectrograph. He compared their spectrograms with the sound spectrograms found in human speech. Anatomically it was found that one of the differences between the vocal tract of apes and man was that the apes lack a fixed tongue root which would be able to form a movable anterior wall of the larynx. Nonhuman primates have long flat tongues, and the tongues appear not able to contribute to the changes in what is described as the supralingual vocal tract shapes that are necessary for human speech. Dr. Liebermann points out that in human speech the tongue moves backward and forward to produce the constant changes in the shape of the pharyngeal region which is necessary for the production of speech. He points out that the cross-section area of the lumen in the human pharynx varies as much as ten times in the production of the vowel sounds *a* and *i*. Dr. Liebermann has stated that the vocal tracts of apes have the resonating characters of a tube which is more or less uniform, although it may be expanded at the end in a trumpetlike fashion.

A number of investigators have suggested that the "aw" sound which some apes make is caused by the movement of the ape's tongue, but an analysis of this vocalization by the sound spectrograph has shown that the change in this vowel sound which in human beings would be modified by the movement of the tongue is actually caused by a change in the amount of excitation of the glottis at the termination of the cry.

Dr. Liebermann has been trying to trace back in man's history where exactly speech may have emerged. He has been taking measurements of skulls and making comparative anatomical studies. His studies suggest that Australopithecus, (the southern man), discovered originally by Dr. Raymond Dart of South Africa, probably was not able to talk. The Neanderthal man may have been able to talk, but this is not certain.

Primates use a variety of sounds to express themselves. Often to the untrained observer one sound will seem very little different from another. In the case of the rhesus monkey, however, up to forty different types of vocalization have been listed. I am not aware that anyone has studied the chimpanzee or other ape vocalizations to the same extent. There is no doubt that there have been listed for them a smaller number of characteristic sounds which are associated with particular emotions and reactions. Facial expressions are also used by all primates for communication. Monkeys make a series of basic faces. The most characteristic is the aggressive face, which is so well shown by the rhesus monkey with his staring eyes and his open threatening mouth showing his teeth. Other animals show what is called a "threat" face, and others show a face which expresses submissiveness. Others have a face which is characteristic for friendliness. For instance, most monkeys who indulge in lip smacking to an observer or another animal are being friendly.

Apes also appear to use many gestures. Two investigators at the University of Nevada, Dr. and Mrs. Allen Gardner, have been working with a chimpanzee known as Washoe in an attempt to communicate with him by means of gestures. They have tried to communicate by using the American sign language which is the language of the deaf in North America. The Gardners decided to use gesturing procedures because the early work of Dr. and Mrs. Hayes at Yerkes with the chimpanzee Vicki had shown that the use of vocalization in attempts to communicate with her were not successful. Generally chimpanzees vocalize when they are excited; however, the hands of these animals are very prominent and their use is prominent in their behavior. Chimpanzees spontaneously use begging gestures when they are caged, and others use even more gestural communication. Films taken at the Yerkes Labs over the years demonstrate a variety of types of manual gesturing which chimpanzees use; quite striking is the gesture used to gain cooperation from another chimpanzee.

There are two methods of communication using American sign language. In one system there is an attempt to produce a manual alphabet; in other words, the positions that the hand makes with the fingers correspond to the letters of the alphabet. The other system, however, consists of a number of manual configurations coupled with gestures that are equivalent to specific words or specific concepts. Two typical examples of the American sign language are given by the Gardners in their recent publications. One of these is the sign for "always," in which the hand is clenched with one finger extended and the arm is rotated at the elbow. In the sign for "flower" the fingers are all extended and the fingers are then touched first to one nostril and then to the other as if a flower is being sniffed.

The Gardners pointed out that when Dr. and Mrs. Hayes were attempting to teach Vicki to speak they took a great interest in the subject of babbling, because in human infants babbling is regarded as experimenting with noise and sounds and is an essential preliminary to the process of speech. During her first year Vicki made quite a number of spontaneous vocalizations, but after that time they progressively decreased to the point where there was no vocal babbling, so no spoken language could be anticipated. The Gardners expected some manual babbling in their baby chimp Washoe, but in the beginning they saw very little of this type of behavior. However, there was a progressive increase in manual babbling, or gesturing, and they were encouraged by movements in which parts of the head and the body were touched. They believed that chimpanzee gesturing might be interpreted or used for communication. This was important, since many of the signs in sign language involve touching parts of the head or the body. They noticed that when Washoe wanted something in a hurry and was not able to get it she often started a flurry of arm waving. The first gesture that Washoe made was a begging gesture. She extended her hand open with the palm directed upward toward either Dr. Gardner or his wife. She often did this when she needed help in various situations or if they were holding something she wanted. It was not much of a problem to persuade her to develop this also into a beckoning movement and thus to turn it into the sign language for "give me" or "come." The impatient flourish with her hand when she wanted something in a hurry was converted by the Gardners into the sign for "hurry," in which the animal shook her open hand from the wrist in a very vigorous fashion.

In a recent publication the Gardners listed 34 signs which Washoe now uses reliably in communicating with them. She rec-

234

Washoe follows Dr. Beatrice Gardner's gesture for "drink."

ognizes the sign when it is given by the experimenters and uses the sign herself. These include signs for come or give me, more, up, sweet, open, tickle, go, out, hurry, here, listen, toothbrush, drink, hurt, sorry, funny, please, food, eat, flower, cover, blanket, dog, you, napkin, bib, brush, hat, I, me, shoes, smell, pants, clothes, cat, key, baby, clean. The sign for "cat," for example, is formed by the thumb and the index finger grasping the cheek or the hair near the side of the mouth and drawn outward. This is the representation of the cat's whiskers. "Clean" is represented by passing the open palm of one hand over the open palm of the other. The sign for "dog" is repeated slapping on the thigh. For "sorry" the fisted hand clasps and unclasps at the shoulder. For "hear" or "listen" the index finger touches the ear.

The types of problem which the experimenters encountered and the way they solved them is shown by the following interesting quote from their publication:

> The differentiation of the signs for flower and smell provides a further illustration of usage depending upon size of vocabulary. As the flower sign becomes more frequent, we noted that it occurred in sev-

eral inappropriate contexts that all seemed to include odors; for example, Washoe would make the flower sign when opening a tobacco pouch or when entering a kitchen filled with cooking odors. Taking our cue from this, we introduced the smell sign by passive shaping and imitative prompting. Gradually Washoe came to make the appropriate distinction between flower contexts and smell contexts in her signing. Although flower in the single nostril form has continued to occur as a common error in smell contexts.

Once Washoe had learned several signs she began to string them together. Strings of two or more signs increased rapidly. Some examples of her combinations are "give me tickle" before the experimenters had ever asked her to tickle them, and "open food drink" to indicate the refrigerator. Signs most commonly used in combination in the early stages were "please," "come," "give me," "hurry," and "more." Examples of this are the "please open hurry" combination and "give me drink please." Then she began to use five additional signs and combinations: "go," "out," "in," "open," and "hear," "listen." Typical examples of combinations she used were these: "go in" or "go out," "go sweet" if she wanted to be carried to a raspberry bush, "open flower" if she wanted to be let through the gate to a flower garden, "open key" for a locked door, "listen eat" at the sound of an alarm clock signaling mealtime, and "listen dog" at the sound of the barking of an unseen dog. Most of these examples of combinations were inventions of the animal herself. This in itself is a fantastic breakthrough in communication between man and animal. Then the writers were able to introduce the concept of "I" or "me" and "you," and as a result at the present time the animal is producing combinations involving these two signs which have the appearance of short sentences.

Another striking breakthrough in communication with apes has been announced recently. This has come from Dr. David Premack of the University of California in Santa Barbara whose work has been supported by the National Institute of Mental Health. This work has also had important bearings on the nature and origin of language. Dr. Premack has a chimpanzee called

Sarah who has up-to-date mastered a vocabulary of one hundred and twenty words, but who apparently has the capability of learning many more—perhaps a thousand. Like Washoe, Sarah has not been taught the alphabet, which, according to Dr. Premack, is not essential for language but is only a device for making a lot of words out of a few simple symbols. The language which Sarah has been taught is one that uses a symbol to represent a word. For example, a banana is represented by a pink square and an apple is a purple triangle. These symbols are made in Dr. Premack's laboratory and are attached to pieces of steel so that they may be arranged on a magnetic board. Sarah spontaneously arranges her combinations of symbols vertically like the Chinese arrange their pictographs—this was her own choice. Furthermore she arranges the symbols in an order that makes sense so that her "sentences" have syntax. Like Bobby, Sarah has learned to type on a typewriter with the normal letters replaced by symbols, so that when she wants to convey a message she simply types it out on the typewriter. Sarah has grasped the concept of sentences such as "Sarah put banana [into] pail [and] apple [into] dish." Conditional abstract sentences such as "If Mary take green [object] then Sarah take red" are also understood by this unusual chimpanzee—or is she that unusual—she is just a chimpanzee that has been taught to communicate with humans. Many other chimpanzees could probably do the same.

These findings alter one's whole philosophical reaction to these apes. The conception that they are stupid or that any animal is stupid because it can't talk is obviously untenable. Those of us responsible for the welfare of these animals now feel a new responsibility.

Jane Goodall has made extensive studies of chimpanzees in the wild and has pointed out that chimpanzees have quite large vocabularies of calls. These calls usually signify some kind of emotion of fear, pain, pleasure, etc. There are food barks, and when these are made other chimpanzees who can hear the call will immediately hurry to the food. If the chimpanzee sees something which alarms him he gives an uneasy "hoo" and the others look intensely in the same direction he is looking. If a young chimpanzee screams with fright or with pain his mother hurries to him at once.

Yerkes chimpanzees have a wide variety of vocalizations, including food barks and screams of excitement and a series of soft vocalizations. Another type of audible response is known as the pleasure pant. If someone is making friendly noises to a young chimpanzee and tickling it in the armpits, it isn't very long before its face assumes a kind of beatific expression and it makes a series of fast short pants known as pleasure panting. Other forms of pleasurable stimulation will also produce this pleasure panting. I have noted something similar to this in gorillas, especially when being tickled.

Jane Goodall has pointed out that chimpanzees in the wild rely a good deal on the sense of touch for communication. Physical contact in general appears to be vital in the emotional life of the chimpanzee, especially during the infant period; presumably as with all infants the mother's touch provides a sense of security for the young animal. Small wild-born baby chimpanzees when they begin their first independent explorations scramble rapidly back to their mothers if any threat of danger occurs. When they become older they still run back to her but do not fling their arms around her and hold on as they did when young. But they press themselves against the mother and maybe hold her hair and even have a quick suckle at the breast to get back the feeling of security. When a chimpanzee in the wild becomes anxious or worried he usually attempts to touch another animal with his hands; when the emotional disturbance is very great, he will very often fling his arms around another chimpanzee. Goodall makes the following comments about this reaction between the apes:

> This embrace is probably the greatest form of reassurance an adult chimp can give or receive. On one occasion David Graybeard, threatened by a huge male baboon, ran screaming to fling his arms around Goliath. And then, as if made brave by his contact with his friend, he ran towards the baboon and threatened it. The deep-seated need for reassuring physical contact shows very clearly when a chimp is threatened or attacked by a social superior. On such occasions he usually continues to scream and make submissive gestures

until the aggressor calms him with a touch. Once young Everett, set upon viciously by Goliath, fled in panic. A short distance away, however, he stopped and hesitantly walked back towards his attacker. He was still so frightened that he turned repeatedly as if to run away again. When at last his zigzag approach took him close enough, he crouched low to the ground, turned his rump to Goliath. He remained thus, screaming and looking back over his shoulder, until the big male reached out and patted him reassuringly, continuing for several moments until Everett's screams died away. Once Figan, threatened by a pugnacious J.B., shrieked in fear and held his hand palm up towards his mother Flo. She responded by reaching out to hold her son's hand until his cries ceased.

The names used by Goodall were the names of chimpanzees she had studied for so long she was able to recognize them and had named them for the convenience of reference.

Goodall points out that chimpanzees, if they are known to each other, exchange greetings when they meet in the wild. This occurs particularly if they meet after they have been apart for any length of time. When an animal comes into a group of chimpanzees to whom he is known, they will often touch him with outstretched hands or even bow to him. Goodall says that many of their forms of greeting are surprisingly similar to our own. For instance, they often kiss each other or press their open mouths onto the neck or shoulder of another animal. A slightly more bizarre method of greeting is found when two male mountain gorillas meet each other; as described by Schaller, they will each reach forward and gently lift the testicles of the other. It is interesting to speculate on a world in which this was a form of greeting among humans.

Goodall has listed a number of calls or sounds together with the expression of the face given by various individuals. For example between relaxed individuals you may hear a soft grunt which is usually given with a relaxed face. This occurs usually in a situation when the group is relaxed and resting or when grooming, or even when it is traveling in a relaxed condition. The response of the other chimpanzees to this sound is often to repeat it. There may be a very soft type of groan given with the same type of face and under the same conditions, and this gets the same response from other individuals. Among other types of noise is a loud barking sound usually made when the apes are eating or when they see desirable food. This is the "food bark" so familiar to us with our caged chimpanzees. Or there may be short, high-pitched single-syllable shrieks when the animals come close to desirable food or start to feed, then soft or loud grunts when they are actually feeding. I have mentioned the existence of pleasure panting; there may also be copulatory pants which are louder and hoarser than the ordinary pleasure panting. Then there is a kind of laughing which consists of soft panting sounds that sometimes become kind of jerky panting grunts. This takes place during the process of social play. Goodall has listed 26 different calls which are significant to the animal. These vary from the pants I have mentioned to hoots, shrieks, roars, barks, whimpers, crying noises, squeaks, and shrieks. A group of excited chimpanzees makes a deafening screaming noise.

II. Ape Sex

ONE of the great triumphs of the Yerkes Center has been its success in breeding apes. At the time of this writing, 203 apes have been born in the Yerkes Laboratories since 1930, which means an average of about 5 a year. In the last three years we have produced 14 baby orangutans in addition to a large number of chimpanzee births. The process of mating and of birth in these big apes is interesting and has some differences from the same processes in human beings.

Female chimpanzees become sexually mature around the age

of eight, whereas the male is likely to become sexually mature at age nine to ten. Full adulthood for chimpanzees and probably also for orangutans and gorillas commences at about twelve years. One of the signs of sexual maturity in apes is the appearance of menstruation. From this time on, the animal is able to reproduce. At the Yerkes Center we have not yet seen any signs of the termination of the menstrual cycle. In our oldest chimpanzee, who is forty-seven, the cycle is continuing. It was also present in the Yerkes chimpanzee Patti, who died at the age of forty-five years. Another feature which characterizes maturity in the female chimpanzee is the periodical swelling of an area of skin in the region of the genitals and anus which is known as the sexual skin. It may become very large indeed. Yerkes describes its size as approximating that of the clenched hand of a man. Very much larger swellings have been seen on some chimpanzees.

The female chimpanzee has a regular sexual cycle comparable with that of human females. The cycle commences with menstruation. This is followed by a time when the genital area is normal. Then there is a period of considerable swelling of the sexual area which is described as tumescence. The time at which this swelling reaches its maximum size is the stage at which the female is receptive to the male and will accept copulation. This lasts a few days, and following that stage, there is a period of detumescence with a disappearance of the swollen area. Then there is a final stage which involves a complete disappearance of the swelling and a phase of inactivity before the menstruation of the next cycle begins. The cycles take about 30 to 35 days, comparable to the cycle for human females. While menstruation also occurs in gorillas and orangutans, they do not have the swelling of the genital area which is characteristic of the chimpanzee.

If a male chimpanzee is placed in a cage with a female chimpanzee, he very rarely takes any sexual interest in this animal until the period of tumescence develops. As far as apes are concerned, copulation occurs only during the few days involved in the mid-third of the menstruation cycle. The female in the wild may receive a large number, as many as eight or ten, males copulating with her in rapid succession when she is in the receptive stage.

Copulation or mating behavior can be initiated by the male, or it can be initiated by the female, who does this by "presenting" herself to a suitable male. There is very little in the way of courtship or presexual behavior of the type shown by humans, although in the chimpanzees there is often a sort of premating activity in the form of a game. According to Yerkes, "Usually the female leads off in a march or deliberate run and the male follows. Either or both may slap the ground with hands or feet as they circle about their cage. Gradually the movement becomes more rapid and the animals exhibit excitement. Finally the female may stop and await the mating approach of the male or he may signal her and establish physical contact. Such behavior as this seemingly occurs only when the two animals are not equally ready to mate."

When chimpanzees actually commence mating the female turns her back to the male and crouches low; the male will then approach her from the back and mount her; he sometimes lays his body along her back. Or he may sit in a more or less semiupright position. The penis of the chimpanzee is surprisingly slender but quite long. He penetrates the vagina very quickly, and the whole procedure is very fast. He does six or eight, rarely more than twenty, thrusts with his pelvis and apparently has an orgasm which rarely takes more than ten seconds to develop. The moment the orgasm is finished, either the female runs off, sometimes screaming, or the male himself withdraws. So the whole process of copulation is a seven- to ten-second affair. The pygmy chimpanzee (a dwarf species of chimpanzee) is said to have a more prolonged copulation.

Not all male and female chimpanzees are expert at this procedure. Presumably in the wild state they have the opportunity of seeing this process going on all the time, and in the caged state they do not get the same opportunity. One typical example of this was an occasion on which we placed a novice male in a cage with a sophisticated female. As he came into her cage he developed an erection. The female saw the erection and immediately

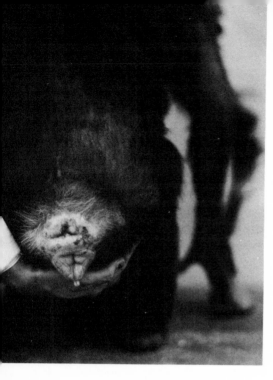

Normal appearance of the anogenital region of a chimpanzee.

turned her back toward him and "presented," obviously expecting him to copulate. However, the male was inexperienced and had no idea what he should do next. The female looked backward at him from under her legs and saw that, stimulated by her "presentation," he had commenced to masturbate. This so enraged her that she turned around and beat him severely.

We once had a young female chimpanzee in the Yerkes group who was used as an educator for males who did not have any idea of the right thing to do from a sexual point of view. Such stupid male chimpanzees would be introduced to this little girl chimpanzee, who rapidly seduced them by showing them the right thing to do and then helping them to do it. After their experience with her the males were then able to return to other females in the colony and have success in their sexual contact with them.

Yerkes, in his volume on the chimpanzees, points out that sexually mature, but inexperienced, male or female chimpanzees often behave ineptly under certain social situations, particularly those which have a sexual connotation. The young caged male chimpanzee has to be taught how to mate, and the female has to be taught how to take care of her infant. The experience of Jim and Anumá, two of the Abreu chimpanzees, bears repeating. Jim was a sexual expert in the Abreu colony, and Anumá, although nine years and four months old, was sexually inexperienced. Even though he was solicited by the females he was unable to perform the act of copulation.

In the mating of chimpanzees it is important not to bring together too abruptly animals who are unacquainted or possibly hostile to each other. They need to be given an opportunity to see each other and make some kind of social relationship beforehand. In the restricted quarters of the Yerkes caging the female cannot get away from the male, and if things do not go well she is liable to be subjected to considerable damage as a result. So the technique of mating in the Yerkes colony, which was adopted long ago by Dr. Yerkes, is to have males and females who are going to be mated placed in adjacent cages so they get to know each other by communication through the wire separating their cages before they are actually put together. This is not necessary,

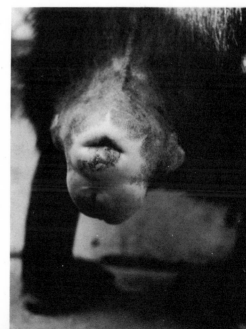

Swollen "sexual skin" of the anogenital region of a chimpanzee that is in estrus (heat).

of course, for animals who already know each other and have proved to be compatible.

I have already mentioned that in the wild the female who is in heat may copulate with large numbers of animals. Goodall in 1965 described as many as 20 males in the wild copulating with a single female chimpanzee in estrus. But in a cage situation where she has only one mate she will copulate with him repeatedly as long as he can get an erection and does not become exhausted or satiated with the experience.

Goodall suggests that the function of the swollen perianal region of the sexually receptive chimpanzee with its bright color is to signal to males, both those nearby and those some distance away, that the female is in fact in estrus and is receptive. Goodall also points out that when a female chimpanzee is in estrus she is usually surrounded by what is described as a "much noisier and more boisterous group than when she is not receptive. Males congregate in her vicinity and follow her closer than at any other time, sometimes threatening if she tries to move away without them." Can there be some comparison here with human behavior?

Jane Goodall also lists some other observations she has made on copulation by the chimpanzee in the wild. In one year she observed 213 copulations and attempted copulations, and in 176 of these the male was the member of the pair who took the initiative. He did this either by approaching the female with his penis erect and his hair standing on end or else by giving a courtship display. Goodall describes various types of courtship display. These include a bipedal swagger, a "sitting hunch," and "tree-leaping," in which the male does a series of leaps and swings through the branches of a tree, usually hanging down, but facing more or less in the direction where the female is located. The male chimpanzee may also indulge in "beckoning." In this case the male stands upright on his legs, raises an arm the same level as his head or higher, and then makes a sweeping gesture toward himself with his arm. Goodall found that 82 percent of the approaches or courtship displays which mature males made were responded to by females. Adolescent males received 77 percent favorable response. The response of the female was usually by

246

turning her back toward the courting male and presenting her genitalia for copulation. On some occasions the males had to touch the females on their rumps before the animals presented for copulation in this way.

On a number of occasions when males approached females to initiate copulation, the females ran away screaming. When this happened the male would sometimes chase the female until she stopped and presented. On other occasions the male would give up, shake the branches of a nearby tree in the direction in which the female had run away, and then just move off to another female. Females were seen to solicit males. A typical method of soliciting is for the female to approach within a few feet of the male, flatten herself in front of him with her limbs flexed, and look back at him over her shoulder. The male will then mount and copulate with the female if he feels in the right mood.

Goodall also records the following example of noncopulatory sexual behavior. When a female who is nonreceptive presents to a male, as may occur under some circumstances as a gesture of submission, or if such a female just happens to stop by, she may be subjected to inspection of the genital area. "Sometimes he merely put his nose near her vaginal opening and appeared to sniff; at other times he poked his finger into the opening carefully, and then sniffed the finger; occasionally he used both hands to part the lips of the vulva, and then poked, peered, and sniffed. Such behavior was often repeated two or three times; one male inspected 18 times in ten minutes while the female reclined beside him."

Male animals with erect penises may also do peculiar things with them. One of our chimpanzees who got an erection from the excitement of seeing some visitors put his penis through the wire separating his cage from that next door, and the animal in the next cage promptly bit the end off of it. One might think this would have taught him a lesson, but on a subsequent occasion it became erect and he put it through again and had another piece bitten off. This animal was a rough, tough, rambunctious creature who would not take a thing from anyone, ape or human, but when he had the end of his penis bitten off he solicited human sympathy in a very active way; he was probably in considerable pain.

In both gorillas and orangutans copulation from the rear is common. Nevertheless, in both these animals a good deal of frontal copulation occurs. On two occasions I have seen a male orangutan sitting with a female's legs drawn across his thighs and his penis in the vagina of the animal, and unlike the chimpanzee, he was thrusting in and out in long, slow strokes and carrying this procedure on for a very long period of time, giving every evidence of enjoying himself. I have also seen a similar procedure with gorillas. The penis of the orangutan is somewhat intermediate between that of the gorilla and the chimpanzee, and in the gorilla it is, even in the erect condition, usually only about 2 inches long.

I have mentioned that chimpanzees have very little play prior to copulation. Nevertheless, interest does occur in various types of sex play, including oral-genital contact. Male orangs and chimpanzees have been seen to lick the vulva of females for quite long periods, and females have been seen to sniff or to lick the male genitalia; sometimes they may manipulate the penis if they themselves are looking for sex. One of our orangs who was quite young and certainly not sexually mature showed great interest in the penis of another animal and would spend the entire day following him around and sucking his penis whenever the animal was not moving—even in some cases moving with him and holding the animal's penis in his mouth. Eventually we found it necessary to separate these two animals, since the animal being sucked never got a break from this behavior. Whether the "sucker" really had a fixation on the penis or was simply using the penis as a substitute for the mother's breast is difficult to say, but there is no evidence that these animals have any particular involvement or interest in the breast except when they are babies and need to suckle.

In gorillas copulation very frequently takes place with the female lying on her back and the male squatting in front of her. The procedure is a longer one than that of the chimpanzee, which is only a matter of seconds, but not as long as that of the orangutan.

248

In the first copulation between a pair of orangutans the ejaculation of the male is quite fast. After a few days it may take 20 minutes including a certain amount of resting but not much active fast pelvic movement, only slow movements. In the wild both orangs and gibbons may copulate while hanging by their hands from the trees. Gibbons have also been observed to copulate with the female crouched on a branch and the male entering from behind. Face-to-face copulation has also been seen in these animals. In a caged situation our orangs most often copulate with the female positioned on her back and the male squatting in front of her with her legs directed toward his shoulders. The male may also lean over her. In new pairings between orangs the female never "presents"—the male chases her and forces copulation. So in a sense it is a form of rape. On one occasion we saw a female appear to initiate copulation; the male lay on his back, and the female squatted on top of him with his penis inside her. Orangs in a caged situation often carry out copulation hanging from the wire roof of the cage in imitation of their treetop copulation in the wild. In the cage type of hanging copulation the female hangs by all fours from the wire roof and the male approaches her hand over hand, also hanging from the roof. In this hanging technique the animals try all kinds of copulatory positions.

When a female gorilla is feeling sexy she often presents and rubs against the wall or the partner or even against another female if she's caged with her. At the time when a gorilla is in heat there is a slight swelling and a slight outturning of the lips of the vulva, just enough to see the pink flesh inside. In the nonheat period this slight turning out is not visible.

Gorillas have picked up a technique of back riding just before or just after heat. Each sex takes turns riding the other. It is hard to say if it is sexual play or just fun, since it also occurs between animals of the same sex. Animals also drink each other's urine on occasions; it is hard to guess the motivation for that activity.

Dr. Yerkes has recorded a female mountain gorilla who was only five or six months old mounting and thrusting against a dog. On another occasion she threw herself on her back and pressed her genitalia against Dr. Yerkes' feet and tried to pull him down on her. She also presented to him on all fours.

Dr. George B. Schaller described a female gorilla at the Columbus Zoo who backed against the bars separating her from a male who was unable to carry on intercourse through the bars but did carry on what was described as a digital intercourse. He also described a mountain gorilla female in the Bronx Zoo who "made advances to the male in her cage by rubbing her rump against him, by holding his hand pressed against her genital area, occasionally she turned on her back with legs spread widely. She fondled and licked the testes of the male. The male in turn rubbed the breast and genital area of the female with his hand."

I mentioned that the gorilla penis is short. One in the Milwaukee Zoo showed a penis about 2.5 centimeters long while the animal was masturbating. At the Washington Zoo there is a record of the erect penis of a gorilla being 5 centimeters long, a figure also supported by the director of the Basel Zoo, Dr. Ernst Lang. In a dead gorilla the penis was measured some years ago and was found to be 7.6 centimeters long. At the London Zoo one was recorded which was 9 centimeters long.

In the National Zoo in Washington a copulation between gorillas has been observed in which the male lay supine and the female straddled him and crouched down on top of him; copulation took place in this position with most of the pelvic thrusts on this occasion being supplied by the female. On another occasion they were observed to copulate standing up with their abdomens together. Copulation was also seen with the male in a dorsal position. However, the position most frequently observed was with the female crouching with her knees bent under her belly and her chest almost in contact with the floor. The male would squat behind her, sometimes placing his hands on her hips, and enter from the rear. Dr. John T. Emlen, when observing the gorillas in the National Zoo in Washington, saw the male thrusting very hard and rhythmically during copulation and after 30 or 40 seconds giving a soft but rather rhythmical hooting duet with the female. The total copulation was only 1 to 1½ minutes long.

Dr. George B. Schaller describes three precopulatory activities of gorillas:

    1. The starting walk: The male approached the female while walking quadrupedally with short, abrupt steps. His body was held very

stiff and erect, and his head was tipped slightly upward and sideways. The male thus advanced toward the female and sometimes circled her. He always averted his head but watched her from the corner of his eye. When approached closely, the female likewise turned her head to the side. 2. Wrestling: The male and female lumbered toward each other bipedally, slowly swinging their arms overhead until close enough to grasp each other behind head and back, a behavior also noted in chimpanzees by Dr. Bingham in 1928. Bent at the waist, they pushed and pulled, and grasped at each other's legs, until finally they toppled over. Then they sat and faced one another, mouths wide open, and emitted almost continuous deep growls and grunts. They mock bit each other's shoulders and they hugged. Several times the male cradled the female in his arms. The whole sequence of events was slow and gentle and appeared ritualistic. 3. Running: The wrestling was several times interrupted when either the male or the female broke loose or led off on a march or run around the cage with the other following closely. The circling of the cage has also been observed by Yerkes (1943) in sexually aroused chimpanzees, which in addition exhibit romping, teasing, petting, eating, fighting, and tantrums (Bingham, 1928).

In the Basel Zoo the director, Dr. Ernst Lang, has seen gorillas copulating face to face and also with the male behind the female. Schaller collected a good deal of data concerning copulation in gorillas and drew attention to the fact that the erect penis can easily be seen in these animals. If the male is sufficiently aroused the vagina is penetrated very quickly, but the animal thrusts only a few times and has an orgasm within about 15 seconds; during the orgasm the male's body becomes very rigid. After the male has reached orgasm, the male and female gorilla may continue to fondle each other with some gentleness, which is a contrast to the behavior of chimpanzees.

The copulatory behavior of apes in captivity shows a great variety. This is not the case in monkeys, in which the postures for copulation are completely stereotyped. Most lemurs and all monkeys copulate with the male mounting the female from the rear and usually clasping her from the back around the chest or waist or on the sides or even hanging onto the fur of the back. In some species the male grasps the female by the ankles. In most species

251

the feet of the male remain on the ground during the process of copulation. Among lemurs, the potto copulates with the partners facing each other, as do bats, whales, porpoises, and some otters.

Among apes there appear to be no sexual jealousies in the sense that no individual female (or females) is preserved for a particular male. There are no permanent leaders of an ape group, and the members of the group fight very little and show very little aggressive behavior to one another. When two animals meet, for example, if they are walking in opposite directions, one will show himself to be subordinate to the other by moving out of the way or greeting the other animal by touching him on the lips or thighs or genitalia. When two groups meet and join with each other, if there is a mature male in each group there is usually a great deal of noise and excitement. The males drum on tree roots if they are available, slap the ground, shake branches of the trees, or vocalize loudly. On such occasions juvenile and young animals, usually screaming, rush out of the way of the big males.

One of the forms of aggression by the male squirrel monkey is to suddenly make his penis become erect in the face of his adversary. This is a real threat, and the procedure is always used by a squirrel monkey when he approaches an inferior or when he wishes submission from a female.

In many monkeys the penis is very highly colored, usually bright red. Sometimes the skin covering the testicles is blue. In a baboonlike primate called a drill, this is a very characteristic development. By simply spreading their legs these animals demonstrate their bright colors, which are in themselves a threat. Then if the penis becomes erect as well, an extreme form of threat is demonstrated. This is used to demonstrate dominance among a colony of drills and is also used to show dominance to other monkeys.

The threat of an erect penis is also used by humans. Some New Guinea tribes tie a long tube onto their penises to simulate erection when they go to war.

Many natural and artificial objects are of a phallic significance—bananas and carrots especially. It is said that many women are excessively frightened of snakes because of their phallic significance. There is no doubt that part of the popularity of cigarettes and especially cigars is because of the phallic significance of these objects. A recent series of TV advertisements for a certain brand of cigars has most blatantly accented the sexual significance of this smoking object. There is no doubt that Madison Avenue can on occasions be more pornographic than any magazine.

Monkeys and apes are often thought of as being homosexual because of the tendency of a submissive male to present sexually to a dominant male. In such cases the dominant male will often mount him and give several pelvic thrusts as a gesture. Such behavior has led some people to believe that this is homosexual behavior. However, it is not at all. It is of interest that many underground newspapers have advertisements in which males who acknowledge themselves as submissive offer themselves to dominant males for sexual activities. This seems to be a case of the submissive behavior of monkeys being carried into the sexual sphere in human activities.

In human beings the procedure of kissing has several connotations. There is a purely social kiss, most commonly on the cheek. There is also a lip-to-lip kiss which is fairly common and is also given sometimes socially, although it usually signifies a sexual attraction between the two people exchanging it, when they are endeavoring to demonstrate interest in each other. It is unlikely that any mouth-to-mouth kissing in humans is completely devoid of some sexual connotation. There is a tense, sexual kiss with considerable oral exploration involving the insertion of the tongue into the opposite person's mouth and contact between the tongue and the interior of the mouth, the other person's tongue, and so on. There is of course the more complex oral exploration which humans are experts in, in relationship to the sucking, licking, and nibbling and light to hard biting of various intensities which some partners do to the genitalia of the other partner.

Chimpanzees and other apes do not have this sexual type of kissing. The kind of primitive kissing which they carry out is always a greeting or has some other social significance.

The tendency to use sex as a kind of game is highly developed in man. Precoital activity involves the manipulation of the breasts and especially the nipples of the woman by the man. Most women's breasts are so sensitive sexually to this type of sexual touch that they receive a good deal of stimulation from it. In fact some women have been known to have orgasms simply from the procedure of manipulation of the breasts. Other precoital activities involve the exploration and handling of the vulva, and sometimes the licking of the vulva with the tongue, which is also done by apes on occasion. Such stimulation leads eventually in the female to rigidity in the clitoris. The advantages of all this sexual play is that it not only conditions the individuals for the sexual act from a psychological point of view, but it causes the secretion of the various fluids which lubricate the vagina and so facilitate the passage of the penis into it.

Since ape penises are thin they probably penetrate into the female vagina very easily, so there is not the same need for presexual play as far as providing lubrication for the act of penetration is concerned. Certain organs in humans which have already been enumerated, such as the lips and the breasts and their nipples and the genitals, have many nerve endings and are very sensitive to any form of stimulation. These are known as erogenous areas. Another part of the body not normally appreciated as being of this nature is the earlobe. We are the only primates who have these pendulous lobes on our ears, though there are some exceptions. Apparently they too show some signs of becoming engorged with blood when the individual is aroused sexually. Presexual play in humans often involves the nibbling or biting of the earlobes. There are cases on record, in both male and female humans, in which orgasm has been reached simply from the stimulation of the earlobes. There is also a spongy type of tissue in the nostril which is erectile in the sense that it can accumulate blood under certain circumstances and become swollen; it certainly does so when one has a cold. But it also accumulates blood, becomes erectile, and makes breathing through the nostrils difficult during the process of sexual arousal, so that even the nose has a sexual connotation.

In all three of the great apes there is little evidence that the female enjoys any kind of orgasm. It is possible that the development of the female orgasm is related to the development of the erect posture. Apes tend to move around on their four limbs rather than walk upright; although they can and do walk upright, they do not do it very often or for long periods of time. This is true also in the case of monkeys. In animals who walk mostly on their four limbs the vagina is more or less horizontal; therefore the female ape or monkey who becomes physically active immediately after ejaculation and withdrawal by the male retains the semen. This would not be the case if the female immediately assumed a vertical position. Furthermore, at least in the case of the chimpanzee, the semen once it has been ejaculated sets into a jellylike condition which also prevents it from running out once copulation is over. If a human female resumed her normal position and normal activities immediately following copulation, the ejaculated semen in her vagina would drain out, since its opening would be directly downward. This would greatly reduce the possibilities of pregnancy. Desmond Morris suggests that nature has intervened here by providing an orgasm for the human female which leaves her relaxed and tired and sleepy and therefore likely to remain in the horizontal position for a considerable period of time after copulation. This is much more favorable to impregnation.

Among humans the amount of sexual play, the amount of orogenital sex, and the amount of noncoital sex in general seem to be related to the social level and possibly to the degree of education and intelligence in the individuals concerned. Many human native tribes have little presexual play in the way we know it. In the uneducated section of the Western community there is relatively less sexual play, and coitus takes place quickly with very little preliminary activity. Thus the more uneducated humans are closer in their sexual reactions to those of the apes. It is an interesting fact that many members of the community, particularly certain religious communities who regard sex as some kind of a sin, think of sex simply as something to be used purely for procreation. The idea of enjoying sex with the other person and indulging in noncoital sex play is abhorrent to them. Sex with them is an in-and-out-forget-about-it kind of behavior. The individuals who framed the sex laws of many of the American states even forbade some types of presexual play. Apparently they thought that in sexual relations we should behave like apes. The type of sex to be obtained from most prostitutes, particularly those of a lower class, is typically the "in and out and off" type of the apes.

Although most human copulation tends to be a face-to-face matter, it is not of course inevitably so. There is a good deal of experimentation, including copulation from the rear. There has been over the evolutionary period a considerable movement of the vaginal passage of the human female, which has swung into a more forward position. Nevertheless in many human females it is still far enough back for penetration to take place from the rear. Man has been very inventive in developing positions for sexual intercourse, and again it is usually a more educated and intelligent type of person who is interested in this type of invention. It is most often the simpler and less educated person or the one who is too busy who sticks to the biologically developed face-to-face form of sexual intercourse.

The human being is the only primate in which the female retains a hymen. This is a small embryonic structure in developing apes and never remains intact as it does in the human. Desmond Morris believes that the explanation of this is that the hymen ensures that the first copulation will not be indulged in lightly because it will be difficult and even painful. So the female is in general not likely to permit a first copulation with anyone with whom she has not been relatively seriously involved. This is part of the whole peer-bonding system which has become an important part of human sexual and social relationships. This peer-bonding between male and female does not exist in the apes.

Literature, particularly early literature, is full of references to the sexual behavior of apes and their desire to have sexual contact with human females. But any woman who believes this would be a thrill would undoubtedly be disappointed by the penises of these animals. A woman ravished by an ape would scarcely feel a thing.

In the Yerkes colony over the years there is no doubt that certain male and female apes have become very attached to certain persons belonging to the staff of the Center who are of the opposite sex. Whether this was just friendship or was in fact related to any kind of sexual feeling or what one might romantically call love, it is difficult to say. Our animals very often show erections in response to certain human females and sometimes to any human female and often even to males, and they often get erections when they are excited.

At one of the Swiss zoos a young lady employee was leaving late one evening and thought there was something wrong with one of the gorillas; it appeared to have caught its hand or something of that sort. The girl opened the cage and came in to see what the problem was. The door, which was self-locking, slammed with her keys on the outside, and she found herself locked in the cage with a gorilla for the night. The animal was apparently very happy to have her company, placed his arms around her, and then took her over to the side of the cage, where he lay down and slept with his arms around her all night. He made no attempt at any sexual play of any sort. After the gorilla fell asleep the girl thought this was the time to loosen the giant hands and withdraw from his hug. However, every time she tried to do this the gorilla partly wakened up and clasped her even more firmly to him. In the morning they were still cuddled together when the members of the staff of the zoo arrived. They were shaken to see what had happened. The girl was dirty, of course, her clothes were torn, and she was in a state of shock, but otherwise she had not come to any particular harm. It seemed that the gorilla was just lonely, and in fact my experience with gorillas indicates they often have this longing for companionship.

Recently I entered the cage where two of our gorillas, Jini and Oban, a girl and a boy, were housed. They are partly grown youngsters, and as soon as I entered the cage they both came over to be stroked, cuddled, and embraced. I spent probably 10 or 15 minutes with them and gave them the little bit of food I had with me. When I got up to go, I found that Jini had folded her arms around my waist and Oban, the little boy, had encircled my legs with his arms. Between them they had inactivated me, and it was almost impossible for me to move. I hobbled with the two of them hanging onto me over to the door and finally managed to extricate myself and get out. Even so, I probably could not have done this had not someone been waiting outside who was prepared to unlock the door for me at the right moment and let me slip out. If these animals had been much bigger I probably would not have been able even to shuffle over to the door of the cage.

There are reports that Trader Horn knew of a case in which a white man shut up a slave girl with a gorilla, having heard that apes were very attracted to human females. He expected that the gorilla would rape her, but the animal made no physical contact at all. He remained in one corner and the girl cried in the other, so there was no result. It was also rumored that the man who did this was later shot by other whites who were horrified by the story of what he had done.

Greek literature refers to the "licentiousness" of baboons and other monkeys. They were said to attack women and children with the object of copulating with them. There is a story in *1001 Nights,* as translated by Sir Richard Burton, in which an Abyssinian baboon is said to have attacked a woman in a Cairo street and tried to rape her. It seems that he was then killed by being bayoneted by a sentry. If such an incident did occur it was probably a straight-out attack by the animal on the woman which was interpreted as a sexual attack. In the book *Those About to Die* by Daniel P. Mannix, the use of baboons in the Roman arena to rape little girls and even to kill them is reported. In *1001 Nights* Scheherazade tells a tale called "The King's Daughter and the Ape." In this Scheherazade describes the daughter of a sultan who was obviously very much of a nymphomaniac—she felt the need for copulation every hour of the day. She was recommended by her servant to take a baboon as a lover. He lived with her, doing nothing but eating and drinking and copulating. Eventually the young lady had to flee to Cairo with her baboon. There she was observed by a Cairo butcher to wine and dine with the ape and then carry out repeated passionate copulations until she swooned away. The butcher killed the ape and offered to substitute in the ape's place, but he found that the girl's sexual appetite completely exhausted him. Finally with the aid of an old woman he produced some extracts which he gave the girl. From her body two worms issued, and after this her nymphomania was cured.

In the Middle East exhibitions have regularly been staged in which tame monkeys were made to copulate with women on the stage. In fact even bears have been known to be used for this purpose. Bernard Heuvelmans describes his experiences of seeing a young, tame baboon assaulting women who were sunbathing on a Mediterranean beach and attempting to copulate with them.

During the Middle Ages and even later, very hairy humans were sometimes thought to be the product of sexual relations between a monkey or an ape and a human. Edward Topsell talks of what he describes as "satyre apes," which he said are shaped like humans, have a lot of hair, live in a solitary condition, and have a great desire for sexual intercourse with women. These satyr apes seem to have had their origin in the stories of various sailors. Mythological satyrs resembled goats more than apes—they had a goat's rear legs and hoofs, and their bodies were covered with hair. It seems very likely that some of the early observations especially of the apes and possibly of baboons resulted in their being interpreted as a type of satyr.

In Voltaire's novel *Candide*, a story is recounted in which Candide and Cacambo, lost in the Amazonian jungle, see two nude girls running along followed by two monkeys who are nibbling at their buttocks. Candide and Cacambo shoot the monkeys, thinking they are saving the lives of the two girls. They find the girls in great grief over the death of what had obviously been their lovers. The possibility that female monkeys have been used by men for sexual purposes is much more likely than women being involved with monkeys. They are referred to frequently in erotic works that originate from Oriental countries. In the West there is even a novel called *My Monkey Wife, or, Married to a Chimpanzee,* published in 1931. In this novel the hero has been in Africa and has brought back with him to England a female chimpanzee whom he used as a housekeeper while he was in the jungle. He accidentally gets married to the chimpanzee instead of to his fiancée and goes back to Africa with the ape, with whom he lives out the rest of his life. The chimpanzee is described as being faithful and loving.

There are many rumors in Borneo that male orangs carry off native women for sexual purposes. The famous naturalist

Georges Buffon in 1766 accepted this fact. Flaubert in his *Quidquid volueris,* reputed to have been published in 1837 (he was only sixteen at the time), described an ape man known as Djalioh who had been produced by sexual intercourse between a male orangutan and a Brazilian Negress. Flaubert's story involves a complicated and rather violent relationship between this ape man and a young married couple.

Tom Harrisson, formerly curator of the museum in Kuching, Sarawak, has recounted a story, written some years ago by an administrative officer who was stationed in Borneo, of the rescue of a Dayak lady who had been captured by an orangutan.

In the latter part of the nineteenth century the gorilla was introduced to the Western world. The original descriptions given of it by Paul du Chaillu, who incidentally was an American, completely misrepresented this pleasant and relatively gentle animal as a ferocious malign creature, black and horrible. Of these adjectives "black" is about the only one that applies. I have mentioned before what a pleasant animal the average gorilla is and, considering his enormous strength, how relatively nonviolent he is. This reputation of the gorilla has unfortunately persisted to the present day. Many people whom I meet and talk to about our animals are extremely surprised to find that their preconceptions of the gorilla are completely inaccurate. The story of King Kong, already mentioned, in which an enormous ape runs loose in Manhattan carrying a young girl in his hand, is also a continuation of this original misconception of the ferocious gorilla.

The human-ape sexual relationship is continued in the famous stories of Tarzan by Edgar Rice Burroughs, in which Tarzan, the son of Lord Greystoke, is captured in infancy from his father and mother in the African jungle and grows up with the chimpanzees who captured him. Later, when he sees an American girl, Jane Porter, in the jungle he immediately falls in love with her. After he has seen her she is attacked by an ape who apparently plans to take her for himself. The ape throws her across his shoulders, leaps into the trees with her, and attempts to make off, presumably with the object of both copulating with her and making her his permanent mate. They are of course chased by Tarzan, who catches them, kills the marauding ape, and so wins the love of Jane.

Boccaccio, who invented the short story as we know it during the fourteenth century, describes the origin of some of the Greek gods. He tells how Vulcan was ejected from Olympus when he was a boy and that he landed amid a tribe of apes on the earth who brought him up.

Dr. C. R. Carpenter, who is at present chairman of the Yerkes Board of Scientific Advisors and is a pioneer in field studies of primates, found that in Burma there was a story about reincarnation connected with gibbons. Gibbons are believed to be disappointed lovers who have been reincarnated in this form. It seems likely that the rather long and mournful call of the gibbon is the origin of this interesting and rather strange story. Some of the natives in these areas will not kill gibbons because of their belief that they are reincarnated humans.

In view of all the stories about apes and human women one might ask, "Have there ever been any hybrids between a man and apes or have there ever been hybrids between the apes themselves?" To this we cannot give a definite answer. There is no real evidence that a successful cross has ever been made between a human and an ape. However, there is no reason at all from the chromosomal point of view why, for instance, a gorilla mated with a chimpanzee should not produce living babies. And it seems reasonable to suppose in view of the evidence we have had from hybridization of other animals that even the orangutan might hybridize with the gorilla and the chimpanzee. However, the orang has a method of sexual intercourse rather different from that of either of the other two apes; under natural circumstances it has at least some sexual intercourse in the trees even hanging from branches. So mechanically it might be difficult to secure copulation between the orang and either the chimpanzee or the gorilla. However, in the state of captivity the new techniques of artificial insemination might make it possible for such hybridization to be carried out without too much difficulty.

There is a rumor that there was a cross between a chimpanzee and gorilla in Georgia many years ago, but I have not yet succeeded in tracking it down to its source. As far as man and apes are concerned there seems to be very little physiological reason why artificial insemination could not be used between man and the apes with a possibility that a viable child might be reproduced. Gorilla and chimpanzee chromosomes are enough like human chromosomes, and similar enough in number to those in man, to make such a hybrid conceivable. And it is surprising that this type of hybridization has not in fact already taken place. What such an animal would be like, and what would be the moral significance of this, it is very hard to say. No doubt it would provide some problems for the ecclesiastics in deciding whether an animal such as this would have a soul or not.

One of the activities that people frequently witness in zoos is monkeys or apes actively parting the hair on each other's bodies or heads and removing and eating what have been thought to be fleas. In fact monkeys do not carry fleas, but they do sometimes carry lice, and these can be removed by their friends and relations. However, what they are more usually doing is picking off little bits of scurf which they may eat. Some years ago I suggested in the journal *Nature* that possibly because of the hair on monkeys and apes there is limited penetration of ultraviolet rays from the sun. In the case of humans the contact of these rays with the skin causes a transformation of substances in the skin oils into vitamin D. This vitamin is necessary to the health of bones and teeth and proper mobilization of the mineral calcium in the body. In the case of monkeys and apes, it was suggested that the oils in the skin leak out onto the surface and saturate small pieces of skin or scurf. This becomes irradiated by the ultraviolet rays of the sun and forms vitamin D, and when apes and monkeys groom each other they eat some of this scurf and so get a minimal amount of vitamin D. This was suggested partly because of the interesting studies which had been done on birds.

At the base of the tail in birds is a little gland called a preen gland. When birds preen themselves they can be seen to stick their beaks into this area and then run their beak through their feathers. In this way they smear oil, which they got on their beaks from the preen gland, over the feathers. Bird feathers are so thickly arranged that practically no sunlight can get through to the skin. However, the oil from the preen gland which is spread over the feathers contains material which is changed into vitamin D by the action of the ultraviolet light in sunlight. In subsequent preenings of feathers, vitamin D formed in the preen gland secretion gets into the bird's mouth and is swallowed. This is the main source of vitamin D for birds. If the preen gland is removed from a bird by a surgical operation, the bird develops rickets, a disease that can be caused by lack of vitamin D. If the feathers are taken and irradiated either by ultraviolet light or by the sun and then ground up and fed to the bird, the bird either does not get rickets or, if it already has the disease, is cured.

It seems with furred and hairy animals that a similar kind of procedure might take place even though furry animals in general do not have preen glands. They do, however, have oil-secreting glands which may perform the same function as preen gland oil. It seems very likely that the preening habits of both birds and furred animals which have been normally attributed to a desire to keep the skin clean are really designed by nature to enable the animal to add vitamin D to its diet.

Grooming has, however, a considerable social function in both monkeys and apes. If an animal grooms another animal it means that animal is accepted, and the same thing applies to humans. An ape or a monkey who will groom your hand, carefully parting any hairs it may see and trying to pick off scabs and freckles, is an animal who is demonstrating to you that as far as he is concerned you are "in" socially. Grooming is a peaceful and non-aggressive demonstration of a relationship. Often during the grooming period, particularly among certain monkeys and also with chimpanzees, there is a rapid movement of the lips called lip smacking. The whole procedure represents a friendly type of greeting.

Masturbation is common among male chimpanzees. It may take place with the hand or with the foot or even by rubbing the penis against inanimate objects. It is common in childhood, but in an animal who is isolated it can become very much more frequent once he develops the ability to ejaculate. Females tend to masturbate less; when they do, they most commonly masturbate with their companions, and it is usually found to be a substitute for sexual intercourse. Masturbation usually disappears when mature congenial animals who are sexually compatible have access to each other.

Julie MacDonald, in her book *Almost Human*, mentions that among baboons in both captive and wild conditions masturbation can be observed in young animals as well as sexually mature animals, although it is more common in males than in females. Dr. George B. Schaller has seen male lowland gorillas masturbate in captivity. He speaks of an animal known as Mambo who was nine years old at the time he was observed and was housed with a mature female at the Bronx Zoo in New York. He was observed stimulating his penis with his hand, working it back and forth between the thumb and index finger. As he continued to masturbate, Schaller records, his eyes became rigid and had a kind of glassy appearance. He also refers to Samson, a lowland gorilla at the Milwaukee Zoo, who was about eight years old and was in a cage with another male. He also stimulated himself with a single hand for some minutes and thrust with his pelvis several times. Schaller did not observe ejaculation in either of these animals.

In the National Zoo in Washington, Dr. John T. Emlen saw a female gorilla playing with her clitoris, and in the zoo in Basel a female gorilla put her infant of three months between her legs and in a squatting position thrust at the baby with her pelvis at least ten times. Masturbation does not seem to have been observed in free-living gorillas.

It is of interest too that Dr. Yerkes in 1928 recorded seeing a captive female chimpanzee push her rear against the front of the cage and on one occasion took the hand of her keeper and placed it on her genital area. It is, of course, not at all uncommon for apes and even monkeys to turn their genital area toward human beings who are passing by the cages. This may not have a sexual connotation and may simply represent the process of "presenting," by which the animal is demonstrating submission to the human person near her.

Monkeys also masturbate. One story is told about a pigtail monkey who had a baby and then, before it was ready to leave

264

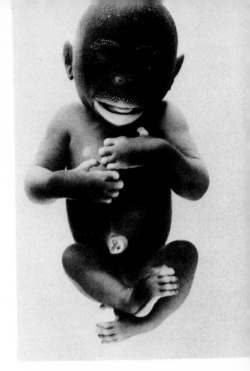

A chimpanzee fetus 126 days old. Notice the human appearance.

her, had a second baby. The first baby became very depressed and would spend long periods sucking his own penis. Perhaps he was using this as a breast substitute.

It is hard to imagine prostitution among nonhuman primates, and yet there are some records in which a female monkey has presented to a male animal in the presence of food in order to take his mind off the food so that she could get more than the share she would have normally been allowed. This could probably be regarded as a form of prostitution.

Extramarital sex in the sense that the female carries on sexual activities with a male, not the dominant male to whom she is attached, has occurred, as we have already mentioned. But the problems of prostitution and extramarital sex are really the products of man's social organization and become noteworthy only because the conventions that man has built up around sexual activities make these acts unlawful in many places.

Prostitution in humans seems to have existed since civilization began. It is recorded among the ancient Egyptians, the Romans, the Arab nations, and the Jews. In fact, wherever humans have taken root prostitution has developed. It is probably related to the fact that for a large number of males with a strong sex drive one female is not adequate. Because of the strong peer-bonding among individuals a man is not able to run around and copulate with any female he fancies or who fancies him. The alternative is to look for more discreet copulation for the payment of a fee. Prostitution is thus probably little more than a civilized demonstration of normal primate sex drive and as such should be appreciated by those individuals connected with the law who have the arrogance to believe it is their duty to decide how the other members of the human race should behave sexually.

Many chimpanzee and orangutan births have been observed in the Yerkes Center. The process takes place fairly rapidly, usually between two and three hours after obvious labor begins. The birth process rarely appears to be difficult or to result in injury to the mother or the child. In the case of Alpha, the firstborn Yerkes chimpanzee, when she was having her last baby, it was obvious that the animal was in labor and yet the baby was not being produced and a Caesarean section had to be performed to produce the child. Subsequently, when Alpha died, it was found that she had a tumor at the bottom end of the reproductive tract. This was why she had not been able to give birth normally. The afterbirth, which includes the membranes and the placenta, is delivered not long after the infant is born and is usually eaten by the mother.

When the baby is born the mother does not seem to be particularly disturbed by the birth; however, she devotes most of her attention to the baby. She usually puts it on her abdomen, and we have even seen the mother orangutan put it on her head, where it immediately clings to her hair. Female apes usually clean the baby up by a licking and grooming procedure. When the mothers are near the point of birth they seem to find it difficult to be comfortable. They change their position constantly. They frequently put their fingers into their vulva and bring them out and

Lada (orang) puts her newborn baby on her head.

smell them and lick them. When birth is imminent the mother ape moves into a crouched delivery position on the floor. The first thing that happens is the extrusion of a yellow fluid from the vulva which the mother may drink. An obvious series of contractions of the uterus occurs just prior to birth, and then the infant is usually delivered quite suddenly after its head is first seen just within the labia of the external genitalia. The mother usually bites through the cord connecting the baby to the placenta, but she does not always do it at once. In both chimpanzees and orangutans I have seen the baby still attached to the cord for quite a number of hours after birth.

Birth of a lowland gorilla Alvila has been described by Dr. Duane Rumbaugh. He tells how the gorilla Vila at the San Diego Zoo, one morning when the birth was imminent, put herself in a prone position with her knees flexed parallel with her

267

body and her face buried in the palms of her hands. Then in what appeared to be quite a normal and uncomplicated chain of events the infant was delivered. From the time that Vila took up the prone position to the time of the birth of the baby was just about one hour. After the birth the mother was seen to manipulate the umbilical cord, then she picked up the baby and pressed it against her. She was seen to lick the baby's head and to wrap straw bedding material around it. The baby supported itself by clinging to the mother's leg and then to her hair. It was probably a very vigorous baby, since it is more usual for the mother to supply part or all of the support for the baby during the first few days of its existence. Vila was very casual about the baby and even pulled it around by its umbilical cord for a period. Then she began to carry it in what was described as a thigh-cradle position in which the baby was held securely by pressing it between the mother's thigh and the lower part of her abdomen. Later, she used her hands more and more for manipulating the infant and for lifting, carrying, and supporting it. During this period she licked the infant's ears, its head, and its face, then she began a detailed inspection of the baby's body, turning it over, inspecting all the orifices by touching them and tasting them and sniffing them. At the end of the first hour after birth the baby began its first vocalizations in the form of whimpers, and the mother answered each time with a kind of guttural grunt. During this period the baby was nuzzling around the mother's abdomen, apparently searching for a nipple.

During the afternoon the baby continued to get stronger and did a good deal of squealing and crying. Although the baby came in contact with the nipple on a number of occasions, it never actually took the nipple in its mouth and sucked. As the day wore on, it got weaker and weaker, and eventually it became necessary to take it away from the mother. This was an unusual situaton, and it is difficult to understand what caused it; under normal circumstances the baby having found the nipple, would have sucked on it, obtained milk, and become stronger, and all would have been well.

Infancy in the chimpanzee and in the other apes spans about

two years. The baby is quite helpless for the major part of the first year, usually completely dependent upon its mother. The baby weighs four or five pounds at birth, and after the early period in which it is supported by the mother it grasps her skin and hair strongly enough with both its hands and its feet to be carried about safely by her. The mother normally holds it and feeds it and of course protects it from the activities of any other apes. These may show interest in the baby, but rarely do they attempt to be violent with it.

The baby is given a playful form of exercise by the mother, and she also teaches it a number of activities, such as how to climb on the various objects in the cage and the wire of the cage. After a year the baby can usually climb about the cage on its own in a fairly skillful fashion and is able to walk about on all fours quite well.

During the first six months the mother is very careful and solicitous of the baby, but in the second six months she tends simply to be watchful and cautious. Then, Yerkes says, "the nurse becomes governess or teacher." However, the baby is still nursed by the mother at the end of the first year, and she may even nurse it almost to the end of two years. During the second year, however, it also eats quite a lot of the food that comes into the cage. It is an interesting thing that even when it is two years old and is a relatively independent animal it still rushes to its mother for protection if it gets frightened. Yerkes said that the chimpanzee child "is playful, energetic, inventive, good-natured, appreciative of favors and affection."

There are quite a number of records of both chimpanzees and gorilla babies being fed at the breast by native women in Africa. The Yerkes chimp babies who are taken from their mothers seem to feel the need of some soft material, particularly toweling of some sort, to hold. It is not at all uncommon to see baby chimpanzees in our nursery holding a towel in one hand and sucking the thumb of the other just like Linus in the comic strip *Peanuts*.

Dr. Duane Rumbaugh, writing about the early life of the gorilla Alvila and the gibbon Gabrielle, points out that three months after birth the little gorilla was very active, climbing all over the wooden dowels which were above her crib. She would hang up-side down in the cage. At about the same time she did this, giving an indication of her arboreal ancestry, she was able to move into the sitting position. The infant gibbon Gabrielle by about four months began to leap about inside the cage and also moved by hanging from the top of the cage and progressing by a hand-over-hand method. This is very characteristic of the adult gibbon and is known as brachiation. At such an age Alvila was not able to perform like this.

Dr. Harry Harlow has shown that the infant rhesus monkeys with whom he worked would accept an object covered in cloth toweling over a wire frame as a substitute for their mother. The baby would spend more time with the toweling-covered artificial or surrogate mother than he would with a simple wire frame mother, even though the latter had a milk bottle attached to it—so it seems that softness and warmth are as important to the infant as any other factor. Probably this is also the most important thing for human babies.

The research workers at the Walter Reed Army Institute of

The infant Gabrielle (gibbon). (Courtesy of Dr. Duane Rumbaugh.)

Research have shown that when the mother and her baby monkey are separated from each other there is an increased excretion of hormone from the adrenal gland which is characteristic of stress. This is increased in both the baby and the mother. Within a few days the mother recovers from this stress, as is demonstrated in the reduction in the amount of excretion of this material. But in the baby the increased excretion apparently goes on for some time, indicating a long-acting effect resulting from the separation.

12. Experiments with Apes and Monkeys

THERE is little doubt both from the evidence provided by evolution and the physiological and anatomical studies of primates that they, especially the apes, are very closely related to men. Therefore, for many experimental studies in both behavioral and medical areas primates are more suitable subjects to study than rats, mice, guinea pigs, etc.

I have already mentioned our studies on the comparative intelligence of different types of primate and the similarity of many of their mental processes with those of human beings. At least they demonstrate the basic patterns of intelligence which are developed to a much greater extent in humans. Some of the experiments we are carrying out with the apes at our Center are described in the following pages.

At the Atlanta Zoo we have placed on loan three female orangutans, each with her baby. One of the females is the orangutan Lada, who, you will remember, had a portion of one lung removed. These animals have all been placed in the one cage and are being studied by Dr. Charles Rogers and Dr. Richard Davenport of the Yerkes Center. One interesting outcome of this particular study was the way in which the two other females turned against Lada and gave her very little peace, nipping her and forcing her to leave any place in the cage where she wanted to be. When, however, we put our biggest and best, and at that time 260-pound, male orangutan (Sampit) in with the group he immediately stabilized the behavior of the females toward one another and Lada was able to live in peace with them. Subsequently we have placed a second male in the group, and the latest results show they all are living together in a very harmonious condition with the baby orangs accepting the presence of the males and the males permitting the babies to take liberties with them which one would never expect from such big and powerful animals.

For some time we have made studies of the effect of alcohol on chimpanzees and some of the other primates. All three types of apes can be persuaded to drink fruit juices which have been flavored with alcohol; in most cases we used a cheap variety of vodka. A chimpanzee has to consume about a quart of vodka before he starts to show any effects and in the drunken state he will behave very much like a human being. Some humans when they are drunk look for company. We have chimpanzees who in such a condition will put an arm around the neck of their cage mate and walk around with him in a fashion typical of a drunken human being. There are other chimpanzees who, when they get drunk, will be noisy and hyperactive just like humans. A third

273

A chimpanzee enjoys a quiet smoke.

type of animal will get drowsy and go to sleep. We have not yet succeeded in getting a chimpanzee addicted to alcohol, although our present studies using much younger chimpanzees have shown that if they are given large quantities of alcohol regularly, they show severe symptoms when it is withdrawn.

Another area in which work is being done is the effect of marihuana on chimpanzees. Dr. Alan Pieper and Dr. Duane Rumbaugh have built a smoking machine which permits an animal to smoke a large number of cigarettes one after the other. Many of our chimpanzees will smoke cigarettes spontaneously. By using a machine which gives a food reward every ten or eleven puffs, it has been possible to get a chimpanzee to sit at a tube and puff it continuously, being rewarded with a piece of food every ten or twenty puffs according to how the machine is set. This work is only beginning, but we have found, for example, that a chimpanzee will smoke sixteen marijuana cigarettes before he shows

274

much sign of behavioral change. The object of these experiments is not only to determine the amount of marijuana that chimpanzees can smoke without visible effect, but also to study the effects of long-term administration of marijuana. We need to know if it will affect the chromosomes and possibly cause genetic defects in the progeny of marijuana-smoking parents. We also need to see what damage to the brain and other organs might occur. Many of our chimpanzees will smoke ordinary cigarettes in a purely imitative and spontaneous way. They hold the cigarette carefully between thumb and forefinger, puffing away and giving every sign of enjoying themselves.

Studies of sleep and motion sickness are also being carried out using chimpanzees and monkeys. In these experiments, conducted by Dr. Adrian Perachio, the monkey or chimpanzee is restrained in a chair and is spun at a moderate degree of acceleration which is not necessarily unpleasant for the animal. With the aid of electrodes which have been connected to the animal it is possible to study its brain activity while it is being rotated in the chair and also to study what happens to the brain waves when the animal goes to sleep or when it is kept awake over a prolonged period.

The spinning of the chair provides centrifugal force which affects the little structures in the inner ear known as the semicircular canals. These structures are responsible for helping us maintain our balance. Up in space the pull of gravity on this otolith organ is not present, and some astronauts have felt a disorientation and a mild nausea for varying periods of time while in space. The phenomenon of motion sickness which most people have experienced is caused by the effects of unusual erratic motion on the semicircular canals. The disorientation and motion sickness experienced by some of the astronauts appear to be related on some occasions to their efforts to sleep. It is hoped that the studies of Dr. Perachio and his colleagues at the Yerkes Center will shed some light on this particular problem and on the general problem of sleep.

I have already mentioned the studies of Dr. Perachio and Dr. Murray on telestimulation, which involves the passing of small fine metal electrodes into the brain. It has been mentioned that the electrodes are connected to a radio receiver, and radio signals may then be used to stimulate the brain. There is an interesting story about this. Several years ago a member of the Emory University faculty gained considerable notoriety and publicity for his comments concerning the "God is dead" controversy. After the telestimulation work at our Center had received some newspaper publicity we received a letter from a member of the general public accusing us of being responsible for the remarks made by the Emory faculty member about God. We had, according to this person, put electrodes in the professor's brain—we were stimulating them by radio and causing him to say all those "dreadful" things.

In addition to the sleep studies, the Yerkes Center is also concerned with other space studies. First, it has a group of monkeys who are kept in a special outdoor compound at the Yerkes field station. These monkeys, whom we might call "space monkeys," consist of a large group of females and a small group of males to

Potential space monkeys try out the quarters they would occupy in orbit.

go with them. The function of these animals is to breed so that we will have high-class rhesus monkeys for future space studies. One of the problems in using monkeys born in the wild for studies in space is that so many of them have a wide variety of diseases. In fact we have found that practically all wild-born monkeys who come into the Yerkes Center show some degree of muscle damage when a biopsy specimen of their muscle is taken for microscopic examination. For space studies it is obviously essential to have animals that are as good as possible from a physical point of view and from a mental point of view as well.

The compound in which these animals are kept has a number of trees in it. It is 125 feet square and is surrounded by a strong wire fence topped by sheet metal so the monkeys can't climb up the wire and escape. When the weather is cold and at night the monkeys take refuge in a trailerlike structure lined with fiber glass. It has a heat pump which heats the trailer in winter and cools it in the summer. In addition to this, Dr. M. N. Golarz and I have a combined space project under the direction of Dr. Walter Jones of the Office of Advanced Research and Technology of NASA and being carried out in association with Dr. Ashton Graybiel and Dr. Jack Thach of the Naval Institute of Aerospace Medicine in Pensacola, Mr. Eugene Mason of the NASA Langley Research Center, and with Dr. Harlow Ades at Northwestern University. The Northrop and Lockheed companies are also associated with this investigation. This project consists of a series of studies directed toward the possibility of putting two unrestrained monkeys into space for periods as long as a year. The original conception of this experiment was that the animals would be attached to the rack of an Apollo spacecraft where the lunar module is normally carried. Once the Apollo was in 100-mile orbit it would discharge the monkey capsule, then turn around and dock with it, fire its engines, push it out another 100 miles, and leave it orbiting at 200 miles above the earth. In another Apollo shot a year later it was planned that the Apollo would rendezvous and dock with the monkey capsule, an astronaut would emerge from the capsule, climb over to the monkey capsule, operate a mechanism which would sweep the monkeys into a carrying cage, detach the carrying cage from the monkey capsule, and carry it back inside the Apollo, which would then return to earth with the monkeys. However, with the cutback in the Apollo program and the changes in many of NASA's other programs, it is much more likely that these monkeys, and also possibly a chimpanzee, will go into space attached to or associated with the manned orbiting workship now known as Skylab.

The association of primates with the space program is by no means new. In fact various subhuman primates have been identified with the space program right from the beginning. Many of these early experiments were carried out from the Holloman Air Force Base at Alamogordo, New Mexico. The first animal to survive after being shot into space was a rhesus monkey called Albert II. However, the failure of his parachute to open resulted in his death on return to earth. This took place in 1949. A German V-2 rocket was used to shoot Albert into space, and he went with it up to an altitude of 83 miles. A third and fourth V-2 were subsequently used. Both had monkeys in them, but both had parachute failures and the animals were lost on their return to earth. On the fourth flight the monkey successfully survived five and a half times the force of gravity on takeoff and twelve to thirteen times the force of gravity on deceleration. This was important because it showed that animals at this high level of intellect could stand the high G's which would have to be imposed on humans as they attempted to move into space.

The fifth V-2 shot had a mouse in it and took place in the summer of 1950. A small camera was included in the capsule, and it showed the mouse in a weightless state, floating around and grabbing anything it touched in order to have contact with something solid. This experiment showed that muscular coordination continued to exist in the weightless condition. Actually this condition was first noted accidentally during World War II when German fighter pilots were attacking Allied bombers from below. The German fighters would dive, then come out of the dive and direct themselves at the bottom of the bomber firing at the apex of their flight; at the last moment they would push the joy stick over, and the plane would flatten out and go into a dive to come down. At the apex of this curve it was found that the pilots experienced a very peculiar sensation which later turned out to be the condition of weightlessness. So it had already been shown during the 1940's that humans could withstand a short period of weightlessness.

Young rhesus monkey in an aircraft flying a Keplerian trajectory which gives twenty seconds of weightlessness at the apex of its flight. The monkey enjoys these weightless periods and has fun floating about.

This method of achieving weightlessness was subsequently used for a number of studies, and the flight path used was described as a Keplerian trajectory. It is possible to obtain 30 to 40 seconds of weightlessness by this method. A number of humans and monkeys have flown these Keplerian trajectories, and the humans found that they very quickly adapted to the short period of weightlessness and were able to carry out tasks requiring quite fine control. This indicated a rapid adaptation to the condition and a possibility that even under conditions of extended weightlessness a human would still be able to handle the controls and carry out effective work.

Young rhesus monkeys flown in the Keplerian trajectory seemed to enjoy the condition of weightlessness. They floated about when the plane reached the apex of its flight path and would kick themselves off from one wall of the aircraft and tumble about until they came into contact with the other wall.

The mouse experiment mentioned earlier was regarded as a significant milestone in the studies of weightlessness and encouraged a number of other experiments to be undertaken.

The next type of rocket used was an Aerobee rocket. In the second of the Aerobee flights the rocket reached 236,000 feet. It contained a monkey and eleven mice. The initial gravitational force at takeoff was seventeen times that of gravity for less than a second and then had a longer period of three to four times the force of gravity which lasted for 45 seconds. All the animals survived these high G's and the brief period of weightlessness that followed without any problems.

The Aerobee III had two monkeys, Michael and Patricia, and two mice. It was fired in 1952. The animals survived the high G's and the brief period of weightlessness. Studies showed that their heart rate, blood pressure, and respiratory systems survived the stresses very well. After their epic flight the animals were placed in the National Zoo in Washington. Pat, however, has since died.

Chimpanzees were used in a number of other studies to test the effects of high-G forces. In 1954 a chimpanzee was placed in a sled running at 630 miles an hour and was stopped in a period of 1.4 seconds. It is said that this is equivalent to running into a brick wall at 120 miles an hour. Colonel John Stapp at Holloman Air Force Base has ridden in a sled going more or less at this speed and stopping in a comparable period of time and survived the experiment. The chimpanzee also survived his rocket sled run.

Chimpanzees were also spun at 105 revolutions per minute. They were exposed to sudden blasts of wind and were subjected to deceleration forces which reached 45 times the effect of gravity. In all these cases they showed no ill effects, which indicated that at least the subhuman primate body and probably the human body were extremely resilient structures.

These studies made it quite clear that man would be able to stand the forces of being launched in a rocket into orbit and then could withstand the enormous forces of deceleration which would be involved on reentry into the earth's atmosphere from orbit and eventual recovery. The studies also led to the design of the couch used in the original Mercury capsule. It is known as a contour couch and fits exactly the form of a man lying on his back with his legs elevated and his knees bent. The same type of couch was used in all subsequent manned space flights.

Chimpanzees at Holloman Air Force Base were taught to carry out all kinds of activities such as pulling levers, operating switches, turning dials, and so on. The signals to move the levers were usually given by flashing lights. These animals were given food by an automatic dispenser. They were flown in Air Force C-131 planes and were persuaded to do their problems under normal flight conditions, under conditions of turbulence, and under conditions of acceleration and deceleration. It was found that they could carry out these problems even under these unusual circumstances.

The first chimpanzee in space was Ham, who had received 250 hours of training before he was rocketed off the earth. He came from the Cameroons in Africa, and he was placed in a Redstone rocket on January 31, 1961, as a preliminary experiment prior to Project Mercury. He was fired downrange in a suborbital flight such as that ridden by Alan B. Shepard, Jr., so Ham's period in space was only very brief.

In the meantime, on May 29, 1959, an Army Jupiter rocket was used to put two monkeys, Able and Baker, up into suborbital flight. They reached 300 miles of altitude, their maximum speed was 10,000 miles per hour, and they went downrange 1,700 miles. They were up for 45 minutes. Able was a rhesus monkey, and Baker was a squirrel monkey 1 pound in weight. She was given a medal of honor and is now called Miss Baker. She has a beautiful new home, built for her by the Navy in September, 1959, at the Naval Aerospace Medical Institute in Pensacola. Her home is 7 feet by 5 feet by $7\frac{1}{2}$ feet. The floor is tiled, and the walls and ceiling are made of Formica. She can be observed through a one-way window. She is taken out on the anniversary of her flight, decorations are placed on her, and a cake is cut in her honor.

Another monkey, named Sam for the School of Aerospace

Medicine from which he came, was a rhesus who went up in a rocket and reached an altitude of 280,000 feet. When he returned to his base at Langley NASA Research Center, he flung his arms around Miss Sam, his cage mate, with what appeared to be great relief. Miss Sam herself was in 1960 shot to an altitude of 9 miles and was up for 58 minutes. Both she and Sam worked very well at the problems they were given while they were in these flights.

The chimpanzee Enos, the only chimpanzee ever to have been in orbit, was a little more than five years old and weighed 42 pounds at the time of his flight. He came from the Cameroons. Before he was put into orbit, he had 1,250 hours of training. He was taught a series of tests which he was supposed to carry out while in orbit. These studies paved the way for a full dress rehearsal for the Mercury launch in which John Glenn was the astronaut. Shortly after the acceleration of the lift-off Enos quickly became absorbed in the jobs he had to do. For example, to obtain either food or drink he had to hit levers. For the whole flight he had to work for ten-minute spells separated by six-minute rest periods. The first orbit took 1 hour 28.5 minutes and was flown at the rate of 17,500 miles per hour. Enos' heartbeat was 105 to 120, his respiration was 20 to 25, and his temperature was 98 degrees Fahrenheit.

During the second orbit there was evidence from one of the tracking stations that the capsule was tumbling. This was because one of the attitude control jets had stuck in the open position. After the second orbit it was decided to bring Enos down. He landed about 200 miles south of Bermuda. When he was released from the capsule, he jumped up and down for a few minutes, presumably with the exhilaration and pleasure of being back on earth, and then he went around and shook hands with all the crew who rescued him. In addition to the tumbling, the temperature in the capsule had gone up to 106 degrees Fahrenheit.

Enos was taken to the main hospital in Bermuda and kept there for the night. He was given a detailed examination and rested, and the doctors that examined him said he was a very fit animal and showed no ill effects from his space flight. The studies showed that the ability of the muscles to control various actions in space was not affected and that one could eat and drink in space despite weightlessness. Unfortunately, in 1962, less than one year after his flight, Enos died of dysentery after a two-month period of illness.

More recently there has been another primate flight, that of the monkey astronaut Bonny, who was flown for $8\frac{1}{2}$ days in orbit and was heavily instrumented for studies of changes in the brain and the respiratory and cardiac systems. A good deal of interesting information was obtained from this experiment, and it was unfortunate that it had to be aborted after $8\frac{1}{2}$ days; it was intended that the monkey would be in orbit for a month. But the capsule lost temperature, though not much, and when Bonny refused to eat and later refused to drink it was obvious that it was necessary to bring him back. He was brought back in a not very good condition but was revived and seemed to be improving when his heart suddenly failed and he died.

There is no doubt, however, that the monkey experiments really paved the way to enable man to make his first hesitant

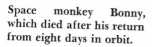

Space monkey Bonny, which died after his return from eight days in orbit.

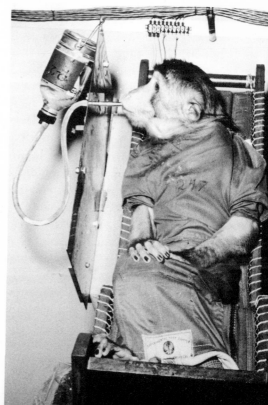

trips into space. It looks now as if the subhuman primate will also tell us how safe it will be for man to spend very long periods of time in orbit and whether it will be safe for him to undertake extensive journeys into space, such as a two-and-a-half-year-long expedition to Mars and back.

Of the more spectacular activities that have been carried out at our Center and which have a direct lifesaving effect, is one known as "cross circulation." One evening the chief physician of the Eggleston Children's Hospital in Atlanta, Dr. Joe Patterson, phoned me and asked if I had a baboon or a chimpanzee which might possibly be used for a cross-circulation procedure with a three-year-old girl. This little girl had had some liver infection, probably infectious hepatitis. When this disease strikes the very young it is sometimes fatal. She had been in a deep coma for some days, and the possibility of connecting her blood vessels with those of one of our chimpanzees was considered. The reason for this was as follows: in the disease hepatitis the virus which causes the disease is particularly destructive of the liver. In a severe attack such as this little girl appeared to have, practically the entire liver would be destroyed. The liver plays many extremely important parts in the normal metabolism of the body, but one of the most important is the converting of toxic or poisonous substances in the blood, which are formed as by-products of the body's normal metabolic activities, into harmless substances. If the liver is destroyed, there is no way in which these substances can be rendered harmless, and eventually they will affect the body. The person suffering from the disease will go into a coma from which he rarely awakes. However, by connecting the blood vessels of the child and the chimpanzee, the child's blood could be passed through the chimpanzee liver, which could clean it of its accumulated poisons. Apparently the poisons in the blood also delay the regeneration of the liver, but removal of the poisons gives the liver a chance to recover, and even in a period of hours enough of the liver may regenerate to enable it to function again. After Dr. Patterson's call the author contacted Dr. Richard Metzgar and Dr. H. F. Seigler, who are responsible for the Yerkes Center's program in immunology, and it was decided to offer one of our chimpanzees, Cassandra, to Dr. Patterson to help treat this little girl. The child's blood group was O, so it was essential that an O-group chimpanzee be used. This is one of the problems in this procedure; most humans belong to the O blood group, and although chimpanzees have the same blood groups as humans, only a small proportion of chimpanzees have this particular blood group. Our colony of eighty-five chimpanzees had only three animals with the O blood group. Cassandra was put to sleep with an anesthetic by our veterinarians, Dr. Michale Keeling and Dr. Garry Moore, her blood was withdrawn, and her veins and arteries were filled with human O-type blood which had been obtained from the hospital blood bank. The child and the chimpanzee were placed side by side in an operating room of the Eggleston Children's Hospital, each on a separate table, the main artery and vein in the groins of both child and chimpanzee were exposed by a small incision, and the vessels were connected by little tubes placed into them and connected with long flexible tubes. The blood passed from the child into the chimpanzee, passed through the chimpanzee's liver, where it was purified, and then went back into the child. This cross-circulation procedure was continued for six hours. Although the child remained in a coma, chemical testing showed that the toxic materials which had accumulated in the blood were reduced to normal level. Eventually it appeared that the brain of the child had been damaged during the long period in coma, and she did not recover.

More recently, however, a five-year-old child who had been in a coma for a shorter time was connected with one of our chimpanzees, Ike. On this occasion the girl and the chimpanzee were connected for 16 hours. They were linked about four o'clock in the afternoon and went all through the night until nearly ten o'clock the next day. At the end of that time the little girl, who had been in a deep coma at the beginning of the cross circulation, was well enough to talk, to remember her address and telephone number, and even to sing a little song. When she did this, everyone in the operating room, doctors and nurses alike, were in tears. She remained out of coma and lived for about three weeks. Then she died of a sudden hemorrhage, probably owing to the exhaustion of clotting substances in her blood. The chimpanzee had, however, done his job well. There is little doubt that the earlier a patient like this can be hooked up to a chimpanzee the better the chance of survival.

The reader of this book may ask, "Why was a chimpanzee used—why not another human being?" The answer to this question is: When a child is suffering from infectious hepatitis, to connect his bloodstream to that of a healthy human being would simply mean giving the healthy person infectious hepatitis, so one finishes up with two patients instead of one. The chimpanzee also receives the virus, and although he will carry it for about two months, he does not show any symptoms of the disease or become ill in any way. Both Cassandra and Ike, the day after the cross circulation, were sitting up eating bananas and looking very pleased with themselves—and in the case of Cassandra, posing for the television news cameras. Interestingly enough, at this stage their bodies were completely filled with human blood, not a drop of chimpanzee blood remaining. However, this happy circumstance could not go on forever. After about three or four days both chimpanzees began to show signs of rejecting the human blood and at this stage it had to be withdrawn, and the animals transfused with chimpanzee O-type blood which for Cassandra was specially flown up to us from the Holloman Air Force Base in Alamogordo. Both chimpanzees then had to be kept in quarantine for two months until they ceased to be infectious. If they had not been put into quarantine they could have infected the members of the Center, both animals and humans, with the disease.

There is no doubt that we have a lifesaving procedure in our hands with the cross-circulation procedure. Many young and valuable lives could be saved in the United States if only the money would be made available to collect chimpanzees with O-type blood and to develop extensive breeding of them. If this is not done very soon it will be impossible to obtain O-type chimpanzees. The selective breeding of these animals would enable us within a few years to build up a bank of O-type chimpanzees. At the moment we feel that it is not desirable because of immunological problems to use chimpanzees a second time for this type of treatment. After having been exposed to human blood they build up antibodies to it. However, if funds were made available it would be possible to study the particular problems involved in delaying or preventing the production of human antibodies by the chimpanzee; this is also a problem in the rejection of heart and kidney transplants.

Most people who even read the newspapers are aware that one of the main problems in the process of the transplantation of organs from one human to another is that of *rejection*. For a time it is possible for the body to accept the organ of another human individual, but only for a time. It soon proceeds to reject it. This can be delayed by the treatment of the recipient with what are described as immunosuppressive drugs, drugs that retard the rejection mechanism but cannot prevent it entirely. Radiation of the recipient of a graft is also used to suppress the immunological mechanisms which result in rejection. It has been demonstrated that in the case of kidney transplants, if the donor kidney is from a member of the family, or better still, from an identical twin, it is much more likely to be accepted. The chances are much slimmer if the kidney is obtained from someone unconnected genetically with the patient.

If there are problems of transplanting kidneys or other organs from one human to another, I am sure you can imagine that these problems would be magnified in the transplantation of a kidney from a chimpanzee to a human being. Yet this has been done, and in one case the recipient lived for eight months with the chimpanzee kidney in place.

Nevertheless, there are still very many problems involved in transplanting chimpanzee kidneys to humans, and the problem of rejection is certainly the most important. Yet there seems to be the possibility that once this problem of rejection is overcome, chimpanzees can be used very widely not only for transplantation of kidneys but of other organs as well, possibly liver transplants, pancreas transplants, and maybe a transplantation of the ductless glands which control so many of the metabolic activities of a person.

These problems are being studied at the Yerkes Center in association with an immunologist and a surgeon from Duke University who share joint appointments with Duke University and the Yerkes Primate Center. They are Dr. Richard Metzgar and Dr. H. F. Seigler. They have done some experimental heart transplants between chimpanzee and chimpanzee, and they are engaged now in a program of kidney transplants also between chimpanzee and chimpanzee because rejection occurs between two chimpanzees just as it does between humans. Dr. Metzgar and Dr. Seigler have been taking steps to accelerate this rejection mechanism with the hopes of bringing it more into the open; thus, they will be able to study it more completely and more effectively design a method of suppressing it.

Some individuals who suffer from a particular type of heart defect require a small battery to be implanted in their bodies, or at least have a small battery attached externally to wires which go to the heart and power a small area of it known as a pacemaker. The rhythmical activity of the pacemaker discharges nerve currents over the conduction paths which stimulate the heart muscle; this results in the contraction of the heart in an orderly and rhythmical fashion. It is when this pacemaker is defective that an artificial pacemaker powered by batteries has to be used. Batteries that are implanted beneath the skin become worn out in time and have to be replaced.

Professor Harold Warner at the Yerkes Primate Center is making a study of how to get electricity for the body without the use of batteries. Actually, most of the chemical activities in the body are accompanied by electrical activity; the body itself produces quite a large amount of electricity. Most of this electricity is produced as a result of the oxidation of the sugar glucose, in the body tissues. Most of the food we ingest is converted ultimately into glucose in the body, and then the glucose is oxidized to produce the energy for growth and movement, repair of tissues, maintenance of the heat of the body, and so on. It occurred to Professor Warner to try to design some kind of structure that would use glucose as a source of energy to make electricity. He has succeeded in producing a little fuel cell powered by glucose which when connected to a small radio is able to make it play for three hours with the consumption of only 1.2 grams (about one-thirtieth of an ounce) of glucose dissolved in water in the process. In other studies he has used fluids extracted from ground-up grass and ground-up leaves in this cell to produce electrical energy. Professor Warner describes the theory behind this fuel cell:

> High school chemistry teachers show that when hydrogen is combined with oxygen in proper proportions and a spark is applied, the resulting release of energy is demonstrated by a flash of light, a loud boom, a pulse of heat, and a bit of "rain." Electrons are exchanged between the hydrogen and oxygen atoms, and energy release is sudden and uncontrolled. In the glucose fuel cell, the hydrogen chemically found in the glucose is also combined with oxygen, but here the exchanged electrons are forced to flow in an external electrical circuit in a controlled manner, and this stream of electrons constitutes an electric current.

The structure of this fuel cell is as follows: a plastic polymer membrane is sandwiched between two platinum electrodes, and the plastic membrane performs as a solid electrolyte. The electrolyte performs the same function as the acid in a battery. In the upper chamber of the fuel cell is a solution of the sugar glucose. It is in contact with one catalyzed surface of the membrane. The hydrogen ions, which are the origin of the electricity, break out of the glucose and travel through the polymer membrane to the side of the membrane where oxygen is present. For each hydrogen ion that travels through the membrane an electron is released which travels through the external electrical circuit to the oxygen side. The oxygen which infiltrates from the other catalyzed platinum electrode picks up the hydrogen ions and forms water. It is the electron which travels in the external circuit which actually provides the electrical power.

Professor Warner plans first of all to implant this glucose fuel cell into a chimpanzee or other ape in order to see if it will produce electricity from the fluids of the body which normally contain glucose. If this is successful, it means that the body itself will be providing the fuel for the fuel cell.

The tests with the chimpanzee, which will cause no pain or inconvenience whatsoever to the animal, will pave the way for the use of this fuel cell for powering the pacemaker for the heart of humans for many years at a time. Eventually, presumably there would need to be only one of these structures implanted in the human being during his lifetime.

Other studies in which Professor Warner is working with various doctors at the hospitals and other scientists at the Center involve the problem of providing the power for an artificial heart. Artificial hearts already exist, but they have to pump and they need substantial power to do this. Professor Warner has suggested that it might be possible to use one of the big muscles of the trunk by unhooking it, hooking it up to an artificial heart, and using its contractions to make the heart beat.

Now the difference between heart muscle and the ordinary muscle of the skeleton called voluntary muscle is that under normal circumstances muscle of the skeleton is used only when we wish it to be used. However, there is a regular rhythmical contraction of the heart muscle irrespective of whether we wish it or not. There is no doubt that certain yogis can slow down the action of the heart muscle, and possibly under sufficiently stressful circumstances it is stopped; it is possible that people who die of so-called broken hearts have, at least subconsciously, been able to stop their hearts in this way.

What Professor Warner proposes is to attach a small electrical make-and-break structure that would give a pulsive contraction to the voluntary muscle by stimulating it to produce the regular cycle of the cardiac heart with the artificial heart.

Professor Warner is also making a study of some of the problems concerned with stroke. This study is being carried out in association with a number of medical colleagues in the Emory Medical School and at the Yerkes Center. When a stroke occurs in a human being, a blood vessel in the brain bursts, blood leaks out into the surrounding brain tissue, and a clot forms. This clot may have a deleterious effect by exerting pressure on the surrounding brain structures. There are also chemical constituents in the blood that may affect the normal functioning of nervous tissue.

Professor Warner has injected an inert substance (silicone) into one of the areas of the brain where strokes occur more commonly and is studying the decrement in function which occurs. He will then inject into a similar area in another animal a similar amount of blood and let it clot there so he will duplicate the effects of a clot spontaneously formed. The difference between the type of a reaction he gets with the silicone and the type that he gets with blood will indicate how much of the damage of stroke is in fact caused by pressure from the clot and how much is caused by some chemical effect that blood has on the nervous tissue. Once these facts are known, it will give a lead to techniques which may be used to ameliorate the effects of a stroke in a human being.

Ever since the Yerkes Laboratories were started 40 years ago, Dr. Yerkes and his colleagues and their successors have studied various aspects of the reproductive physiology of chimpanzees. However, it is only within more recent years that techniques have developed which enable us to estimate with accuracy the level of certain hormones in the animal which cause the various changes taking place during the reproductive cycle and the cycle of pregnancy in human beings and in animals.

Recently the Ford Foundation granted a substantial sum of money to be shared among the Yerkes Primate Center, Emory University Medical School Department of Medicine, and the Harvard Medical School for a study of reproductive physiology of apes. The study will be carried out with the object of discovering if chimpanzees, orangutans, and gorillas can be used for experimental work concerned with human reproduction and population control. Dr. Charles Graham of the Yerkes Primate Center will be coordinating the work at Emory and will be studying various aspects of the reproductive cycle of chimpanzees and other apes.

It is planned to take regular measurements of the ape's temperature, which varies slightly at different points of the reproductive cycle. This will be done by placing a tiny radio transmitter about an inch long and half an inch thick under the skin in the chimpanzee and connecting it to a little temperature sensor. This will radio information on the temperature level to a receiver that will record how it rises and falls.

Dr. John Preedy, who is chief of endocrinology at the Emory Medical School, is studying the amount of female sex hormone compounds in the blood and those excreted in the urine.

Dr. Janet MacArthur of the Harvard School of Medicine is studying the hormones produced by the pituitary gland, which is situated just underneath the brain. The hormones produced by this gland control the production of the female sex hormones by the ovary. In this way it will be possible to relate the temperature changes with the changes in the pituitary hormone and female sex hormone levels in the blood. Furthermore, Dr. Graham will be taking samples of the tissue lining the uterus of the animal which react in a specific way with the hormones. He is also studying the types of cells produced by the animal's vagina and observing in the case of the chimpanzee the incidence of the swelling in the sexual skin and the times at which the animals menstruate. He hopes eventually to make a study through surgical procedures of the process of liberating an egg from the ovary. In the end it will be possible to correlate all these different aspects of the female sex cycle in a way that will be very meaningful in terms of the human reproductive cycle, a procedure which would be quite impossible to do with human beings.

When the full details of the cycle are properly known, it will be possible to find satisfactory ways of interrupting the cycle to prevent conception or it will give a better understanding of the nature of malfunction in human females and will point a way to correcting these problems.

Dr. Graham has also been carrying out a number of studies for some years on the effects of female sex hormone and certain cancer-producing substances on the production of reproductive cancer.

Recently some scientists at Emory Medical School, Dr. Zuker M. Naib and his colleagues, believed that they found evidence that a certain type of herpes virus which exists in the female reproductive tract may play an important role in the production of cancer in that region of the body. Dr. Graham is also collaborating with this group in a study of this particular problem.

Earlier in this book we talked about some of the groups of monkeys being studied by Dr. Irwin Bernstein at the field station; we mentioned a group of pigtail monkeys he was studying and also a group of mixed species of animals.

We have pointed out how the leader of the pigtail group was subsequently deposed by the number three male, but it is of interest that apart from this type of conflict, the group is a very stable one. It is organized into a very definite hierarchy in which each animal knows its place, and perhaps this is the reason why it is so stable. There are now more than thirty animals in this group. Dr. Bernstein himself has described it as a highly successful organized society.

In the mixed species group it was a different story. At one time six different species were represented in this group, but they failed to form a stable organized society. Many severe fights occurred. According to Dr. Bernstein, this seemed to be the result of a lack of communication. He says that monkeys who belong to the same species have a communication system which seems to facilitate the development of a comfortable social organization in which the conflicts are reduced to a few at the top. However, in a mixed species group the individuals do not understand the signals that the different species make, and so they fail to evolve into a peaceful organized society. Maybe there is a lesson here for the United States and for the world. It certainly appears as though the whites and the blacks are not able to communicate adequately in this country, and maybe this is a significant reason for the strife which exists at this time.

Dr. Bernstein has groups of other monkeys which he is studying at the field station. These include Java monkeys, also known as crab-eating macaques. He also has a group of green or vervet monkeys. He started with a male and a female adult of the latter group, and there are now a dozen or more animals in this group, all of whom are descendants from the original pair of adults. The importance of this particular group is that Dr. Bernstein is able with them to study the social behavior of highly inbred animals.

Breeding projects at the field station have produced a number of young hybrid monkeys. Under normal circumstances in nature there is a mechanism which prevents mating between species.

But under certain circumstances in the wild this can be broken down, and in captivity many species of monkeys which do not seem to mate naturally in the wild can be hybridized. For example, Dr. Bernstein has been able to cross a Celebes black ape with a pigtail macaque and also with a Moor macaque. He has also succeeded in crossing a pigtail macaque with a crab-eating macaque. But it is of interest that he has also seen natural hybrids from these two last species in the jungle in Malaya.

The studies of groups of primates have proved most valuable in discovering the factors involved in the formation of peaceful or aggressive societies. Recently, in collaboration with the Walter Reed Army Institute of Research, Dr. Bernstein was able to set up a project for making a biochemical study of the stresses involved in the formation of hierarchies. For example, in a normal group of monkeys which has formed a hierarchy, presumably the male is under some degree of stress compared with some of the less important animals who have no responsibility in the group. There is also stress involved in the fights between the leaders, and presumably the winners and losers of the fights show differing degrees of stress. There may also be different degrees of stress in other sections of the hierarchy. One of the best ways of determining stress is to estimate the amount of stress hormone that is excreted in the urine following its liberation into the blood by the adrenal gland. Collection of the urine and analysis of the level of stress hormone will give an indication of the degree of stress to which the animal is being subjected. This has very important implications for the control of groups of persons or soldiers which form the various units of the Army. It will be remembered that in the Special Forces in Vietnam there was a substantial rise in the excretion of the stress hormone by the officers and by the radio operator, following notice of an enemy attack, but only a transitory rise which rapidly fell to normal or below normal in the men.

While Dr. Bernstein's studies have been mostly on groups of animals at the field station of our Center, he has made one or two field trips, one to Barro Colorado Island in Panama and one to Malaya in the area of Kuala Lumpur. During the latter trip he was able to make a study of groups of pigtail monkeys and Java monkeys (crab-eating macaques) in the wild, and was able to make some observations of gibbons.

Dr. Stuart Altmann of this Center, a distinguished student of primates in the wild, has been making detailed studies of wild baboons in east Africa. Dr. Altmann was one of the pioneers in the field studies of primates and was one of a small group (which includes the chairman of our board of advisers) which began to bring some sense into what appeared in many cases to be the aimless behavior of groups of monkeys in the wild state.

The baboon groups which Dr. Altmann has been studying may contain a large number of individuals, sometimes as many as two hundred. These social groups act to support each other and also to protect the young baboon while it is growing up. The young baboon also learns from his elders where to find food and water and shelter and what to do to protect himself from predators such as leopards or cheetahs.

The baboon group is divided up into dominant males, subordinate males, females, weaned juveniles, younger juveniles, and infants. When a baboon troupe moves across the savanna the subordinate males act as the protectors at the front or rear of the group, and the infants and the females remain in the center of the group with the dominant males close to them. Even when it is resting, the group retains this arrangement more or less. However, when danger threatens, the dominant males will move through the troupe to take the leading positions as scouts and lead the subordinate males to do battle with the enemy. It is difficult to surprise a group of baboons because every few seconds they look up from whatever they are doing and scan the country around. Since there can be as many as 200 baboons in a group there are 400 eyes keeping a watch on what's going on around. It therefore becomes very difficult for a predator and certainly for a human to get very close to such a group.

Dr. Altmann was particularly interested in the problems of survival for the baboons. He was studying where they obtain their essential natural resources such as food and water, and the location of sheltered groups of trees or groups of rocks where they could sleep at night with some degree of protection. Baboons have to avoid predators such as leopards, lions, and cheetahs, which are typical of the animals which may attack them. They are also in danger of heat stroke. How they avoid this is yet to be discovered. Dr. Altmann was interested in the birthrate, the death rate, and the migration of animals from one group to another, and he studied the seasonal changes in the life of the animals and the competition between the various groups of baboons. Although they have a reputation of being vegetarians, on occasions they attacked and ate small mammals.

Two other medical experiments which are of interest are being carried out by the veterinary pathologist at the Center, Dr. Harold McClure. They are being performed on a group of monkeys inherited from the U.S. Air Force which have already been discussed and a group of baby monkeys and apes who are being studied in a leukemia project financed by the U.S. Department of Agriculture.

One of the problems in keeping milking cows is that from time to time an individual may develop leukemia. There is some evidence from studies with lower animals that there is a particle in the milk of animals that have leukemia which can pass the disease on to the young. Whether this particle is a virus or not is not known for certain, but there is a good deal of evidence that it is. It thus becomes important to know whether the milk which comes from leukemic cows could induce cancer in human beings. It is not always very easy in a big herd of milking cows to be immediately aware if one should develop leukemia, and such milk could be passed on to humans.

We have a number of baby monkeys and some baby apes who are being fed milk which comes from leukemic cows in an attempt to demonstrate whether this milk is or is not safe for higher primates such as apes and ourselves to drink. So far we have not had any evidence that it is unsafe, but these experiments have only just begun and it is not possible to infer very much from the results at this moment.

In addition to the projects we have discussed, a very large number of other projects are being partly carried on by members of the staff in collaboration or association with outside investigators. Dr. Michale Keeling and Dr. Wesley Bonner, for example, are involved with members of the biochemistry department of Emory University in a study on the growth hormone of the pituitary gland. They are also making a study of the agents which cause a particular type of encephalitis, a serious disease of the central nervous system which can be caused by a variety of agents. The particular type of encephalitis which Dr. Keeling is studying in association with Dr. Robert F. Kibler from Emory University is an allergic encephalitis in which the damage to the central nervous system comes from an agent to which the body has hypersensitivity.

Some of the other members of the Center, for example, Dr. Johannes Tigges, are interested in the accessory optic pathway in the brain in primates and in humans. This is a type of study which calls for detailed and meticulous investigation of the brains of these animals with complex staining procedures.

Dr. Sohan Manocha and Dr. Todata Shantha have been studying the distribution of enzymes in the different parts of the brains of monkeys and apes. The enzymes, of course, are essential chemical constituents of the brain because they provide the metabolic activities for the brain without which it would not work at all. There are a very large number of enzymes in the brain, and Dr. Manocha and Dr. Shantha have recently published a book in which several of these enzymes have been identified and mapped in different parts of the brain. This type of work has very important applications in many practical aspects of the study of the central nervous system.

In addition to all these researches which are being carried on, continuous studies are proceeding on the control, the breeding, and the husbandry of great apes and the method of treating them for different diseases. Dr. Keeling and Dr. Bonner, our veterinarians, are very heavily engaged in the process of keeping our animals in good health and condition and have shown a great dedication to their work.

One of the problems, for example, which we have come across in the orangutan and the chimpanzees is infection of the air sac. There is a big sac which may contain air under the chin in apes which connects to the windpipe by a small opening. We are not quite sure what the function of this air sac is; presumably in the wild it is used as some kind of resonating device when the animals are calling, but they rarely seem to use it for this purpose when caged. Sometimes they inflate it with air, but generally they do not.

When the air sac of one of our orangs gets infected it may even fill up with pus. The bacteria that get into the sac and do this are often organisms which are resistant to the ordinary antibiotics, and the animal can become quite sick and may die as a result of this infection. Even at this moment one of the biggest and best of our male orangs has come down with this condition, and we are hoping that our veterinarians will be able to solve this problem and bring this animal back to normal health and life.

Our apes may get all kinds of diseases similar to those which man is heir to. We have mentioned that they get polio and infectious hepatitis. They also may sometimes get measles, and we have had one case which looked very much like chicken pox. They may get infections of the urinary tract. They often get diarrheas, and in fact almost any disease one can think of that human beings get, it is possible to find in apes. Probably if one worked with enough of them for long enough one would find even the rare diseases turning up in the chimpanzees. The reader might remember the account of Jama, our Mongoloid chimpanzee, who was the first example of Mongolism occurring in a primate other than man. This, of course, has very important and interesting implications from the point of view of evolution, showing that the gene pools of the human and the great ape are really very close together.

Dr. M. N. Golarz and I have also found a muscle disease in one of our chimpanzees, Todd, which is strikingly similar to a a form of human muscle disease. Apes therefore do have human diseases, even rare human diseases, and are obviously ideal experimental animals in which to study human health and disease.

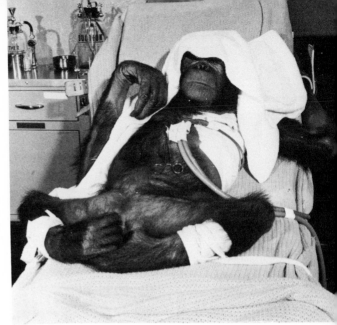

Lada (orangutan) relaxes after her operation. She has placed a towel over her head.

Two young gorillas in the nursery want to see more of the outside world.

A young gorilla poses after a morning drink of milk.

The author and His Serene Highness Prince Rainier, Prince of Monaco, have a consultation with some orangutans in the Yerkes nursery.

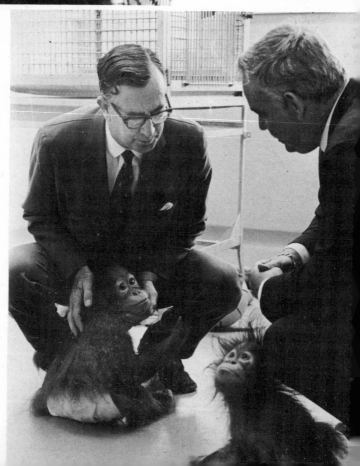

Two orangs in the nursery pose for the photographers.

Two young gorillas play in nursery like human children.

Baby chimpanzee supports his weight with one hand.

Two chimpanzees at ease. Wendy grooms Josie.

Mother and baby chimpanzees. Wendy and her son "Bob."

Madame Ladygin Kohts and her chimpanzee Joni.

Chimpanzee profile (Martha).

Young orang in the nursery greets the photographer.

A recently born chimpanzee feels apprehensive about his medical examination.

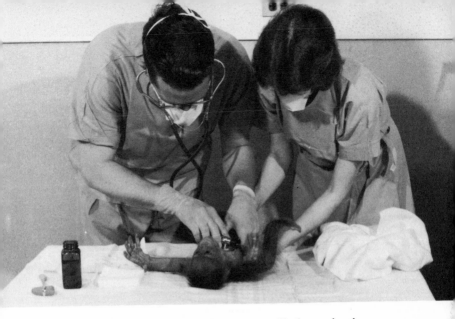

Our firstborn orangutan, Seriba, gets a medical examination.

A Celebes black ape (really a monkey—not an ape).

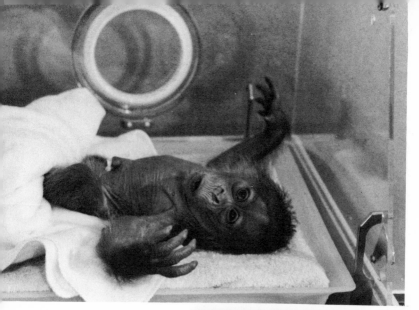

A newborn orang in a human
baby incubator.

Gabrielle (gibbon) with her
rope. (Photograph by courtesy
of Dr. Duane Rumbaugh.)

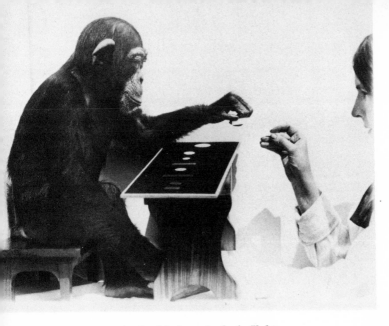

Joni matching samples for Madame Ladygin Kohts.

A beautiful Sumatran orangutan in the zoo of His Serene Highness Prince Rainier in Monaco. His name is Jojo.

Two of Dr. Yerkes' first chimps when they were youngsters. Wendy (left) and Pan.

Lyn, a chimpanzee, giving a big yawn as a symptom of drug withdrawal.

Dr. Irwin Bernstein at the Yerkes field station with two spider monkeys (long tails) and Benito holding his foot.

Gorillas are friendly people.

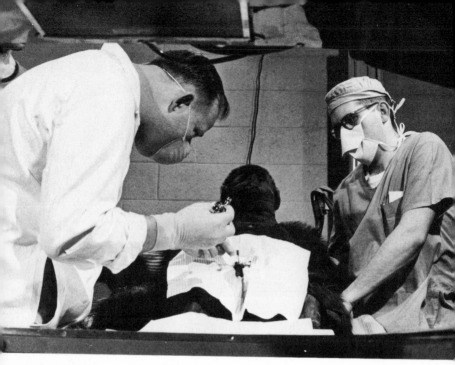

Sample of bone marrow being withdrawn from Mary Lou with the hope that its study might help her condition.

Moos (chimpanzee) taking part in an auditory acuity (sharpness of hearing) experiment.

Joe Mendi, a performing chimpanzee from the Detroit Zoological Park. (From the Yerkes Archives.)

Chimps that are ice hockey players now performing in *Holiday on Ice*. (Photograph by courtesy of their owner and trainer, Werner Muller.)

Bimba working on a spatial maze, aided and abetted by Dr. Austin Riesen.

The first Yerkes twins: Tom (left) and Helene. Photographed in 1934.

Left; Shamba, a subadult female gorilla, showing the typical gorilla walking stance as she comes up the front of her cage. She weighs 114 pounds and is the oldest gorilla in the colony. Right; Proboscis monkey (*Nasalis larvatus*), Honey Ong. She had originally been rescued from the sea by Barbara Harrisson of Sarawak, Borneo.

A group of pig-tailed macaques in the outdoor compound. In the foreground, an adult female, Bernadette, following her infant and accompanied by another female, Jan.

Behavioral studies may encompass the entire lifespan of the animals. Dr. R. K. Davenport, Psychobiologist, records the social interactions of young captive-born chimpanzees for comparison with the behavior of wild-born animals.

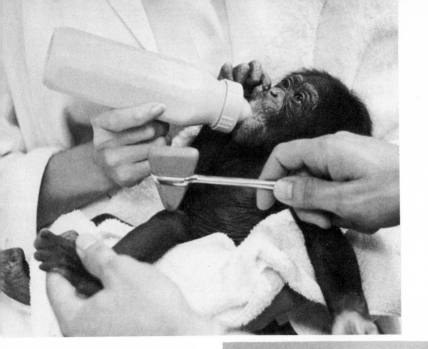

Atlanta, one-day-old chimpanzee receiving her first feeding and physical examination . . . reflexes normal, weight 3.98 pounds. She was the first chimpanzee born in Atlanta.

Gabrielle (gibbon) at nine and a half months. (Photo courtesy of Dr. Duane Rumbaugh.)

13. Ape People and Human People— Are They Related?

I HAVE often been asked, "Did man really come from apes?" or "Which ape did he come from?" Man did not come from any of the existing apes. The present-day apes represent the specialized end products of a particular type of life, and man is still very much a generalized primate. However, there is little doubt now that both man and apes did come from related ancestors. Early man had many of the characteristics which persist in the apes. He has lost these apelike characteristics as he has progressed toward the condition which has been described "as the most dangerous and malignant product of creation—man."

In many ways man differs from the apes, particularly as far as his structure is concerned. One of the outstanding differences is his apparent hairlessness. When Desmond Morris used the title *The Naked Ape* for his recent book he gave the impression that man has in fact lost virtually all his body hair compared with the apes. This is of course not so. The hairs in man have been greatly reduced in size and become extremely fine, but they are still there. It has been pointed out by some authors that man is actually a more hairy animal than the anthropoid apes themselves. In both the head and the back man is a much more hairy person than the gibbon or the chimpanzee, and his head is a great deal more hairy than the head of the orang. He has actually been described as "an abundantly haired primate."

One scientist has shown that if you take the skin of a six-month fetus of a man, an orang, a gibbon, a chimpanzee, and a macaque, the head of the human fetus can be shown to have 880 hairs to a square centimeter, the orang 383, the gibbon 546, and the chimpanzee 400, but the macaque has 1,240. So he is a much more hairy animal than man or the apes. On the back, a human fetus at six months has 688 hairs per square centimeter, the orang has rather more, 937, but both the gibbon and the chimpanzee have considerably fewer, 440 and 420. The macaque has 1,406, so also in body hair he is much more hairy than either man or the apes. One might say that all the apes are substantially less hairy than monkeys and that man's apparent nakedness is simply a result of the relative insignificance of his hairs.

The follicles which produce hairs are sometimes at right angles to the surface of the skin and are sometimes on an angle. The hair as it grows out points in the direction of the hair follicles. The general direction of the hairs in particular parts of the body is known as a "hair tract." On the human back the hairs are directed toward the midline. But in the apes the hairs are directed away from the midline or the area of the vertebral column. This is a significant difference between man and apes.

Other profound differences between man and apes include the proportion of the various parts of the skull and the cranial capacity of the skull, that is, the volume of the skull which is devoted to housing the brain. If you look at the skulls of apes and of man, you find that a disproportionate amount of the skull in apes is devoted to the face and a relatively small part is devoted to harboring and protecting the brain. This is reversed in man. In the evolution of man there is a gradual regression backward of the face, which projects forward in the apes, so that the angle of the front of the face in man is more or less vertical. In most apes the angle is about 45 degrees. The size of the upper and lower jaws in man thus becomes shorter, and the teeth are crowded together in a much shorter jaw. These changes in the face are also accompanied by other changes. Anyone who has looked at an ape's skull in any detail will observe that it has a very flat nose. Man differs very substantially from the apes in having a nose which has prominent nasal bones to support it. The whole nasal structure, which is built up of bone and cartilage, sticks out in a way which is not seen in any ape. The only thing similar to it is the nose of the proboscis monkey, and that is not a comparable anatomical structure with that of man.

Another significant point to observe about the head is that ape ears do not have the lobule which hangs down from the ear in man.

The increase in man in the part of the skull which is devoted to harboring the brain presents an extremely striking difference between man and apes. In the chimpanzee, gorilla, and orangutan the brain or the part of the skull which holds the brain is only about 600 cubic centimeters, whereas the human brain occupies about 1,400 cubic centimeters. Some of the fossils believed to be a part of man's evolution and history have a cubic capacity of about 900 cubic centimeters. That is certainly the upper capacity which the brain of any apelike creature or any ape is likely to reach. I do not know any records of living apes who have shown a cranial capacity as high as 900 cubic centimeters. However, I have measured an Australian aboriginal skull which did in fact have a capacity of 900 cubic centimeters. On the average the size of the human brain is about twice that of the apes. It is interesting that the porpoise has a brain which is even greater than that of man and reaches as high as 1,400 or 1,500 cubic centimeters. What is more, it is a great deal more convoluted than that of man. The convolutions of the brain are apparently developed in order to increase the total area of gray matter of the cerebrum, where the thinking and the coordinative part of the brain is located. The greater the amount of gray matter, the greater the possibility of integration and abstract reasoning. This of course suggests that the porpoise has these abilities. Whether we can demonstrate this will depend upon the degree to which we are eventually able to communicate with these animals.

Apart from the size, however, the brains of man and the ape are the same; distinguished scientists such as Dr. Grafton Elliot-Smith have said that "no structure found in the brain of the ape is lacking in the human brain; and, on the other hand, the human brain reveals no formation of any sort that is not present in the brain of the gorilla or the chimpanzee."

Man's skin differs in many respects from that of the apes. The skin of man has underneath it a bed of thick subcutaneous fat which is actually adherent to the back of the skin. This is not the case in the apes, as anyone who has had the opportunity to skin both humans and apes (and there are not many such people) will testify.

Another characteristic distinction of man is the much greater length of the legs compared with the arms. In apes it is the reverse, and in the case of the gibbon this greatly increased arm length is most striking; it is also obvious in the orang.

It is an interesting thing that while still in the uterus and up until the time of birth man is very much better developed in the upper part of the body, including the forearms, than he is in the legs; in fact the proportion of arms to legs in man is much greater at birth and during the fetal stage than it is later. It is only after birth that there is an increased growth of the legs by comparison with the arms. During the 1920's a European scientist, Professor L. Bolk, produced a theory that man was, in fact, really a precocious fetal ape. The fetuses of apes look more humanlike than apelike in their proportions. I find this theory rather appealing; it means in effect that man has been born at a progressively earlier period in development. Even though the period in the womb now may be as long, the development has been progressively slowed down so that man has been born and grown up with the fetal ape characters. The ape has developed faster *in utero* and superadded onto the human basic structure the specialized characteristics which are found in each of the different kinds of ape.

Another interesting difference between man and ape is that the big toe in apes is opposable—it is not closely attached to the rest of the foot as it is in humans, and it is more like a thumb. It sticks out at an angle and is separated from the rest of the foot; it can, in fact, be used for grasping in all the big apes.

There are a number of other anatomical differences to a greater or lesser degree between man and the apes. There is a difference in the number of vertebrae in the thorax and the lower part of the back in the various apes and in man. Nearly all humans have 17 vertebrae in this area, most chimpanzees and gorillas also have 17 vertebrae, and so do the gibbons, but most orangs have 16 vertebrae in this area.

Another point we must make is related to erect posture: in the skull of the ape the opening through which the spinal cord connects with the brain is more toward the back of the skull because their predominantly four-legged progression causes the head to be turned forward. In man, whose head has to be carried horizontally in order to obtain unrestricted vision, this opening is brought around to the base of the skull. This enables the head to sit balanced on top of the spinal column, supported there by the appropriate muscles.

Teeth are extremely important in trying to determine the relationship between apes and humans and also in attempts to assess the nature of certain fossils. Anthropologists can get a pretty good idea even from a single tooth whether the original owner was a man or an ape. Monkeys, apes, and men have 32 teeth in the skull, whereas animals such as the lemurs, which are not true primates (they are known as prosimians), have 34 teeth. So a skull has to have 32 teeth if it is to belong to the true primate group.

If you look at the top of the molar teeth, you find that there are a series of bumps present on them; these bumps are essential for chewing up the rough material that is present in food. The ungulates, which include animals such as the horse, have a complex series of corrugations on the molar teeth because they are used for chewing on hard grass which needs a very efficient grinding mechanism to break it up before it goes down to the stomach. Monkeys have four bumps, or cusps, on the top of each molar; apes have molars with five cusps, and this is also characteristic of man. These five cusps are arranged in such a way that the spaces between them are modified to form a Y shape. The pattern on these teeth is then known as the "y-five" pattern. It seems to have existed in teeth for some 26,000,000 years.

Even though apes and man have molar teeth which are apparently almost identical, there are in fact differences in the sizes of the cusps which make it possible for an expert to distinguish whether a tooth came from an ape or from a human or a humanoid being.

Another difference between the teeth of man and those of the ape is the very large canine teeth which are found in the apes. In these animals they are long and powerful and project down beyond the line of the other teeth. In the human skull the canine is greatly reduced in size and is normally only as long as the rest of the teeth in the mouth.

The shape of the palate is also diagnostic as far as distinguishing between a human and an ape is concerned. The arch formed by the teeth in the palate varies a good deal. It is broader and shorter in man, and much more elongated in the apes. If the fossil skull shows a short, broad type of arch in its palate, it is more closely related to man than to the apes.

Somewhere around 70,000,000 years ago, in what is known as the Eocene Period in the geological time scale, the first hint of primatelike creatures appeared. There is evidence from fossils that this period was a warm one, that there were many tropical forests that spread way up into the north and down into the south, and that even in parts of Europe there existed moist and humid jungle.

There is a group of small animals living today about the size of rats, but which has a completely different type of dentition from rats; these animals are known as tree shrews. Tree shrews are believed to be very similar to the animals who were the forerunners of the massive collection of primates which exist on the earth today. Although these forerunners resembled the tree shrews, it is not my belief that the present-day tree shrews are closely related to the primates. They have some fundamental neurological differences from true primates. Nevertheless, it is almost certain that animals similar in structure to these present-day tree shrews started the whole race of primates. These animals ranged over the jungles in Europe and other parts of the world for many millions of years. Then from about 45,000,000 years ago, during the Oligocene Period, came some fossils which are recognizable as monkeylike animals, but there were perhaps 600,000,000 years of evolution before these first primates appeared on the earth. These early monkeylike fossils were discovered in Egypt. There is a very famous depression in the desert about 60 miles south of Cairo which is known as the Fayum Depression. Apparently in Oligocene times this Egyptian Fayum was a swamp lying on the border of the Mediterranean Sea and was very rich in trees and other elements of the jungle.

The first of these monkeylike creatures was called Oligopithecus, meaning "the monkey from the Oligocene Period." Animals resembling the New World monkeys were never found in the Old World. Apparently the New World monkeys represent a separate development of their own. Humanlike fossils have been found in Africa, India, China, the Middle East, France, Gibraltar, Germany—but not in North or South America.

The thing that led the finders of Oligopithecus to decide that it was a monkey rather than some other type of animal was that it had 32 teeth. In addition the molar teeth of this fossil had four cusps, which is also characteristic of monkey molars.

Like the progenitors of many present-day mammals, the first Oligopithecus was a tiny animal, probably 10 or 12 centimeters high only; the animal that was the forerunner of the line of horses was scarcely more than that size.

During this early Oligocene Period apparently the New World monkeys and the Old World monkeys separated, and the New World monkeys then developed into the typical forms that we know of in South America; the Old World monkeys developed

321

into the wide variety of forms which are now found in Africa and Asia.

Another discovery in the Egyptian Fayum was a fossil jaw. The extinct owner of the jaw was called Parapithecus and seemed to have been about the size of a modern-day squirrel monkey. It had very primitive teeth, but nevertheless it had already the simple dental formula which we find in Old World monkeys and also in anthropoid apes. What made this jaw so interesting was that the pattern of the cusps on its molar teeth was a simplified form of the pattern we find in the molars of anthropoid apes and man, so apparently 40,000,000 years ago apes had begun to diverge from the monkey line. However, the slope of the jaw seemed to be more like that of a modern preprimate known as the tarsier. The modern representatives of the tarsier are found today only in Borneo and in the Philippines. Tarsiers are small, slender animals with very long legs enabling them to jump considerable distances. They have big, round, saucer-shaped eyes and the ability to swivel their head on the spinal column through 180 degrees so that in fact some of these animals have been seen with their arms clasped around a tree and the head looking backwards, as if it had been put on the wrong way round.

Many years ago the distinguished anthropologist and anatomist Professor Frederic Wood Jones, with whom I had the privilege of working during the 1930's, claimed that humans were descended directly through animals related to the tarsier. Later I was a member of the laboratory of Professor Sir Wilfrid E. Le Gros Clark, in the University of Oxford, and he also pointed out the similarity between Parapithecus and the tarsiers. Sir Wilfred had spent some time in Borneo studying these animals. The fossil Parapithecus provides evidence that this animal was a tiny apelike creature showing similarities to the tarsiers and supports strongly Professor Jones' original suggestion.

Another small skull found in the Egyptian Fayum was that of Propliopithecus. It was found more than a hundred years ago. This animal was about the size of a small gibbon and had teeth like the modern gibbon. Propliopithecus appears to be a stage beyond Parapithecus in the development of apelike characteristics and was a little later in the time scale. The important thing about these findings was that they suggest that man and the apes developed through a small ancestor related to the modern tarsiers, without going through any stage of evolution which could be described as a "monkey stage." It appears, in fact, that the monkeys diverged somewhere around 40,000,000 years ago and simply developed a form of evolution of their own. In 1957 an additional Propliopithecus skull was found in Czechoslovakia.

By the beginning of Miocene times, which started about 35,000,000 years ago, there is some evidence that a great variety of different types of primatelike creatures existed, and fossils of apes from the early Miocene Period have been found in Kenya and other parts of central Africa. There was a great variety of sizes ranging from that of a smaller gibbon up to that of a large ape similar to the chimpanzees and gorillas. The limb bones of these Miocene apes which have been found indicate that they were of a much lighter build than the big apes of today, and presumably because of this they were much more active and probably much more agile individuals. The bones of the limbs also suggest from their length and shape that the animals were probably much better at running along the ground than they were at swinging from the branches of the trees. The elongated arms associated with tree-swinging habits which are found in the modern orangutan and gibbon and to a lesser extent in the chimpanzee had not yet developed and are thus probably a more modern specialized development of these animals.

Around the middle of the Miocene Period, some 20,000,000 years ago, there lived an animal which showed many similarities to the modern chimpanzee; his fossil remains have been named Proconsul. He was discovered on an island in Lake Victoria in Kenya by Dr. Louis S. B. Leakey, a distinguished and internationally famous anthropologist who has made an amazing number of finds in the area of human and anthropoid fossils and who probably has done as much as any other living person to fill in the gaps concerned with man's and ape's evolution.

It is very likely that Proconsul gave rise eventually to the modern apes. It was found in a large number of sizes, some quite small and some quite large, and it is possible that the larger variety gave rise to the modern gorillas. So we seem to have identified the origins of most of the apes. We have not yet found the origins of man himself.

The palate of Proconsul was elongated and U-shaped, which is characteristic of apes. The first evidence of the evolution of man came in the 1930's, the same decade in which Proconsul had been found, when Dr. G. Lewis of Yale University found in the Siwalik hills of India a part of a skull in which the palate showed the same kind of broad arching found in humans and not the narrow U shape which is characteristic of apes.

Subsequently Dr. Leakey found another upper jaw, this time in Africa, which was almost identical with the skull found by Dr. Lewis. Dr. Lewis' animal has been called Ramapithecus.

Ramapithecus not only had this arched palate, but it also had very small teeth, especially the canines, and the molars had a simple structure which suggested that they were transitional in the development of the manlike dentition as distinct from the apelike molars of the other apes of that time.

Many fossils have been found from the time in which these Miocene apes were flourishing, including one called Limnopithecus, which was similar to the modern gibbon, and also a famous fossil, Dryopithecus, which was one of the earliest fossil apes to be found and appears to have been about the size of a modern chimpanzee.

Many species of Dryopithecus have been described, and they vary considerably in the anatomy of their teeth. In some of them the teeth appear more like the chimpanzee, in others more like an orang, and in others more like the gorilla. From Dryopithecus may have developed the orangutans on the one hand and Proconsul which was the forerunner of the chimpanzee and the gorilla on the other.

The thighbone of Dryopithecus indicates that it was a lightly built animal, probably of considerable agility. Its armbones did not show the excessive arm development characteristic of the modern apes.

So at the end of the Miocene Period and the beginning of the Pliocene Period about 14,000,000 or 15,000,000 years ago, the animal which was probably going to develop into man (Ramapithecus) had already made its debut on the world's stage, and so had the progenitors of the apes (Dryopithecus).

Another fossil has been found called Oreopithecus which probably weighed about the same as a modern-day chimpanzee and was about the same size. The appearance of its teeth and other skeletal characters led to suggestions by some scientists that it could have been on the direct line to man, but subsequent studies showed it was an ape that did not quite make the human line and came to an evolutionary dead end.

While evidence had been accumulating from the explorations in the Egyptian Fayum and other parts of Africa about the early origin of the primates, particularly apes and man, some key skulls in the later evolution of man had already been discovered. One of the first of these was found as long ago as 1856 in the Neander Valley close to Düsseldorf in Germany. It was definitely a human skull, but it was different from any human skull that had been seen up to that time.

I have mentioned that among the differences between human skulls and ape skulls are those in the teeth and the shape of the palate. In addition, the ape skull has very strongly developed eyebrow ridges, and the front of the skull slopes backward so that there is really very little of the forehead such as we see in the human skull. The top of the skull is flat instead of being arched.

The skull found in the Neander Valley was for this reason named the Neanderthal man. Although it was obviously human and had a good cranial capacity well in the human range, it did have the strong eyebrow ridges and the sloping forehead of the apes. The skull was given to Rudolf Virchow, the founder of modern pathology, to examine, but his mind was directed more toward pathology than toward anthropology. He declared that it was a pathological human skull, and as a result its anthropological importance was not realized until a quarter of a century later.

Subsequently other Neanderthal skeletons were found associated with bony deposits of other animals which certainly do not exist on earth today, such as the mammoth. A conception began to emerge toward the end of the nineteenth century that maybe this was the skull of a more primitive man who lived about 100,000 years ago.

However, a real bombshell was produced by a Dutch physician, Dr. Eugène Dubois, who was working in the Dutch East Indies from 1887 to 1895. Dubois found the top of a skull and a thigh bone in his diggings. The shape of the top of the skull indicated that the size of the brain must have been within the human range, and yet the bone was flattened as it was in apes and had enormous eyebrow ridges and no forehead. It seemed for certain to be some primitive type of ape man. The femur (thighbone) which had been found provided a strong indication that the owner of the skull probably walked erect in the way we do today. It was called Pithecanthropus, which translated from the Latin means "ape man."

Some scientists at that time, about 1890, regarded the skull as that of the missing link. Others claimed that it was simply a large gibbon, and yet its cranial capacity showed it to be 900 cubic centimeters, which is within the human range.

Subsequently, in 1936–40, further valuable anatomical specimens of Pithecanthropus were discovered in Java. These included a lower jaw with several teeth, an adult skull, the back part of another skull together with the upper jaw and teeth, part of the top of a third skull, and also an infant's skull, the last being found at Modjokarto in central Java.

Forty miles southwest of Peking at a Chinese village called Choukoutien a Canadian anatomist, the late Professor Davidson Black, in 1927 found a molar tooth which had the characteristics of a human tooth but was primitive in a number of respects. On the basis of this tooth he coined the name for another extinct man, Sinanthropus (China man). Continuing his excavations, Black found in 1929 an almost complete skull and some portions of jaws and teeth. Before the Japanese invasion of China interrupted the work, he found the remains of several more skulls. He actually had the remains of fourteen individuals, both young and old people, by that time. These were skulls or portions of skulls, and in addition he had teeth and parts of jaws from forty other individuals, including parts of thighbones and some armbones, some wristbones and a collarbone. These Chinese fossils showed very great similarity with the Javanese fossils and were both dated back to the early Pleistocene Period, about half a million years ago.

There is no doubt that the China man stood erect just like the Java man. In the Chinese skulls the brain capacity was found to vary between 850 and 1,300 cubic centimeters, the average being 1,075 cubic centimeters. The Javanese skulls have an average of only 860 cubic centimeters, but very few of these have been found, so the difference in cranial capacity may be only statistical.

More recently scientists have decided that both the China man and the Java man are close enough to modern man to be called *Homo.* Since they were erect they both now come under the single species *Homo erectus,* and it seems fairly certain that *Homo erectus,* who lived half a million years ago, existed all around Asia. There is some evidence that a comparable type of man also was occupying Germany about that time and probably other parts of Europe as well.

Ramapithecus was an apelike creature who just showed the beginnings of human development and who lived 13,000,000 years ago; *Homo erectus* was definitely human who still showed some links with the apes and who lived 500,000 years ago so that between these two there was a tremendous gap.

However, in 1924 some workers in a limestone quarry near Taungs in South Africa were blasting rocks, and after one explosion they picked up a small skull. They thought it had a kind of human look about it and sent it to the anatomy department of the medical school at the University of Witwatersrand in Johannesburg. The professor of anatomy at that institution was Raymond Dart. Dart saw both apelike and humanlike characteristics in this skull and called it *Australopithecus africanus,* the "African southern ape." Some people at the time that Dr. Dart described his find thought he was really describing a kind of chimpanzee. However, he had the support of Dr. Robert Broom, who worked with Dart to find further examples of this type of primitive man. Raymond Dart found his skull and published the details about it in 1924, and in 1925 the famous antievolution trial was held in Tennessee in which the state of Tennessee convicted the teacher

Australopithecus (Zinjanthropus) skull reconstructed by R. J. Clarke under supervision of P. V. Tobias. Photo by R. Campbell and A. R. Hughes from *Olduvai Gorge* by P. V. Tobias (Cambridge University Press, 1967), vol. II.

John Scopes of teaching evolution, described as "a theory that denies the story of the divine creation of man." The conviction of Scopes showed that in 1925 there were a number of extremely primitive human beings alive and living in Tennessee. The climate for the reception of Dart's discovery was not a good one. He has pointed out that he had letters from all over the world, some of which informed him that he would roast in hell for claiming that his discovery was related to a human. Anthropological discoveries since that time have shown conclusively the correctness of Professor Dart's claims for Australopithecus who apparently lived 2,000,000 years ago.

Subsequently Dr. Louis Leakey went on to find further specimens which supported Dr. Dart's theories. The skull which Dart had been given was filled with material which when removed provided a cast of the interior. The skull was that of a child of about six years of age. One of the things that impressed Dart was that the hole at the base of the skull through which the spinal cord passes was underneath the skull instead of toward the end of it, indicating that the ape man-child had carried his head like a human and had almost certainly walked erect. The surfaces of the fossil molars were very similar to those of a human child, and the canines were also small instead of being enlarged like an ape's. Thus Australopithecus was no longer in the trees; he was a ground-living animal, and probably came down originally out of the trees because he could find more food on the ground than he could find up there.

This jump from the quadrupedal posture to the erect posture was probably one of the most important jumps that the progenitors of man made. In doing it they liberated their forefeet to become hands to perform all kinds of manipulations and activities which would be impossible for other animals to do. Monkeys and apes are of course halfway into this condition. An animal that is completely erect has its arms and hands free to carry materials, including food, for long distances back to the family group; but also, because it is standing on its hind legs, it is taller and thus able to see predators more quickly. Most scientists believe that the adoption of the erect posture freed the hands for other activities and locomotion. Dr. Sherwood Washburn of the University of California has, however, suggested the reverse. In other words, the tendency of apelike ancestors to use tools was responsible for the progressive development of the erect posture, since this posture would aid them in using tools better and more constantly. Animals such as chimpanzees do in fact use tools; this has already been referred to in an earlier chapter in this book. Dr. Washburn believes that tools may have been used by the earlier primates 10,000,000 years ago instead of about 500,000 years ago as most scientists believe.

Among the Australopithecine fossils that were found was one by Dr. Robert Broom which seemed to belong to the same group as Australopithecus but which Broom called Paranthropus. Paranthropus was a large-built animal, and his fossil remains went back chronologically at least as far as Australopithecus. After a considerable amount of exploration and the discovery of other

Paranthropus remains, it appeared that Paranthropus was probably not on the direct line to modern man at all, but was an aberrant offshoot like Oreopithecus, which developed up to a certain point and did not proceed on to modern man.

In the meantime discoveries by Leakey showed that apparently Australopithecus-like animals were all over Africa 2,000,000 or 3,000,000 years ago, and were actually toolmakers and tool users. This genus of Australopithecines he called Zinjanthropus, "East African man." It is probable that Paranthropus was not a tool user and that *Australopithecus Zinjanthropus* was. If this was so, there is no doubt of the reason why Australopithecus progressed and Paranthropus did not.

It is possible that the great apes have not changed very much for some millions of years because of their failure to adopt a truly erect posture, but in the last 2,000,000 years we have had a change from an apelike *erect* man, Australopithecus, to the modern man of today. The pace of the evolution of man once his primary characters were established has been phenomenal.

The brain of the Australopithecus was small, reaching only about 600 cubic centimeters; it was still only half the size of the brain of modern man but was probably a little above that of the largest chimpanzee, since the 600-cubic-centimeter capacity is an upper limit for them.

Australopithecus had much more forehead than any ape has, and the eyebrow ridges, although heavy, were greatly reduced compared with the modern ape. He had a palate very much like that of the human palate, and the canines of Australopithecus were much more like those of a human than those of an ape.

The general picture of the hominids who formed the Australopithecine group in Africa 2,000,000 years ago shows that they were apelike men of small stature, with a brain very little bigger than that of the gorilla and the chimpanzee, and a skull and jaw more human than ape. The dentition was definitely human in nature, and the animals were, of course, erect. Professor Dart has suggested that these early man-apes were killers and that this is where the lethal activities of modern man came from. So modern man is a "killer ape" as well as an apparently "naked ape."

In 1968 Dr. Elwyn Simons, distinguished director of the Peabody Museum of Natural History at Yale University, announced at the Second International Congress of Primatology the discovery of the lower jaw of a species of ape known as Gigantopithecus, which apparently lived in the middle Miocene Period, about 20,000,000 to 25,000,000 years ago, which means that it is a much earlier fossil than Ramapithecus. The large teeth obviously belonged to a new form of higher primate for which evidence had been found just before World War II in Chinese drugstores in Hong Kong and Canton. The drugstores in these parts of the world sell dragons' teeth, which are supposed to have a rejuvenating effect when ground up and consumed. Among the so-called dragons' teeth were large teeth which obviously belonged to a new type of primate. The animal that owned them must have been a very big animal. It was therefore christened Gigantopithecus (big monkey). Later, whole lower jaws were found containing the same kind of teeth, and it appears that these belonged to a very large ape which roamed across the plains of China about half a million years ago, about the same time that *Homo erectus* was wandering in the same regions.

Dr. Simons and Dr. S. R. K. Chopra of Punjab University in Chandigarh, India, announced at the Second International Congress of Primatology in Atlanta, Georgia, in 1968 that they had discovered a more or less complete lower jaw of an animal which they also placed in the genus Gigantopithecus, but they claimed that it was a new species of the genus and placed its age back in the middle Pliocene, approximately 10,000,000 years ago, which made it quite an ancient ape and comparable in age with that of Ramapithecus. Gigantopithecus appeared to have come into the anthropoid line from Dryopithecus. Although similar to the Chinese Gigantopithecus, the new species found in India showed a number of primitive features not found in the Chinese species. These included teeth with low crowns without any tendency for the formation of the multiple cusps found on the teeth of the Chinese fossils. Ramapithecus has been found in almost the same region as Dryopithecus.

Dr. Simons feels that 15,000,000 years ago both Ramapithecus and Australopithecus were derived from a species of Dryopithecus, which he now believes can be placed in its proper position in the history of man. Dr. Simons believes that his Gigantopithecus find is closer to the early hominids than the African apes and suggests that the Asian giant ape of India must represent an early branch derived from the same group of apelike animals which ultimately produced modern man.

The structure of the teeth shows that Gigantopithecus ate more like a man than like an ape, using the same kind of grinding action as man.

Dr. Simons' work, in fact, suggests that from a Parapithecus type of individual was developed a Gigantopithecus; from that developed Dryopithecus; that animal gave rise on the one hand to the orangutan, gorilla, and chimpanzee, and there is another branch which extended from Gigantopithecus, to Ramapithecus, to the Australopithecines, and through them to *Homo erectus* and modern man.

At what stage man became a meat eater as well as a vegetable eater it is not possible to say. There is, however, some evidence that Australopithecus was something of a hunter, and he must have eaten meat as well as vegetables. In the caves in which his remains have been found broken animal bones have also been discovered. It seems possible that some of these bones had been broken in a particular way so that they could be used as tools.

One cannot talk about the older fossil finds without referring to the Olduvai Gorge in East Africa. Olduvai Gorge has been Dr. Leakey's fossil gold mine. He and his workers have found not only Australopithecine remains but also the further remains of Paranthropus and those of *Homo erectus,* and they have even found modern man in the same site.

Dr. Leakey's results of the last few years have also demonstrated that in the Olduvai Gorge there are fossil remains that appear to be intermediate between the Australopithecus and the *Homo erectus* remains, and we are now fairly certain that this is the root from which modern man has come. The big difference between Australopithecus and *Homo erectus* was the dramatic increase in the size of the brain from about 600 cubic centimeters to around 1,000 cubic centimeters, which brings it into the range of modern human brains.

The tools of *Homo erectus* were much more advanced than the primitive bone tools of Australopithecus; they even included a type of hand ax. There is some evidence that *Homo erectus* used fire to start animals from cover when engaged in hunting, and there is no evidence that he used any form of cultivation; he probably formed hunting bands and did not stay very long in one place. In a sense the behavior of the Australian aborigine probably resembles these early hunters. The Australian aborigines are a primitive race of people who came to Australia within the last 50,000 years, probably in dugout canoes or something of that sort, from the neighboring islands of the north. They were isolated for many years in Australia until the white man arrived around the end of the eighteenth century. The aborigines live in groups in an area where they hunt for animals and dig for vegetables, roots, and so on. When they have eaten out the food in the vicinity of the camp, they simply pack up and move on to the next area. They hunt wild animals, but the only wild animals available are the kangaroo and some other marsupials. There are no true mammals in Australia that are indigenous except rats and mice, which came to the country on floating logs from time to time from other parts of the world. There is also the dingo, a wild dog descended from the original dogs brought in by the first men who arrived in Australia. The reason why Australia does not have the typical fauna of other parts of the world is that it has been cut off from the rest of the world since Cretaceous times, about 100,000,000 years ago. In other words, it was isolated even during the early period of the development of mammals, many millions of years before any progenitor of man appeared on the scene. Therefore the evolutionary direction the animals in Australia took produced unusual creatures such as kangaroos and other marsupials. In the absence of the competition of more sophisticated animals elsewhere, these creatures were able to build up a marsupial "civilization," if it can be called that, throughout Australia.

This is why no primitive skulls have ever been found in Australia. However, on one occasion I had the opportunity, when I was working in the Australian Institute of Anatomy in Canberra, Australia, to describe and study in detail the skull known as the Cohuna skull. This had an enormous palate and virtually no forehead. It had very large eyebrow ridges and a flat top of the skull—in other words, it shows many characteristics of the early human skull, and yet it had a cranial capacity of about 1,000 cubic centimeters, well into the human range. This skull had apparently been carried around by one tribe of Australian natives as a kind of religious relic, and they were persuaded to give it up only with great difficulty. The skull, from what I now remember of it after thirty-five years, was very similar in appearance to those recently discovered in Kow swamp near Sydney in Australia. This exciting find in an Australian swamp of a number of skulls and parts of skeletons suggests that *Homo erectus* of the Java type may have found his way to Australia tens of thousands of years before the progenitors of the Australian aborigines.

About 400,000 years ago there was a great increase in the sophistication in the tools which the prehumans were making. A number of these were found in the valley of the Somme River in France in the neighborhood of a town called St.-Acheul. These types of tool then became known as the Acheulean culture. This was the culture of *Homo erectus,* and it probably lasted up to about 75,000 years ago, but *Homo erectus* seems to have disappeared some 300,000 years ago. However, there is some evidence that the Swanscombe skull found in the Thames Valley in England, and the Steinheim skull found near Steinheim in Germany, represent the skulls of a more modern type of *Homo erectus* which had not yet reached the stage of being *Homo sapiens.* Probably this advanced type of *Homo erectus* occupied the 200,000-year period between the last true *Homo erectus* that has been found and the appearance on the scene of the Neanderthal man.

The Neanderthal man came on the scene about 100,000 years ago and produced an even more sophisticated kit of tools. He used fire regularly, and even hearths have been found on the floors of the caves which he inhabited. He was in fact the original caveman. He was much less of a migrant than *Homo erectus.* It is a sobering thought that a number of young people from many different countries, including America, have gone back to living in caves on the shores of some of the Greek islands. Their dress and social relationships seem to have reverted to those which we believe were characteristic of Neanderthal man. This regression back thousands of years by groups of intelligent, educated young people is a disturbing circumstance.

Neanderthal man lived up to about 35,000 years ago, and then a new culture appeared, the Cro-Magnons. They lasted until about 10,000 B.C., which brings them very close to the beginning of history.

While the Acheulean tool culture belonged to *Homo erectus,* the Neanderthal man brought in a new culture called the Mousterian from Le Moustier in southern France. There is good reason to believe that the Neanderthal men descended from the Swanscombe and Steinheim men. The Neanderthal man had prominent eyebrow ridges, and his chin receded like that of an ape; it was not square like that of a human. His cranial capacity was close to that of the modern human, but he was short in stature and was obviously built very powerfully. The Neanderthal man appeared to die out quite abruptly 35,000 years ago; but he had remained quite primitive. Even the latest specimens of the Neanderthal skulls are still very primitive and some are even more primitive than some of the earlier specimens. This regression makes it unlikely that the Neanderthal man was the originator of our own stock, at least as far as those in Europe are concerned.

In the Middle East, however, there was evidence of the development of a type of Neanderthal which approached that of modern man. This Neanderthal man was, in fact, closer to the Cro-Magnon man. The latter appeared about 35,000 years ago and was probably the cause of the elimination of the Neanderthal. These people had much more sophisticated tools and were big-brained individuals, the size of their brain being fully into the range of modern man. They were consummate artists—they were the people who painted the cave drawings that I described earlier in the chapter "Ape Aesthetics." The Cro-Magnon man was not only an artist in painting; he was also an artist in sculpture. A number of caves show the outlines of animals incised in the walls, including a fine set of horses in a cave at Cap Blanc which is near Les Elyzies in France. These people also made statues.

The Cro-Magnon people were so called because the remains of some of them were found near the town of Cro-Magnon in southern France. They appear to have been a finely built race, to have been tall and muscular, with finely developed modern heads. Their facial features were refined like those of modern humans without the apelike characteristics of the Neanderthals.

At the time the Cro-Magnon man, who appears to have been light skinned, appeared in Europe it is almost certain that Africa also contained people who were progenitors of the present-day Bushmen in Africa. But as far as is known, the modern Negro was not in Africa at that time, about 35,000 years ago. Where he came from is still a mystery. The exact ancestry of the Mongoloid people is also unknown. However, it was during this period 35,000 years ago that man first invaded North and South America and migrated into Australia. The new evidence from Kow swamp in Australia suggests that *Homo erectus*-like individuals may have got to Australia many thousands of years earlier.

In a cave in Grimaldi on the Riviera two skeletons have been found which belong to the Aurignacian culture, but they seem to be Negroid in appearance. Possibly they represent an invasion into the southern part of Europe of a race of Negroid peoples from Africa. In fact some scientists have drawn attention to the similarities between some of the Aurignacian cave paintings and the cave art which the modern Bushmen in Africa practice today. However, it is uncertain that the Grimaldi skeletons are in fact Negroid, and the anatomical evidence is rather tenuous.

The Cro-Magnons appeared to have been able to make crude clothes out of skins, although the Neanderthals may have done this to some extent also. Like the Neanderthals they used caves, bushes, and rocks for shelters, but they also put up some type of tent and apparently also built dwellings or houses more or less under the earth; on occasions they even constructed rounded huts.

About 10,000 years ago modern man appeared on the scene. He was scarcely distinguishable from the Cro-Magnon and with his arrival modern history begins.

The Dutch anthropologist Dr. Adriaan Kortlandt has produced what he calls a "dehumanization hypothesis" concerning African ape evolution. According to Dr. Kortlandt, during the

336

Pliocene and early Pleistocene periods, from 8,000,000 to 10,000,000 years ago, the Hominidae of Africa evolved in semi-open woodlands and grassy savannas. The Hominidae included the progenitors of apes and man, and this environment favored the emergence of a hominid, that is, a human, type of behavior. But the apelike animals who were going to develop into humans invented the spear and were able to kill with this at a distance. With this kind of offensive weapon the hominids drove the other apelike animals back into the dense forests, a habitat unfavorable to hominid behavior patterns. And so the hominid patterns of the original apes faded away and in some cases degenerated completely.

It appears that man penetrated into chimpanzee territory about 300,000 years ago, that is, during the later Acheulean times. This is the time of the first clearly recognizable stone spearheads which have been found.

Dr. Kortlandt carried out experiments with chimpanzees using a stuffed leopard. When this was exposed to chimpanzees whose habitat was the savanna, the chimpanzees attacked the beast of prey by means of clubs, in some cases more than 2 meters long.

Judy (chimpanzee) and the author enjoy a joke and a drink together at the International Primatology Congress in Atlanta.

The clubs were handled very much as a human being would handle a club of that size. But in a number of trials conducted on chimpanzees dwelling in the rain forest the stuffed leopard was not hit at all. Only remnants of the clubbing technique were observed. The savanna-dwelling chimpanzees not only showed a tactical cooperation between the chimpanzees attacking the stuffed leopard but also received vocal support from the onlookers. The forest dwellers did not show the same sort of concerted action. It is of interest that the film *2001: A Space Odyssey* has a preliminary session in which the development of the use of clubs among apes is demonstrated in a very realistic fashion.

Dr. Kortlandt also found that the savanna chimpanzee spent more time in the bipedal position and walked more often on his hind legs than did the animals who lived in the forest. Kortlandt thus believes that the chimpanzees have many more human characteristics and are much closer culturally to humans than has previously been believed, but by being driven back into the forest by developing man, they have lost many of these humanoid abilities which they had developed in the lightly forested and savanna areas. The chimpanzee as we know it today is really a regression.

There is a school of thought, of which the famous anthropologist and anatomist Sir Arthur Keith was a great protagonist, which believes that brachiation was the primary cause of the erect posture. Brachiation is the process of hanging in the trees by the arms and progressing by swinging hand over hand through the branches. The gibbon is the ape which has developed this type of progression to perfection. It is also well developed in the orang. This led the body to adapt to a vertical position. Then it is postulated that weather conditions caused a destruction of the forests and many of the human progenitors were forced out of the trees onto the plains. Since they were used to their bodies being vertical, these animals were more easily able to adapt to the upright position on the ground than the progenitors of the chimpanzees and gorillas, who were not brachiators, and so the erect posture was born.

338

14. Conservation of the Ape People

EACH year apes become harder and harder to obtain. It is impossible to buy orangs in this country and in many others; it is still possible to obtain gorillas, but they, too, are harder to get than a few years ago. The reason for this is that the numbers of these animals in the wild are diminishing rapidly. The number of orangs left in the wild amounts to only 3,000 or 4,000. This is a crisis number and indicates that this noble human cousin is well on its way to extinction. Export of orangs is

339

banned from Borneo and Sumatra, the only two places left in the world where they still exist in the wild. Once they extended over most of Southeast Asia, even reaching to India. Their contraction to such a small localized area is caused partly by pressure of human population and partly by hunting. They continue to decrease despite the export ban. Smuggling of young orangs, especially out of Sumatra, continued at least until very recently, and the method of catching the young is especially destructive. It is the same wasteful method that is also used to capture young chimpanzees and gorillas. This is simply to locate a mother with a baby and shoot her. The baby will remain clinging to its dead mother and can easily be removed. The orang babies may fetch $50, sometimes less, to the hunter but can bring $3,000 to $4,000 on the world market (the chimpanzee sells for about $600). Two orangs sold at auction recently in California brought $10,000 each. Baby apes are most sought after for international trade because at 15 to 25 pounds they are easily handled, and freight charges, even air freight charges, are quite low. Large apes would require massively strong transport cages and a fortune in air freight for transport.

In hunting it would be just as easy to shoot the mother with a tranquilizer dart as to kill her, and she would thus be saved for further breeding in her natural state. It takes a mother ape nine or ten years to become sexually mature, and then she is said to have at least twenty years of breeding; in our experience she has much more than this. There is no more certain way of exterminating a race of animals than by systematically eliminating the breeding females. Unfortunately, many of the native hunters who obtain the babies for the trade are interested in obtaining the mothers' carcasses for food, and in some cases apes are killed solely for this purpose. Most hunters and in many cases the people that handle the baby apes are ignorant of proper feeding, disease protection, and treatment for the young animals that have come into their keeping, and many baby apes die on the way to their destination. It is estimated that only one baby survives out of two or three obtained in this way.

Most of these apes go to zoos, and some are used for circuses and music hall variety entertainment. Few research institutes other than Yerkes Center use great apes. The orangs which we now have at Yerkes we found already in this country in the hands of a dealer. We believed they would do much better with us than anywhere else, and of course the fourteen babies they have produced adds significantly to the total number now in captivity.

Our success in breeding these animals gives hope that if they do die out in the wild we will be able to keep breeding them and at least preserve the species in captivity for posterity. Our present rate of breeding is much greater than is needed to actually maintain the colony. We now have more than thirty orangs. We also have eighty-five chimpanzees, and it has been some years since we purchased any of these animals for our colony. We obtain at least ten baby chimpanzees a year, and this number too is many more than are needed to maintain the colony. We have only fifteen gorillas, but they are a big, strong, healthy bunch of animals. They are, however, still adolescent with the exception of Shamba, who came from "Africa USA" in Hollywood, where she had appeared in a film with Clarence, the cross-eyed lion. Shamba is a female of breeding age, and although some of our males are fairly big and husky they are not quite sexually mature. However, we hope that in the not too distant future we will start having gorilla babies and that we will be able to maintain this species, too. We are in a position now with our three groups of apes that we need no longer purchase any of these animals on the market, so we make no demands on the animals still in the wild. On the other hand, because of our forty years of experience in handling and breeding great apes, we are in a position to be the world's source of all three apes. In fact we could, if necessary, meet in due course the world zoos' demands for great apes, and they would no longer need to be captured from the wild for this purpose.

The wild apes could still be maintained in the wild if only a limited number of babies were withdrawn a year for the legitimate world market, but the first step is for the countries where these animals live to make it a serious offense for either foreigners or their own people to kill them. A certain number of babies could be obtained each year with the aid of a tranquilizing gun.

Some attempt should also be made to establish the areas where these animals live as reserves and to prevent housing development, industry, including mining, and roads from going into these areas. The absence of a road is an excellent way of reducing the number of people who will penetrate into the reserve. Despite the laws banning export of animals, smugglers will still operate if the rewards are high. Although orangs may not be legally exported from Borneo or Sumatra, they still get out, and there is evidence that personnel belonging to the Indonesian Army and the U.S. armed forces in Southeast Asia have played a part in this smuggling trade.

Apes in the wild live in developing countries, and it may seem unfair to the people of those countries that they should not be permitted to develop areas of their own countries because of the presence of apes there. Perhaps these countries could be paid a certain sum each year by the wealthier nations, possibly through UNESCO, to establish and maintain and police such ape reserves. It would be appropriate that the administration of such a plan be under the control of an international organization such as UNESCO. Such a suggestion may seem too idealistic in our present materialistic world, where nothing is safe from destruction or pollution, but the great apes took 40,000,000 years to develop from their mammalian stock; when they are gone they are gone forever, and their passing will make our lives poorer. It is some comfort that the Yerkes Center may keep these animals alive in captivity for posterity, but that is a small compensation for their disappearance from the forests of the world.

There is an International Union for the Conservation of Nature with headquarters in Switzerland which is doing yeoman work in its attempts to preserve not only apes but many other endangered species, and the American Wild Animal Propagation Trust is also working actively and effectively in this area, so all is not yet lost in the battle to preserve the ape people for posterity.

Bibliography

The volume of knowledge of nonhuman primates is already huge, and it is beyond the competence of any one person to encompass it all. In a book such as this, therefore, it is necessary to draw on the experience and knowledge of scientific colleagues, both alive and deceased, to amplify the story. I express my gratitude to the authors and books listed below for the help they have given me in the compilation of *The Ape People*. Every effort has been made to give adequate reference to these sources without affecting the flow of the story, but indulgence is craved from those who feel that they deserved a more specific reference.

Animal Problem Solving, A. J. Riopelle, ed. London, Penguin Modern Psychology, 1967.

ARDREY, ROBERT, *African Genesis.* New York, Atheneum, 1961.

———, *The Territorial Imperative.* New York, Atheneum, 1968.

BORGESE, ELIZABETH MANN, *The Language Barrier, Beasts and Men.* New York, Holt, Rinehart & Winston, 1968.

———, *The White Snake.* New York, Holt, Rinehart & Winston, 1968.

BOULENGER, E. G., *Apes and Monkeys.* London, George G. Harrap & Company, 1936.

The Chimpanzee, G. H. Bourne, ed. Basel, Karger, 1969. 2 vols.

CLARK, W. E. LE GROS, *The Antecedents of Man.* Chicago, Quadrangle Books, 1960.

———, *History of the Primates.* London, Phoenix Books, 1958.

EIMEL, S., and DEVORE, IRVEN, *The Primates.* New Jersey, Time-Life Books, 1965.

HARRISON, RICHARD J., and MONTAGNA, W., *Man.* New York, Appleton-Century-Crofts, 1969.

HARRISSON, BARBARA, *Orang-utan.* New York, Doubleday, 1963.

HAYES, CATHY, *The Ape in Our House.* New York, Harper & Brothers, 1951.

HOOTEN, E. A., *Up from the Ape.* New York, Macmillan, 1947.

———, *Why Men Behave Like Apes and Vice Versa.* Princeton, N.J., Princeton University Press, 1940.

HOWELL, F. CLARK, *Early Man.* New Jersey, Time-Life Books, 1965.

HOYT, A. MARIA, *Toto and I.* Philadelphia, J. B. Lippincott, 1941.

IRVINE, WILLIAM, *Apes, Angels, and Victorians.* London, Readers Union, Weidenfeld and Nicolson, 1956.

KELLOGG, R., and O'DELL, SCOTT, *The Psychology of Children's Art.* San Diego, California, C.R.M., Inc.; distributed by Random House, New York, 1967.

KELLOGG, W. N., and KELLOGG, L. A., *The Ape and the Child.* New York, McGraw-Hill, 1933.

LAPIN, BORIS, and FRIDMAN, EMAN, *Monkeys for Science.* Moscow, Novosti Press Agency Publishing House, 1966.

LORENZ, K., *On Aggression.* London, Methuen & Company, 1968.

MACDONALD, JULIE, *Almost Human.* Philadelphia, Chilton Books, 1965.

MANNIX, DANIEL P., *Those About to Die.* London, Panther Books, 1960.

MORRIS, DESMOND, *The Biology of Art.* New York, Alfred A. Knopf, 1962.

———, *The Human Zoo.* New York, McGraw-Hill, 1969.

———, *The Naked Ape.* New York, McGraw-Hill, 1967.

MORRIS, RAMONA, and MORRIS, DESMOND, *Men and Apes.* New York, Bantam Books, 1968.

NAPIER, J. R., and NAPIER, P. H., *Handbook of Living Primates*. New York, Academic Press, 1967.

NESTURKH, M. F., *The Origin of Man*. Moscow, Progress Publishers, 1965.

OBERJOHANN, HEINRICH, *My Friend the Chimpanzee*, trans. by Monica Brooksbank. London, Robert Hale, 1957.

Primates, Phyllis C. Jay, ed. New York, Holt, Rinehart & Winston, 1968.

REYNOLDS, VERNON, *The Apes*. New York, E. P. Dutton, 1967.

ROSENFELD, A., *The Second Genesis*. Englewood Cliffs, N.J., Prentice-Hall, 1969.

SCHALLER, GEORGE B., *The Mountain Gorilla*. Chicago, University of Chicago Press, 1965.

———, *The Year of the Gorilla*. Chicago, University of Chicago Press, 1964.

SCHULTZ, ADOLPH H., *The Life of Primates*. London, Weidenfeld & Nicolson, 1969.

TOBIAS, P. V., *Olduvai Gorge*, vol. 2. Cambridge, Cambridge University Press, 1967.

TUTTLE, R. H., "The Way Apes Walk," *Science Journal* (November, 1969), p. 66.

VAN LAWICK GOODALL, JANE, *My Friends the Wild Chimpanzees*. Washington, National Geographic, 1967.

WOOD JONES, FREDERICK, *Man's Place Among the Mammals*. London, Edward Arnold, 1929.

WOOD JONES, FREDERICK, and PORTEUS, S. D., *The Matrix of the Mind*. London, Edward Arnold, 1929.

YERKES, R. M., *Almost Human*. New York, Century Company, 1925.

———, *The Chimpanzees*. New Haven, Yale University Press, 1948.

YERKES, R. M., and YERKES, A. W., *The Great Apes*. New Haven, Yale University Press, 1929.

ZUCKERMAN, S., *Functional Affinities of Man, Monkeys and Apes*. New York, Harcourt, Brace & Company, 1931.

Index

347

357